Collins

Advanced Modular Scie

Biology

A2

Series Editor: Mike Bailey

Mike Bailey

Keith Hirst

This book has been designed to support A A Biology specification B. It contains some material which has been added in order to clarify the specification. The examination will be limited to material set out in the specification document.

Published by HarperCollins*Publishers* Limited
77-85 Fulham Palace Road
Hammersmith
London
W6 8JB

www.CollinsEducation.com
Online support for schools and colleges

First published 2001
Reprinted 2001
ISBN 0 00 327752 6

British Library Cataloguing in Publication Data
A catalogue record for this publication is available from the British Library

Cover design by Chi Leung
Design by Ken Vail Graphic Design
Edited by Kathryn Senior
Illustrations by Illustrated Arts
Picture research by Caroline Thompson
Index by Julie Rimington
Production by Kathryn Botterill
Commissioned by Martin Davies
Project management by Kathryn Senior

Printed and bound by Scotprint

The publisher wishes to thank the Assessment and ualifications Alliance for permission to reproduce examination questions.

You might also like to visit
www.**fire**and**water**.com
The book lover's website

Acknowledgements

Every effort has been made to contact the holders of copyright material, but if any have been inadvertently overlooked the publishers will be pleased to make the necessary arrangements at the first opportunity.

The publishers would like to thank the following for permission to reproduce photographs (T = Top, B = Bottom, C = Centre, L= Left, R = Right):

Ace Photoagency/J & H Robins, 23, C Thomas, 118L;
Allsport/D Rogers, 92T;
Heather Angel, 124BC, 137C&TL, 150, 156, 165C, 171CL;
Animal Photography/Sally Anne Thompson, 111CR, 131T&BL;
Ardea London/F Gohier, 143TR&TL, J-P Ferraro, 149CR, Weisser, 171BR;
BBC Picture Archives, 118R;
Mr D Banerjee, 72R;
Beechams Pharmaceuticals, 198;
Biophoto Associates, 5, 6, 34, 100, 106CR;
Anthony Blake Photo Library/T Robbins, 191R, G Buntrock, 191L;
Bruce Coleman Ltd, 29, 111TL&TR&CL, 121, 125, 126, 131C&BC, 133B, 133C, 140C, 142, 143C, 144, 168B, J Johnson, 31, A G Potts, 164L, 178;
Environmental Images/P Glendall, 182T;
GettyOne Stone, 44, 127;
GlucoWatch® Biographer (registered trademark of Cygnus, Inc. Redwood City, California, USA), 18;
Ronald Grant Archive, 122R;
Holt Studios International/N Cattlin, 8, 189, 208;
Frank Lane Picture Agency/Silvertris, 26BL, P Moulu/Sunset, 27TR, D Hosking, 28B, B Borrell, 171CR, R Wilmshurst, 213;
NHPA/G Bernard, 132, S Dalton, 133T, 171TL, 143CR, E A Janes, 64, N Wu, 102, 130, H Ausloos, 108T, G Lacz, 124BL&BR, S Robinson, 149BC, A.N.T, 149BL, 172C, 175, D. Woodfall, 161, 172T, 185B, G Edwards, 164R, W Zepf, 165T, N A Callan, 137CL, J-L Le Moigne, 192C, L Campbell, 192CR, A Williams, 185CL, 192T; H van Ingen, 188, H Palo Jnr, 143CL, R Erwin, 28C;

Natural History Museum, 79;
Orbis International, 68, 72L;
'PA' Photos, 37, 140T;
Planet Earth Pictures/M Read, 179;
Popperfoto/Reuters, 27BL, 48R;
Range/Bettmann/UPI, 168T;
Res-Q Products Inc. www.hypothermia-ca.com, 30;
Rex Features Ltd, 48L, 120;
Photo by Alan Robinson, 108C;
Science Photo Library, 20, 24, 25, 26TR, 41, 51, 52, 60, 71, 75, 82, 87, 96, 97, 106CL, 113, 114, 119, 122L, 124CR, 137TR&CR, 154;
Still Pictures/E Parker, 2T, N Dickinson, 2B, H Giraudet, 141, J Cancalosi, 184;
Fiennes/Stroud/Howell/Sygma, 86, 92C;
C&S Thompson, 11;
John Walmsley, 157;
Woodfall Wild Images/M Powels, 159, D Woodfall, 182C, 183.

Front cover:
Images supplied by: Science Photo Library (top left)
Bruce Coleman Ltd/Dr M P Kohl (centre)
Science Photo Library (top right)

To the student

This book covers the content needed for the AQA Specification B in Biology at A2-level. It aims to give you the information you need to get a good grade and to make your study of advanced science successful and interesting. Science is constantly evolving and, wherever possible, modern issues and problems have been used to make your study stimulating and to encourage you to continue studying science after you complete your current course.

Using the book

Don't try to achieve too much in one reading session. Science is complex and some demanding ideas need to be supported with a lot of facts. Trying to take in too much at one time can make you lose sight of the most important ideas – all you see is a mass of information.

Each chapter starts by showing how the science you will learn is applied somewhere in the world. At other points in the chapter you may find more examples of the way the science you are covering is used. These detailed contexts are not needed for your examination but should help to strengthen your understanding of the subject.

The numbered questions in the main text allow you to check that you have understood what is being explained. These are all short and straightforward in style – there are no trick questions. Don't be tempted to pass over these questions, they will give you new insights into the work. Answers are given in the back of the book.

The Key Facts for each section summarise the information you will need in your examination. However, the examination will test your ability to apply these facts rather than simply to remember them. The main text in the book explains these facts. The application boxes encourage you to apply them in new situations. Occasional extension boxes provide extra detail not required for your examination. These are interesting to read and will support your studies beyond A2-level.

Past paper questions are included at the end of each chapter. These will help you to test yourself against the sorts of questions that will come up in your examination. There is also a section (Chapter 16) that covers synoptic assessment questions to help you prepare for the synoptic element of your final examination.

Good luck!

1 Energy in living organisms

View over the Amazon basin. Like other rainforests, this was considered to be a valuable sink for carbon, but is it?

The atmosphere that surrounds the Earth is unique; no other planet that we know of has a blanket of gases that enables it to support life. For many living organisms the key component of this blanket is oxygen, a by-product of the photosynthesis and a vital requirement for aerobic respiration. However, in the modern industrial world, it is carbon dioxide that is attracting our attention. This by-product of respiration, and vital ingredient for photosynthesis has been building up as a result of our burning fossil fuels, and many people are now concerned that this might be having global effects, such as global warming and climate change.

Rich rainforest regions are an important 'sink' for carbon dioxide, helping to absorb some of the excess produced by us. However, researchers have realised very recently that these huge forests don't always do what we think they should. In 1998, a report revealed that, under the right conditions, 10% of all the carbon dioxide in the Earth's ecosystems is locked up in the forests of the Amazon basin. In 1993, for example, the Amazon was storing a massive 0.7 trillion kilograms of carbon dioxide. However, this only happens when the climate in the Amazon is cool and wet. When it is warmer and drier, as has happened in the recent El Niño episodes, the Amazon basin actually produces more carbon dioxide than it stores. In 1992, for example, it added 0.2 trillion kilograms of carbon dioxide to the atmosphere.

Researchers are now trying to find out what makes the Amazon a sink or a source for carbon dioxide. This delicate balance is an important factor for countries to consider as they cooperate to try to manage carbon dioxide production.

1.1 What does energy mean to you?

Think about the last time you were running about playing football or tennis, or the last time you were dancing at a party; you had plenty of energy, but where did it come from? Most people would answer a question like this with something like, 'From my muscles!' or 'From the pizza and chips I had at lunch time!'. Both would be true to a certain extent but if you think about the question more deeply it starts to get really fascinating.

Ultimately, all our energy and all the energy used by all organisms on Earth comes from the Sun. But we can't gain enough energy to dance the night away by sunbathing: we need plants to do that for us. Plants have a wonderful collection of

biochemical mechanisms and pathways that allow them to absorb sunlight and use the light energy to convert water and carbon dioxide into sugars; they literally make food from thin air. The plant then uses more energy to build up the basic sugars into more complex molecules; starch, fats, proteins. When we eat plant foods, we digest the complex molecules back into simple ones, and then strip out the energy that the plant put there using light. Respiration – the process that does this in the body – is essentially the reverse of photosynthesis. In this chapter we look in more detail at these two vital biochemical processes that enable life on Earth – including us – to exist.

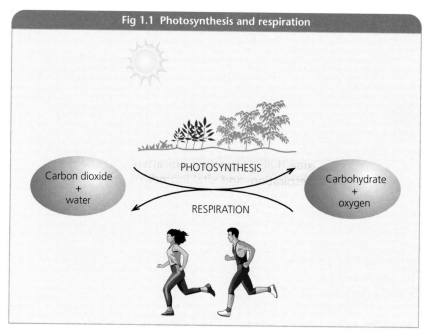

Fig 1.1 Photosynthesis and respiration

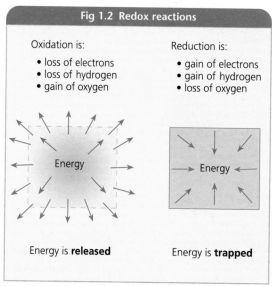

Fig 1.2 Redox reactions

Oxidation is:
- loss of electrons
- loss of hydrogen
- gain of oxygen

Reduction is:
- gain of electrons
- gain of hydrogen
- loss of oxygen

Energy is **released**

Energy is **trapped**

Basic principles

Before going into the various stages of photosynthesis and respiration, it is important to cover some basic principles.

Fig 1.1 gives a general overview of photosynthesis and respiration. You may remember the summary equations for photosynthesis and respiration from your GCSE studies.

Photosynthesis:

$$6CO_2 + 6H_2O + [Energy] \rightarrow C_6H_{12}O_6 + 6O_2$$

Respiration:

$$C_6H_{12}O_6 + 6O_2 \rightarrow 6CO_2 + 6H_2O + [Energy]$$

As you can see, these two equations are actually the reverse of each other. Chloroplasts contain chlorophylls and other pigments that absorb light energy and use it to power a series of **reduction reactions** that **reduce** carbon dioxide and water to glucose to provide the plant with an energy store.

Most of the reactions of aerobic respiration occur in the mitochondria. Again, the process is a series of chemical reactions but this time they are **oxidation reactions**. Their objective is to **oxidise** glucose into carbon dioxide and water, releasing the stored energy and making it available for immediate use by the organism.

It is important for you to understand oxidation and reduction reactions really well. It is also useful to appreciate the central role that **adenosine triphosphate** (ATP) plays in energy storage. Before we go into photosynthesis and respiration in detail, the next two sections introduce these important concepts.

Oxidation and reduction reactions

First some definitions of oxidation and reduction reactions (see also Fig 1.2):

- **Oxidation reactions** take away electrons or hydrogen atoms from molecules. Oxidising agents take away electrons. Most oxidation reactions are **exothermic** – energy is released.

- **Reduction reactions** add electrons or hydrogen atoms to molecules. Molecules that supply electrons in a chemical reaction are called reducing agents. Most reduction reactions are **endothermic** – they require an input of energy.

Whenever a chemical is oxidised, another must be reduced, since electrons and hydrogen atoms can't just disappear or exist on their own. This means oxidation reactions and reduction reactions always occur together; they are often referred to as **redox reactions**. Photosynthesis and respiration both consist of a complex chain of reactions in which electrons are passed from one molecule to another like juggling balls.

In photosynthesis, the overall point of reduction is to capture light energy so that the plant can use and store it. Similarly, oxidation in respiration allows plants to release energy from stored food.

Photosynthesis, respiration and ATP

The energy in organic molecules could be released in one go – rapid, uncontrolled oxidation. This is what happens when substances burn. This is no use to the body. Most of the energy would be lost as heat, and

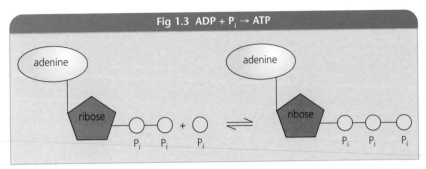

Fig 1.3 ADP + P$_i$ → ATP

the high temperature would be lethal. Instead the body uses enzymes to break down food fuels such as fats, proteins and carbohydrates step by step, releasing energy in small, usable amounts.

This energy is transferred to ATP, ready for use. ATP stores energy within the cell, and releases it instantly for reactions that need it, such as muscular contraction. ATP breakdown is usually a **coupled reaction**; the ATP breakdown is coupled with reactions that need energy.

Adenosine triphosphate, as its name suggests, contains three phosphate groups. You will remember from the AS book that the energy released from the respiration of glucose is used to add inorganic phosphate (P$_i$) to adenosine diphosphate (ADP) to

produce ATP (Fig 1.3).

$$ADP + P_i + [Energy] \rightarrow ATP$$

ATP is also formed during photosynthesis, when light energy absorbed by chloroplast pigments is transferred as chemical energy.

About 33 kJ of energy is required to combine one mole of inorganic phosphate with one mole of ADP. This is more energy than is needed to form bonds in most molecules. This means that ATP is a particularly good 'store' of energy. When ATP is broken down again into ADP and P$_i$, these 33 kJ of energy are released.

What is the advantage of having this universal 'intermediary'? ATP can quickly provide the energy required for most synthetic reactions in all living cells.

1 Energy is important in the human body in lots of ways. Give an example of:

a a part of the body that generates a lot of heat;

b a part of the body where active transport is used to pump substances in or out of cells;

c a synthetic reaction that needs energy.

1.2 Photosynthesis

At GCSE you learned that energy is needed to reduce carbon dioxide to carbohydrate. You now need to understand that this reduction requires a supply of electrons, and you should know how the process of photosynthesis provides this.

Photosynthesis can be divided into two separate phases. The text that follows and Fig 1.4 provide a brief summary.

1 The light-dependent reactions

These capture energy from light and produce a supply of electrons for the light-

independent reactions. Energy captured from sunlight and captured by the pigment molecules is used to split water, to create ATP, and to produce NADP, a molecule necessary for the fixation of carbon that occurs in the light-independent reactions.

2 The light-independent reactions

These use the energy and electrons produced in the light-dependent reactions to reduce carbon dioxide. They do not require light and so can take place in the light or the dark. Carbon dioxide is fixed from atmospheric carbon dioxide to form first a 3-carbon molecule, and then a 6-carbon sugar – glucose.

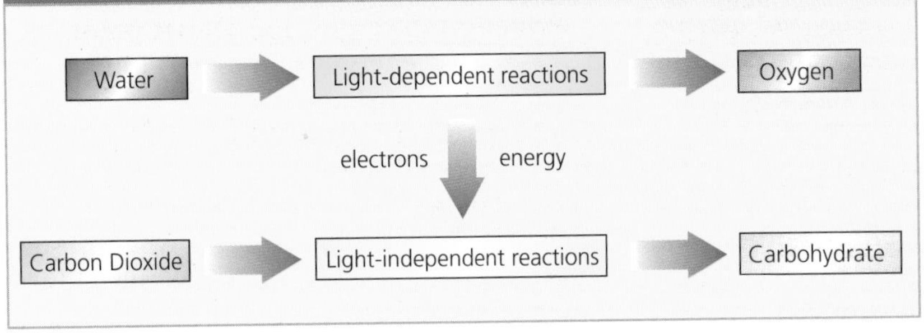

Where do these reactions occur?

Photosynthesis takes place in the chloroplasts (Fig 1.5). The light-dependent reactions occur in the **thylakoids** of the chloroplasts. The phospholipid membranes in these layered structures contain different pigments that absorb light energy. Chlorophyll and

Fig 1.4 Phases of photosynthesis

Water → Light-dependent reactions → Oxygen

electrons   energy

Carbon Dioxide → Light-independent reactions → Carbohydrate

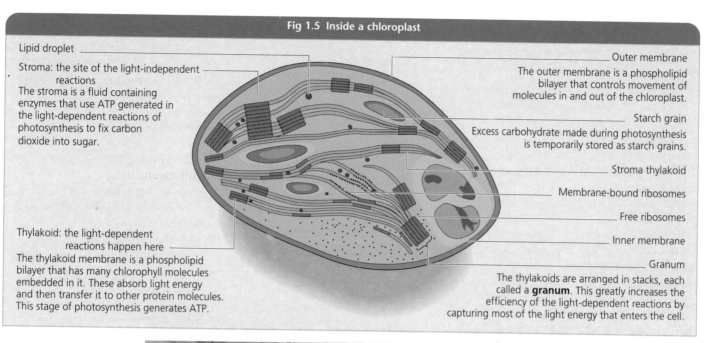

Fig 1.5 Inside a chloroplast

Lipid droplet

Stroma: the site of the light-independent reactions
The stroma is a fluid containing enzymes that use ATP generated in the light-dependent reactions of photosynthesis to fix carbon dioxide into sugar.

Thylakoid: the light-dependent reactions happen here
The thylakoid membrane is a phospholipid bilayer that has many chlorophyll molecules embedded in it. These absorb light energy and then transfer it to other protein molecules. This stage of photosynthesis generates ATP.

Outer membrane
The outer membrane is a phospholipid bilayer that controls movement of molecules in and out of the chloroplast.

Starch grain
Excess carbohydrate made during photosynthesis is temporarily stored as starch grains.

Stroma thylakoid

Membrane-bound ribosomes

Free ribosomes

Inner membrane

Granum
The thylakoids are arranged in stacks, each called a **granum**. This greatly increases the efficiency of the light-dependent reactions by capturing most of the light energy that enters the cell.

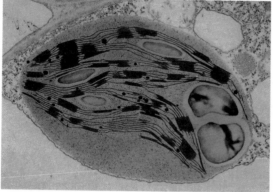

False-colour electron micrograph showing the structure of the chloroplast in detail.

carotenoid molecules are arranged in groups, centred on chlorophyll *a* molecules. The light-independent reactions of photosynthesis occur in solution in the **stroma**.

Both sets of reactions are kept separate from other reactions in the cell by the outer chloroplast membranes. The products of photosynthesis are rapidly removed from the chloroplast. Carbon dioxide readily diffuses through the outer membranes of the chloroplasts into the stroma. Carbohydrate can be transported out though the membrane. Starch grains form temporary sites for storing excess carbohydrates produced during the day. During the night, carbohydrate may be released from the starch grains and translocated to other parts of the plant.

2 How is the chloroplast adapted for its functions?

The light-dependent reactions

The light-dependent reactions of photosynthesis provide the energy and electrons needed for the later, light-independent reactions. An overall summary is shown in Fig 1.6.

What we call 'chlorophyll' is in fact several different compounds. These include chlorophyll *a*, chlorophyll *b* and the carotenoids. Energy captured by all of these

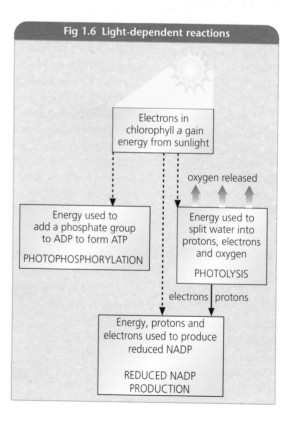

Fig 1.6 Light-dependent reactions

Electrons in chlorophyll *a* gain energy from sunlight

oxygen released

Energy used to add a phosphate group to ADP to form ATP
PHOTOPHOSPHORYLATION

Energy used to split water into protons, electrons and oxygen
PHOTOLYSIS

electrons | protons

Energy, protons and electrons used to produce reduced NADP

REDUCED NADP PRODUCTION

APPLICATION — Why the colours in light are crucial to plants

White light is a mixture of light of different colours; these are easily seen in a rainbow, or when light is passed through a prism. Each colour of light has a different wavelength; blue light has a wavelength of approximately 450 nm; red light has a wavelength of approximately 650 nm, with the other colours in-between. Objects appear to be different colours because of the wavelengths of light they absorb and reflect. A white object reflects all wavelengths of light while a black object absorbs all. An absorption spectrum shows how much light specific objects or molecules absorb at each wavelength. The diagram top right shows the absorption spectra of the different pigments in a chloroplast.

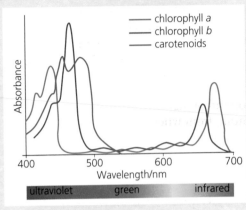

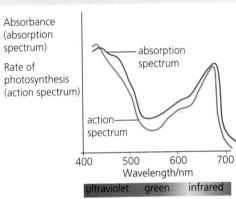

1 a What are the main colours of light absorbed by chlorophyll *a*?
  b Explain why chlorophyll appears green.
  c What colour would you expect carotenoids to appear?

An action spectrum for photosynthesis shows the rate of photosynthesis at different wavelengths of light. The diagram below left shows an action spectrum for photosynthesis, and combines it with the absorption spectrum for a leaf.

2 a Copy the graph. On your copy, draw the action spectrum of a leaf if it contained only chlorophyll *a*.
  b Explain why it is an advantage to the plant to have several different pigments in its chloroplasts.

3 Brown seaweeds photosynthesise, but their pigments are obviously different from those of green-leaved plants. Pigments are soluble in organic solvents such as acetone. Describe how you would use paper chromatography to find which pigments a brown seaweed contains [see Chapter 5, pages 70-73, AS Biology].

APPLICATION — They changed the atmosphere

Cyanobacteria are primitive organisms related to bacteria. They may well have been amongst the first living things on Earth and seem to have changed little in the last 3000 million years. These tiny organisms almost certainly helped to change the atmosphere from an inhospitable mixture of carbon dioxide, methane and ammonia into one containing enough oxygen to support animal life.

Cyanobacteria contain the pigment chlorophyll. This is identical to the chlorophyll found today in almost all plants. Some cyanobacteria are remarkably similar in structure to the chloroplasts found inside the green cells of more modern plants.

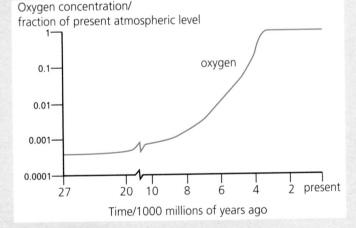

1 How is the structure of the cyanobacterium similar to that of a chloroplast?

However, in bright light cyanobacteria behave differently from modern plant chloroplasts. They give off hydrogen gas as well as oxygen. Scientists trying to find alternative fuel sources grew cultures of cyanobacteria in small plastic containers.

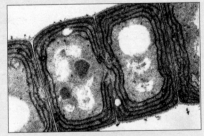

Electron micrograph showing the structure of cyanobacteria

They calculated that cyanobacteria placed in a tank measuring 8 m × 2 m × 2 m could produce enough hydrogen to supply the fuel needs of an average house. Energy from the Sun is 'free', and you might expect that this idea would have been developed further.

2 Suggest reasons why it has not.

pigments is transferred to groups of chlorophyll *a* molecules. Chlorophyll *a* is one of a special group of compounds that can absorb light energy and use it to boost the energy level of electrons from the hydrogen atoms in water. Electrons can be compared to satellites orbiting Earth. To move a satellite into a higher orbit requires energy, for example from firing a booster rocket. Similarly, energy is required to boost an electron into a higher orbit around the nucleus of an atom, from where it can be passed on to another atom more easily.

Chlorophyll *a* absorbs light energy and the excited electrons that it then contains are used to power several very important redox reactions – **photolysis**, **photophosphorylation** and **NADP production**.

Photolysis

Energy from excited electrons in chlorophyll *a* molecules is used to split water molecules into protons (H^+), electrons (e^-) and oxygen.

$$\text{water} \xrightarrow{\text{Energy from excited electrons}} \text{protons} + \text{electrons} + \text{oxygen}$$
$$2H_2O \qquad\qquad 4H^+ \quad + \quad 4e^- \quad + \quad O_2$$

This reaction is known as **photolysis** (*photo* = using light, *lysis* = splitting).

The oxygen is released to the atmosphere. This reaction is the source of almost all the oxygen that makes up 20% of the atmosphere, which covers the Earth with a gas blanket ten miles deep. That's a lot of oxygen. Millions of tonnes of oxygen are present in the atmosphere only because of the work of photosynthetic organisms over millions of years. Without it there would be no animal life on Earth.

Photophosphorylation

Energy from excited electrons can also be used to produce ATP. Because the energy comes from light, this method of producing ATP is called **photophosphorylation** (*photo* = using light; *phosphorylation* = adding a phosphate group).

$$ADP + P_i + \left[\begin{array}{c} \text{energy from} \\ \text{excited electrons} \end{array} \right] \rightarrow ATP$$

Production of NADP

The electrons released from water molecules by photolysis are eventually used to reduce carbon dioxide to form glucose. However, electrons cannot react directly with carbon dioxide. The excited electrons in chlorophyll *a* molecules are transferred to a very useful compound called **nicotinamide adenine dinucleotide phosphate** (NADP).

With each electron that NADP takes up, it also accepts a proton, and so it does not become negatively charged. The transfer of electrons and protons to NADP requires energy that is obtained from excited electrons in other groups of chlorophyll *a* molecules.

$$NADP + \text{proton} + \text{electron} \xrightarrow{\text{Energy from excited electrons}} \text{reduced NADP}$$
$$NADP + \quad H^+ \quad + \quad e^- \quad \rightarrow \text{reduced NADP}$$

Reduced NADP (which can also be written as NADPH) can donate electrons to reduce carbon dioxide directly, and for this reason is known as a **reducing agent**. The reduction of carbon dioxide occurs during the light-independent reactions of photosynthesis, which is covered in the next section.

KEY FACTS

- The reactions of photosynthesis can be separated into the light-dependent reactions and the light-independent reactions. Both occur inside the chloroplast.

- The internal phospholipid membranes that make up the thylakoids within chloroplasts contain light-absorbing pigments. To maximise light absorption, thylakoids are arranged in stacks called grana.

- The light-dependent reactions occur in the grana.

- When chlorophyll *a* molecules absorb light energy, some of their electrons become excited, gaining energy that can be used to carry out chemical reactions.

- Energy from excited electrons in chlorophyll *a* molecules is used to split water, producing protons, electrons and oxygen. This reaction, known as **photolysis**, produces most of the oxygen present in the atmosphere.

- Energy from excited electrons in chlorophyll *a* molecules is also used to produce **ATP**. This method of producing ATP is known as **photophosphorylation**.

- This same source of energy is used to add to **NADP** the protons and electrons that have been obtained by splitting water. Reduced NADP is produced; this is a reducing agent that is later used to reduce carbon dioxide to carbohydrate in the light-independent reactions of photosynthesis.

The light-independent reactions of photosynthesis

All of the food produced by photosynthesis ultimately feeds the world's population of animals, including humans. But that isn't why plants evolved the process. Photosynthesis developed to provide plants with the energy that *they* require for respiration. Plants are the ultimate self-sufficient unit. Like all other organisms, their cells need to respire 24 hours a day to maintain the metabolic reactions essential to life.

As we have seen, the light-dependent reactions of photosynthesis occur during the day, but cease at night. Although the light-independent reactions of photosynthesis carry on after dark, they do so for no more than a few seconds. This is because there is a limited amount of NADP available to reduce and a limited amount of ADP for conversion to ATP; these compounds need to be manufactured constantly using light energy. To prevent the plant dying overnight, it has evolved a way to transfer energy to a more stable and storable form – **carbohydrate**.

Crop plants are the ultimate food storing plants. The ears of these wheat plants are packed with carbohydrate produced by photosynthesis

The energy from ATP and the electrons from reduced NADP are used to reduce carbon dioxide from the atmosphere and build it into carbohydrate. This carbohydrate provides a longer-term store of energy and can be used as building blocks to produce all the other organic molecules – such as fats and proteins – that are needed for growth.

In the light-independent reactions of photosynthesis, carbon dioxide molecules are eventually linked together to make much larger molecules such as glucose, which has six carbon atoms. This process occurs in stages, just like building a wall from individual bricks:

- In the first step, an **acceptor molecule**, an organic molecule that will combine with carbon dioxide, incorporates carbon dioxide into its structure. This reaction forms a **3-carbon acid**. As carbon dioxide gas has become part of an organic molecule rather than part of the atmosphere, it is said to have been **fixed**.

- The 3-carbon acid is not a carbohydrate; it must be converted into one. This reduction reaction requires energy from ATP and electrons from reduced NADP. Both are supplied by the light-dependent reactions of photosynthesis. The 3-carbon acid is reduced to a **3-carbon sugar**.

- The acceptor molecule for carbon dioxide is regenerated so that more carbon dioxide can be fixed.

3 What limits the length of time the light-independent reactions can take place after light is 'switched off'?

4 Look at Fig 1.7 and give an example of:
a an oxidation reaction;
b a reduction reaction;
c a hydrolysis reaction.

Fig 1.7 Reducing the 3-carbon acid

ATP → ADP + P_i reduced NADP → NADP

Glycerate 3-phosphate (GP)	Glycerate 1,3 diphosphate	Glyceraldehyde 3-phosphate (GALP)
3-carbon acid	3-carbon acid	3-carbon sugar

Fig 1.8 Regenerating ribulose bisphosphate

3 molecules
Carbon dioxide
1-carbon molecule

3 molecules
Ribulose bisphosphate (RuBP)
5-carbon molecule

6 molecules
Glyceraldehyde 3-phosphate (GALP)
3-carbon molecule

5 molecules

1 molecule
Glucose
6-carbon molecule

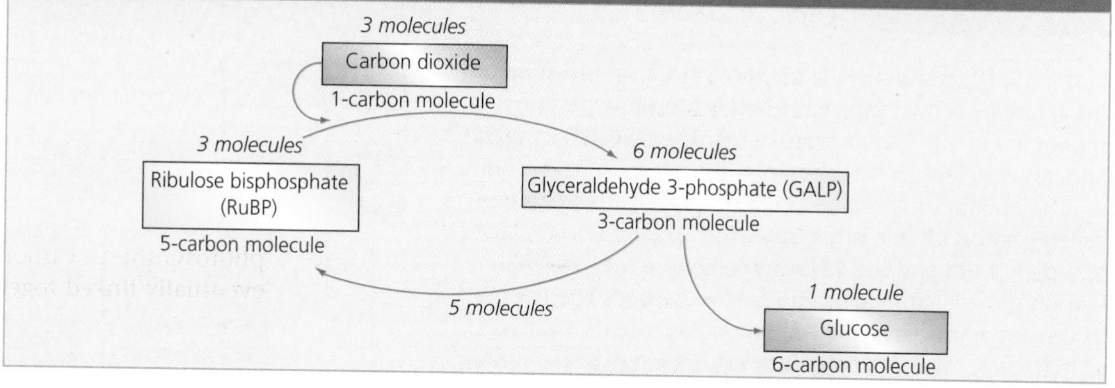

Fixing carbon dioxide

The process of absorbing carbon dioxide from the atmosphere so that it can become part of carbohydrate in the plant is called **fixing** the carbon dioxide. The enzyme **Rubisco** (**ribulose bisphosphate carboxylase**) is used by plants to combine carbon dioxide with the 5-carbon acceptor molecule, **ribulose bisphosphate (RuBP)**. This forms a highly unstable 6-carbon compound that splits up immediately to form two molecules of the 3-carbon acid called **glycerate 3-phosphate (GP)**.

Reducing the 3-carbon acid

Converting glycerate 3-phosphate into carbohydrate requires both ATP and reduced NADP that are produced in the light-dependent reactions of photosynthesis (Fig 1.7). The ATP and reduced NADP force electrons into the glycerate molecule. This forms a 3-carbon sugar molecule called **glyceraldehyde 3-phosphate (GALP)**.

The reduced NADP has now lost electrons to the glycerate; it has been oxidised. It returns to the site of light-dependent reactions where it can regain energy and electrons to become reduced NADP.

The ATP has lost energy to the glycerate,

forming ATP and P_i. These also return to the site of light-dependent reactions where energy from excited electrons will be used to reform ATP. Plants don't miss a trick when it comes to 'molecular recycling'.

Regenerating the acceptor molecules

Glyceraldehyde 3-phosphate can be converted into a whole series of other sugars, including glucose. It can also be used to synthesise lipids and proteins. However, in order to keep the production of glyceraldehyde 3-phosphate going at a high rate, plants need to use some of the glyceraldehyde 3-phosphate they make to regenerate ribulose bisphosphate. Fig 1.8 shows one of these pathways.

5

a What is needed to convert glyceraldehyde 3-phosphate into ribulose bisphosphate?

b Two groups of the same species of plant were exposed to the same total amount of light. Group A received the light in one continuous period. Group B were given alternate periods of a few seconds light and a few seconds darkness. The total photosynthetic yield from Group B was greater than that from Group A. Suggest why.

KEY FACTS

- The light-independent reactions occur in solution in the stroma of the chloroplast.

- The acceptor molecule for carbon dioxide is **ribulose bisphosphate**. It incorporates carbon dioxide into its structure. Carbon dioxide is said to have been **fixed** by ribulose bisphosphate.

- The enzyme **Rubisco** catalyses the reaction in which carbon dioxide and ribulose bisphosphate produce two molecules of **glycerate 3-phosphate**.

- ATP and reduced NADP are used to reduce glycerate 3-phosphate to the sugar **glyceraldehyde 3-phosphate**.

- Some of this glyceraldehyde 3-phosphate is used to synthesise other carbohydrates and organic molecules.

- The rest of it is used to regenerate the acceptor molecule ribulose bisphosphate.

The Calvin cycle

In the 1950s, researchers led by Melvin Calvin investigated the pathway shown top right. This is the same pathway shown in Fig 1.8, but in more detail. The researchers used apparatus similar to that shown in the diagram below right.

The apparatus contained cells of a *Chlorella* (a tiny one-celled photosynthetic organism). The apparatus was placed in a dark room and the *Chlorella* cells were supplied with carbon dioxide containing radioactive carbon. The contents of the apparatus were mixed thoroughly, then a light was switched on. At five-second intervals Calvin placed a few of the cells into hot ethanol to kill them. Homogenates of the killed algal cells were analysed using two-way paper chromatography. This technique involves running the chromatogram with one solvent, then turning the paper through 90° then running it with a different solvent.

By using this technique, Calvin's team was able to investigate the organic compounds produced during photosynthesis. The diagram below shows two of the chromatograms he obtained. The dark spots contain radioactive carbon compounds.

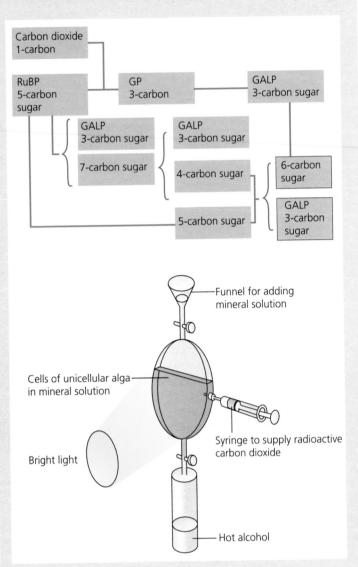

After 5 seconds

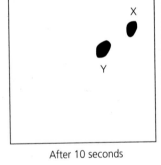

After 10 seconds

1 Identify substances X and Y. Give reasons for your answers.

In another series of experiments, Calvin's team used similar techniques to investigate the effect of light and dark periods on the compounds formed in the light-independent reactions. The graph on the right shows the results of one of these investigations.

2 Explain why, when the light is switched off:
 a the curve for ribulose bisphosphate falls;
 b the curve for glycerate 3- phosphate rises and then levels off.

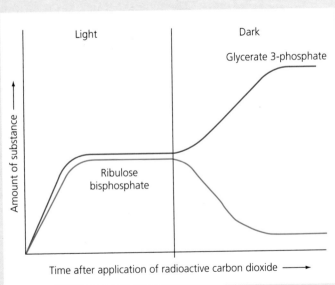

1.5 Aerobic respiration

In a bonfire, the energy from the carbohydrates that make up wood is released very quickly, and the burning cannot be easily controlled. Much of the energy is therefore wasted – the bonfire never seems to last long enough! In respiration, the energy in sugars is released in a series of small steps that are more easily controlled and less energy is wasted.

Overall, respiration is the reverse of photosynthesis, but the processes and reactions involved are not a direct mirror image. Respiration splits up carbohydrate molecules into carbon dioxide and water, releasing energy to form ATP along the way. There are two forms of respiration, aerobic and anaerobic. Aerobic respiration requires oxygen whilst anaerobic respiration does not. Here, we look only at aerobic respiration in detail.

Aerobic respiration has four stages

- **Glycolysis** This is literally *sugar splitting* – glucose molecules are split into pyruvate molecules that contain 3 carbon atoms. Each molecule of glucose is split to produce 2 molecules of pyruvate with a net gain of 2 ATP molecules.

- **The link reaction** Pyruvate is oxidised to form acetyl coenzyme A.

- **The Krebs cycle** Electrons and carbon dioxide molecules are removed from acetyl coenzyme A.

- **The electron transfer chain** Transport of electrons down a series of electron carriers transfers energy that is used to produce ATP.

Note that **anaerobic** respiration is basically just the first stage of aerobic respiration, i.e. glycolysis, which doesn't go any further because there is no oxygen available.

When wood burns, the process of oxidation and energy production happens rapidly, releasing large amounts of heat.

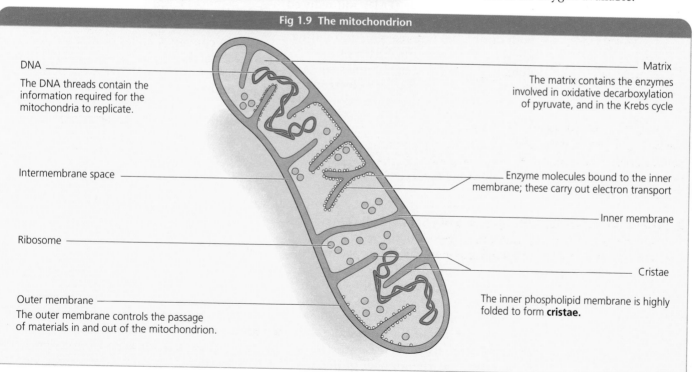

Fig 1.9 The mitochondrion

DNA
The DNA threads contain the information required for the mitochondria to replicate.

Matrix
The matrix contains the enzymes involved in oxidative decarboxylation of pyruvate, and in the Krebs cycle

Intermembrane space

Enzyme molecules bound to the inner membrane; these carry out electron transport

Inner membrane

Ribosome

Cristae

Outer membrane
The outer membrane controls the passage of materials in and out of the mitochondrion.

The inner phospholipid membrane is highly folded to form **cristae.**

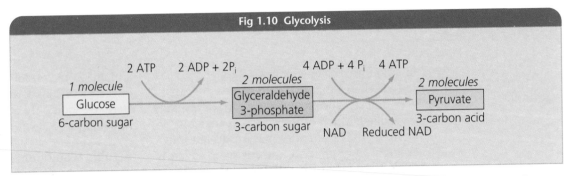

Fig 1.10 Glycolysis

Mitochondria; the site of aerobic respiration

Before going on to see the events of each stage, it is important to realise where these different reactions occur within the cell. Fig 1.9 shows the internal structure of the mitochondrion and shows where reactions in the different stages of respiration take place.

Site of the individual stages

- The reactions of **glycolysis** occur in the cytoplasm.

- The pyruvate produced by glycolysis diffuses into the matrix of the mitochondria where the **link reaction** forms acetyl coenzyme A.

- Acetyl coenzyme A then enters **Krebs cycle**, a cycle of reactions that also occur in the mitochondrial matrix.

- Reduced **nicotinamide adenine dinucleotide (NAD)** and reduced **flavine adenine dinucleotide (FAD)** and reduced NAD, *important oxidising agents* produced both during the link reaction and during Krebs cycle, pass to the cristae of the mitochondria. These membranes contain the proteins involved in the **electron transfer chain**. Electrons pass down this chain and are eventually transferred to NAD and FAD, releasing enough energy to produce ATP. Of all the stages of respiration, the electron transfer chain produces the most ATP.

The link reaction, the Krebs cycle and the electron transport chain are all dependent on each other and all occur within the mitochondria. As in the chloroplasts, the molecules concerned with energy transfer, in this case the molecules of the electron transport chain, are held close to each other in the phospholipid membranes of the cristae. The folding of the phospholipid membrane into cristae increases the surface area and therefore the number of the 'energy-transfer molecules' that can take part in respiration.

Glycolysis

Glycolysis is the first stage of respiration. The overall process of glycolysis, which takes place in the cytoplasm, is illustrated in Fig 1.10.

Sugars are not very reactive, so to start the process, 2 molecules of ATP are used to add two phosphate groups to the 6-carbon sugar. The phosphorylated 6-carbon sugar is then broken down into 2 molecules of the 3-carbon sugar **glyceraldehyde 3-phosphate**. This is then converted into 2 molecules of **glycerate 3-phosphate**, a reaction that is the reverse of the one we saw in the light-independent reactions of photosynthesis.

Glyceraldehyde 3-phosphate is then converted to **pyruvate**. This is an **oxidation reaction**. Electrons are removed from the glyceraldehyde 3-phosphate and transferred to NAD. The energy released is used to convert 4 moles of ADP + P_i to 4 moles of ATP. There is thus a net gain of 2 moles of ATP from every mole of 6-carbon sugar broken down during glycolysis. (Remember that molecule and mole are not the same thing – a mole of ATP and a mole of sugar both contain the same number of molecules.)

The end products of glycolysis are **pyruvate** and **reduced NAD**. Reduced NAD is generated at several stages in respiration; we shall consider the fate of all the NAD produced later in this section.

The link reaction

This stage of aerobic respiration links glycolysis, which occurs in the cytoplasm, with the Krebs cycle, the main ATP-generating phase that occurs in mitochondria. Fig 1.11 on the page opposite gives an overview of the link reaction.

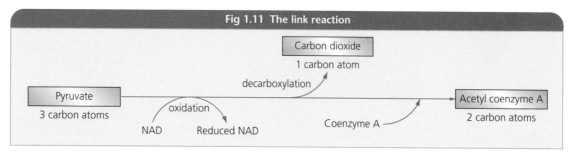

Fig 1.11 The link reaction

At the start of the link reaction, pyruvate produced by the process of glycolysis leaves the cytoplasm and enters the mitochondria. There, NAD removes electrons from the pyruvate, oxidising it to a 2-carbon acetate molecule and carbon dioxide. The acetate is picked up by a carrier molecule – **coenzyme A** – and **acetyl coenzyme A** is formed. Because a carbon atom is removed from pyruvate in this process, and because the pyruvate is oxidised, this reaction is termed **oxidative decarboxylation**.

6
a When oxygen is in short supply, for example in muscles during exercise, there is insufficient oxygen to oxidise all the pyruvate. What happens to the pyruvate that is not oxidised? You may need to refer to Chapter 12 in the AS book.
b In anerobic conditions, pyruvate accepts electrons from reduced NAD. Explain the effect this will have on glycolysis.

The Krebs cycle

Acetyl coenzyme A then enters a cyclic series of reactions called the Krebs cycle, named after Hans Krebs, who discovered the sequence. The reactions of the Krebs cycle, summarised in Fig 1.12, occur in solution in the matrix of the mitochondria. The main goal of the Krebs cycle is to provide a continuous supply of electrons to fuel the next stage of respiration, the electron transport chain. The Krebs cycle itself produces only a small amount of ATP.

At the start of the Krebs cycle, acetyl coenzyme A joins the 2-carbon acetyl part of the molecule onto a 4-carbon acceptor acid to form a 6-carbon acid. Two molecules of carbon dioxide are then removed, and the resulting 4-carbon acceptor acid is recycled. Several electrons are also transferred to NAD and FAD, forming reduced NAD and reduced FAD, respectively, and one molecule of ATP is formed.

During the link reaction and the Krebs cycle, all three carbon atoms are removed from pyruvate (the end product of glycolysis) and are released as free carbon dioxide (Fig 1.12a). All the electrons removed from the three carbon atoms in the pyruvate molecule are transferred to NAD or FAD to produce reduced NAD or reduced FAD (Fig 1.12b).

7 The several reactions of Krebs cycle all occur simultaneously in the same solution in the matrix. Each reaction is catalysed by a different enzyme. Explain how so many different enzyme-controlled reactions can occur simultaneously in the same solution.

Fig 1.12 The Krebs cycle

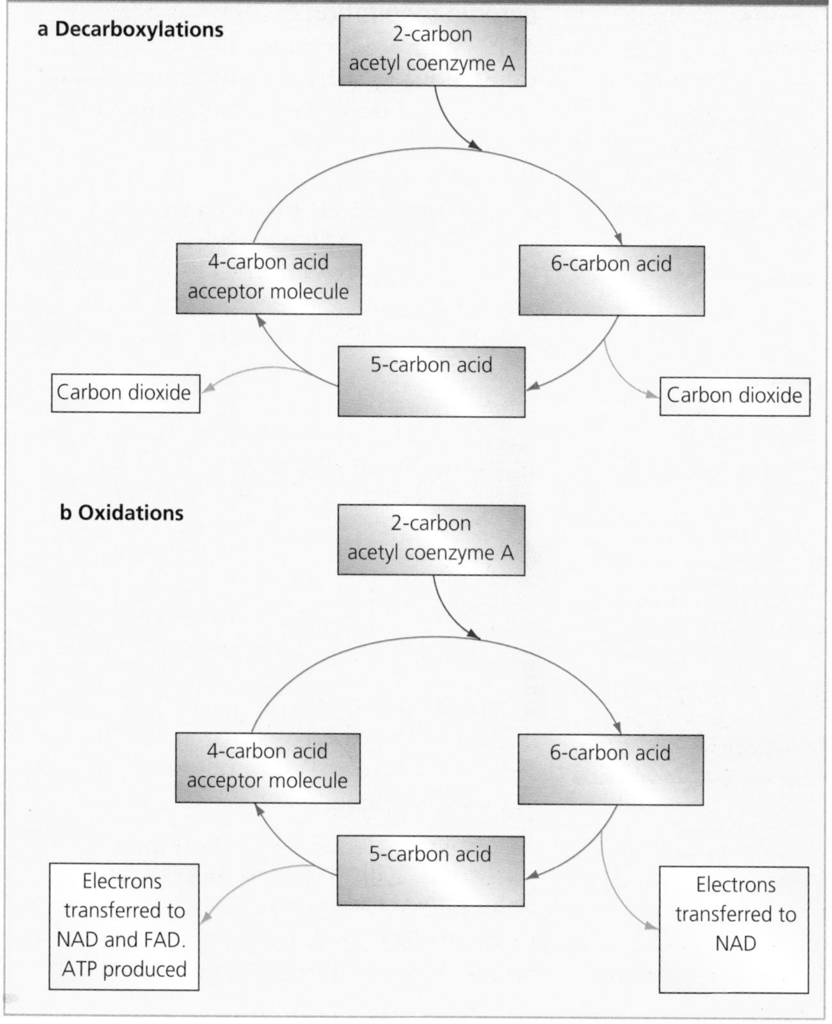

a Decarboxylations

2-carbon acetyl coenzyme A

6-carbon acid

5-carbon acid

Carbon dioxide

4-carbon acid acceptor molecule

Carbon dioxide

b Oxidations

2-carbon acetyl coenzyme A

6-carbon acid

5-carbon acid

Electrons transferred to NAD

4-carbon acid acceptor molecule

Electrons transferred to NAD and FAD. ATP produced

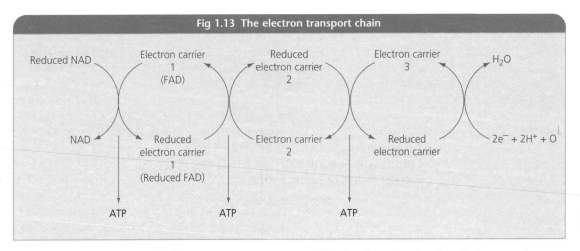

Fig 1.13 The electron transport chain

The electron transport chain

The electrons transferred to NAD and FAD during the Krebs cycle play a key part in the production of large amounts of ATP during the final stage of aerobic respiration. A summary of the reactions that occur in the electron transport chain is shown in Fig 1.13.

Reduced NAD and reduced FAD transfer their electrons to a chain of electron carrier molecules embedded in the phospholipid membranes inside the mitochondria. When electrons are transferred from reduced NAD or reduced FAD along the chain of electron carriers, they provide the energy to power the active transport of hydrogen ions from the outer mitochondrial space across the inner mitochondrial membrane.

The movement of hydrogen ions sets up a large hydrogen ion gradient, creating the pressure for hydrogen ions to go back out of the inner mitochondrial space. There is only one route – through an enzyme that spans the membrane. As hydrogen ions pass through this enzyme, it attaches P_i groups to ADP molecules to form ATP.

The passage of one mole of electron pairs along the chain of carriers from reduced NAD provides enough energy to move sufficient hydrogen ions to produce three moles of ATP. The first electron carrier is FAD, so only two moles of ATP are produced from reduced FAD.

The final carrier in the chain transfers electrons to oxygen atoms. Each of these oxygen atoms picks up two protons and two electrons to produce a molecule of water, which is released back into the cell.

$$2e^- + 2H^+ + O \rightarrow 2H_2O$$

How much ATP is produced during aerobic respiration?

ATP is produced in two different ways during respiration, by **substrate phosphorylation** and by **oxidative phosphorylation**. Substrate phosphorylation occurs:

- during glycolysis: there is a net production of 4 moles of ATP per mole of glucose;

- during Krebs cycle: 1 mole of ATP is produced per circuit.

Oxidative phosphorylation occurs when electrons from reduced NAD and reduced FAD flow along the electron transport chain.

- 3 moles of ATP are produced for every mole of electron pairs that are transferred from reduced NAD into the electron transport chain.

- 2 moles of ATP are produced from every mole of electron pairs that are transferred from reduced FAD into the electron transport chain.

Table 1.1 shows the number of moles of reduced NAD and reduced FAD produced from one mole of glucose during the different stages in aerobic respiration.

Table 1.1 NAD and FAD produced during aerobic respiration		
Stages of aerobic respiration	**Moles of reduced NAD formed**	**Moles of reduced FAD formed**
Glycolysis	2	
Formation of acetyl coenzyme A	2 (1 per pyruvate)	
Krebs cycle	6 (3 per turn)	2 (1 per turn)

8 Calculate the number of moles of ATP produced from 1 mole of glucose during aerobic respiration. Show your working.

9 Anaerobic respiration occurs in the absence of oxygen. It is basically just glycolysis. Bearing this in mind, estimate how much ATP is produced from 1 mole of glucose during anaerobic respiration. What do you think is the significance of this for life on Earth?

Energy transfer in photosynthesis and respiration: a summary

A comparison of photosynthesis and respiration is shown in Fig 1.14.

In photosynthesis, reduced NADP acts as an electron donor to the carbon. In respiration, a similar compound, nicotinamide adenine dinucleotide (NAD) accepts high-energy electrons from carbon and becomes reduced NAD in the process. You can always remember which one of these two is involved in photosynthesis and which in respiration if you remember that the one with the P, NADP, is used in photosynthesis and the other, NAD, is used in respiration.

Reduced NAD therefore contains a great deal of energy. This energy can be released by transferring the electrons to oxygen. The electrons are not transferred from reduced NAD to oxygen directly; the series of oxidation reactions that transfer the electrons makes up the major part of respiration.

During respiration, carbon is oxidised. Four electrons are removed from each atom of carbon, which is exactly the opposite of photosynthesis. Whereas energy is required to add electrons to organic molecules in photosynthesis, removing electrons in respiration releases energy.

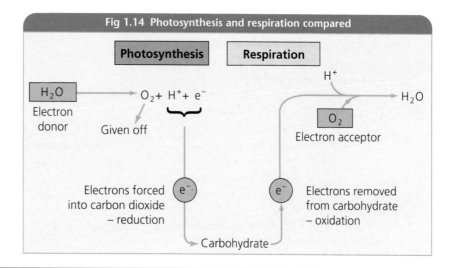

Fig 1.14 Photosynthesis and respiration compared

■ During glycolysis, glucose (6C) is oxidised into two molecules of pyruvate (3C) with a net gain of two moles of ATP and reduced NAD.

■ The pyruvate undergoes oxidative decarboxylation and combines with coenzyme A to produce acetyl coenzyme A (2C)

■ In Krebs cycle, acetyl coenzyme A (which contains 2 carbons) is combined with a 4-carbon acceptor molecule to form a 6-carbon organic acid. This 6-carbon acid then undergoes decarboxylation and oxidation to regenerate the acceptor molecule.

■ Reduced NAD is produced during glycolysis, the formation of acetyl coenzyme A and the Krebs cycle. Reduced FAD is also produced during the Krebs cycle.

■ Electrons from reduced NAD and reduced FAD are transferred to electron carrier chains on the cristae of the mitochondria. As the electrons pass along these chains of carriers, ATP is generated.

■ At the end of the electron carrier chain, electrons, protons and oxygen combine to form water.

■ A total of 38 moles of ATP is produced during the aerobic respiration of one mole of glucose.

1 The diagram shows part of the light-independent reaction of photosynthesis.

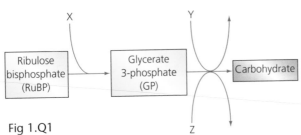

Fig 1.Q1

a In which part of the chloroplast does this series of reactions take place? (1)

b Name the compound labelled X on the diagram. (1)

c Name the two compounds, labelled Y and Z on the diagram, which are necessary for the reduction of glycerate 3-phosphate to carbohydrate. (2)

d Give one possible fate of the glycerate 3-phosphate other than being converted into carbohydrate. (1)

Total (5)

BY01 Feb 1995 Q6

2

a Describe how chloroplasts could be isolated from leaf tissue to investigate their structure and function. (4)

b How is the structure of a chloroplast related to the part it plays in photosynthesis? (4)

Total (8)

BYO1 Feb 96 Q8 parts (a) and (b)

3

a The process of photosynthesis can be subdivided into two stages, one dependent on light, the other independent of light.
  i Complete Table 1.Q3 to show the substances used in and the end products of each of these stages. (Do not include solar energy.) (2)
  ii What are the functions of reduced NADP and ATP in the light-independent stage of photosynthesis? (2)

b The graph in Fig 1.Q3 shows the effect of temperature on the rate of photosynthesis.
  i Explain why increasing the temperature from X °C to Y °C increases the rate of photosynthesis. (2)
  ii Explain why increasing the temperature from Y °C to Z °C decreases the rate of photosynthesis. (2)

Total (8)

BYO1 June 99 Q6

	Light dependent stage	Light independent stage
Substances used	1 Water	1 Reduced NADP
	2 Inorganic phosphate	2 ATP
	3 ADP	3
	4 NADP	4
End products	1 ATP	1 NADP
	2	2 ADP
	3	3 Inorganic phosphate
		4 Carbohydrate

Table 1.Q3

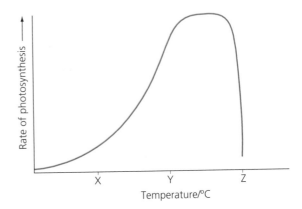

Fig 1.Q3

4 Fig 1. Q4a shows some steps in the light-independent pathway of photosynthesis.

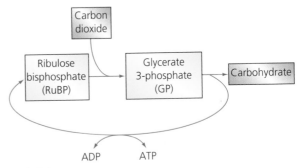

Fig 1.Q4a

a What two substances, produced in the light-dependent reaction, are required for the conversion of glycerate 3-phosphate to carbohydrate? (2)

Some algae were allowed to photosynthesise in the presence of radioactively labelled carbon dioxide. After a time, the light was switched off. Throughout the investigation the amounts of glycerate

3-phosphate and ribulose bisphosphate were measured. The results are shown in Fig 1. Q4b.

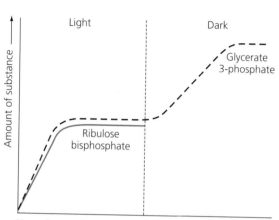

Fig 1.Q4b

b Suggest why, after the light was switched off, the amount of glycerate 3-phosphate
 i increased immediately; (2)
 ii levelled out after a time. (1)

c i Complete the graph by sketching a curve to show what would happen to the amount of ribulose bisphosphate when the light was switched off. (1)
 ii Give an explanation for your answer to (c) (i). (1)

Total (7)

BYO1 Feb 96 Q6

5 The diagram in Fig 1.Q5 represents an outline of cellular respiration.

a
 i Complete the boxes on the diagram to show the number of carbon atoms contained in each molecule. (2)
 ii Complete Table 1.Q5 to show the names of Stages X and Y, and the part of the cell in which each stage occurs. (2)

	Name of stage	Part of cell in which it occurs
Stage X		
Stage Y		

Table 1.Q5

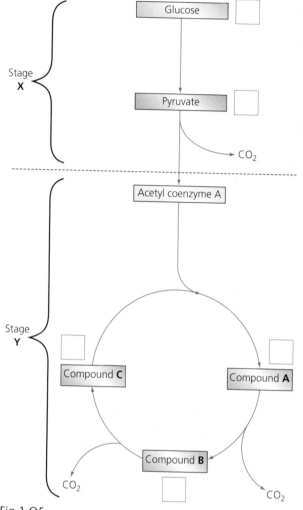

Fig 1.Q5

b Explain what happens to the hydrogen produced during Stage Y. (3)

Total (7)

BY01 June 98 Q5

2 Homeostasis

People with diabetes have trouble controlling their blood glucose level. If the problem is severe, someone with diabetes needs to check their blood glucose levels every few hours and sometimes up to ten times a day. This involves the finger-prick test – a drop of blood is taken from the finger and placed on a test-strip that then indicates the concentration of glucose in the blood. It doesn't sound so bad, but imagine having to do that 10 times a day. The good news is that a new type of watch, the Glucowatch® Biographer can monitor blood glucose levels painlessly, without the need to draw blood. It also has the advantage that it can take measurements much more frequently.

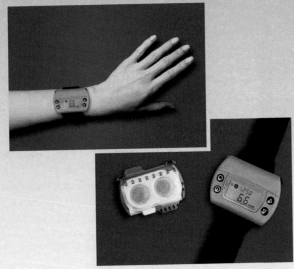

For some people with diabetes, this watch may be better than a Rolex!

The Glucowatch® Biographer checks blood glucose levels every twenty minutes by sending tiny electric currents through the skin. This attracts glucose to the surface of the skin. The sensor in the Glucowatch® Biographer has tiny gel discs that sense the level of glucose in the blood. The monitor gives a reading of the blood glucose level, and sounds an alarm if this becomes dangerously high or low. In the future, this system could be linked to an automatic insulin pump, permanently connected to the person's blood supply. This would allow the pump to respond directly to the blood glucose level, mimicking the body's normal method of maintaining homeostasis.

2.1 What is homeostasis?

All cells in the body need to be in the best physical and chemical conditions possible if they are to function properly. Keeping every cell at the optimum temperature, with enough water and food is a complex task that involves many systems in the body; biologists call this overall control mechanism **homeostasis**.

The word *homeostasis* means *steady state* and refers to the fact that conditions inside the body need to be maintained within certain limits. Some factors – such as temperature and blood pH – are kept within very narrow limits. Others, such as blood glucose, can vary within a wider range without adversely affecting the individual.

For all homeostatic mechanisms you should focus on three basic aspects:

- What causes the change? For example, a rise in external temperature causes the body's temperature to start to rise.

- What detects the change? If body temperature starts to rise, this is detected by the hypothalamus in the brain.

- How is the change corrected? To reduce its temperature, the body sweats, blood vessels in the skin dilate, etc.

You have already come across some important examples of homeostasis. You learned how important it is to keep the water potential of the blood plasma constant in the AS book in Chapter 2. Then, your work on exchange surfaces in Chapter 3 gave you some idea how various animals have become adapted to keep their body temperature within narrow limits. In this chapter of this book you will learn about the homeostatic mechanisms in the human body that keep blood glucose concentration and core body temperature within limits.

Stimulus and response

Homeostasis involves mechanisms that correct changes that occur in the body. These changes are usually brought about by a stimulus. A stimulus can be *external* – it can come from outside the body, or it can be *internal*. When we eat a meal rich in carbohydrate, for example, the absorption of glucose into the blood raises blood glucose concentration. This is an **internal stimulus** that changes conditions inside the body. In a healthy person, the body then responds by producing a hormone that reduces the amount of glucose in the blood, readjusting the balance back towards normal. The way that the Glucowatch® Biographer monitors changes in blood glucose concentrations also involves a stimulus and a response, although these are obviously mechanical rather than physiological. The stimulus is an increase in blood glucose concentration – if this is great enough, the watch responds by sounding an alarm.

Although the stimulus and response are important in homeostasis, they are not the whole story. In order for the body to respond to a stimulus, it must first detect it using a **receptor**. Then, it must have a way of bringing about the response – it must have an **effector**. In most pathways, receptors and effectors are linked by a **coordinator** (Fig 2.1). Control of body temperature involves a homeostatic pathway that has a coordinator (see Section 2.4).

Receptors and effectors

All cells in the body can detect stimuli of one kind or another and all living cells are able to respond to stimuli. For example, when you get a speck of dust in your eye, the stimulus, the dust particle, is detected by touch receptors embedded in the delicate membrane on the surface of the eye. They bring about the automatic blink response to rid the eye of its foreign body. This sort of response is a **nervous response**.

In nervous responses, the receptors are connected to the effectors by nerve cells called **neurones**. In other responses, the link between receptor and effector may be chemicals called hormones carried by the blood. For example, when you are frightened, the adrenal glands, small glands next to the kidneys, release the hormone adrenaline. This has many different effects in the body – it increases heart rate, it diverts blood away from the digestive system to the muscles, and it increases breathing rate. This is the 'fight or flight' response that enables the body to be ready to face a dangerous situation, or to run away from it as fast as possible.

Feedback systems in homeostasis

Receptors and effectors work together in homeostasis in **feedback systems**. In a feedback system, a condition in the body is monitored constantly by a receptor and signals are sent to the effector to produce a response that causes the conditions in the body to return to normal. Fig 2.2 illustrates a negative feedback system that is part of the homeostatic response that regulates blood glucose. This mechanism is covered in detail in the next section.

1 Draw diagrams similar to Fig 2.2 to show one negative feedback process that occurs:

a when the body temperature rises;

b when the body temperature falls.

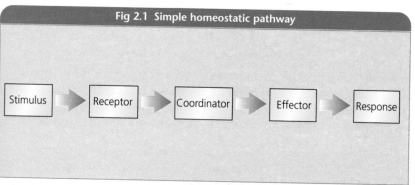

Fig 2.1 Simple homeostatic pathway

Stimulus → Receptor → Coordinator → Effector → Response

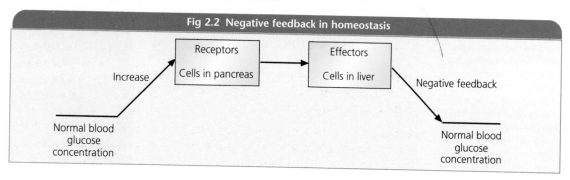

Fig 2.2 Negative feedback in homeostasis

If the response reverses the effect of the original stimulus, the system is described as **negative feedback**. If a response enhances the effect of the original stimulus, this is **positive feedback**. In homeostasis, most feedback systems are negative since these allow the 'fine-tuning' that keeps conditions within physiological limits. Positive feedback systems regulate rather dramatic conditions that do not occur often – such as the onset of puberty (see Application on page 21).

In healthy people, receptor cells in the pancreas detect a rise in blood glucose concentration. They respond by secreting insulin. The insulin affects liver cells so that they return blood glucose concentration to its original level.

2.2 An example of homeostasis: regulation of blood glucose

The control of blood glucose is a classic example of homeostasis. Two negative feedback systems work together to detect and correct a rise or fall in blood glucose, maintaining it within limits that the body can tolerate safely. But why does blood glucose need to be regulated? While other organs can cope with greater variations, the brain needs special attention. This vital organ needs a constant and well-controlled supply of glucose. Although it uses about 25% of the total glucose used by the body, the brain cannot store this important food fuel. The blood must contain between 60 and 120 mg of glucose per cubic decimetre of blood (60–120 mg dm^{-3}) so that it can supply the brain cells. If blood glucose strays outside these limits, even for a few minutes, brain cells can suffer and the central nervous system may not function correctly.

The pancreas plays a central role in regulating blood glucose since it acts as both receptor and effector; the brain is not involved at all. As you can see from the micrographs of sections through the Islets of Langerhans (below), there are two distinct types of cell in this region of the pancreas, **alpha cells (α)** and **beta (β) cells**. The two types of cell secrete different hormones, **glucagon** and **insulin**, which have opposite effects on blood sugar concentration. Fig 2.3 shows an overall summary of how these two hormones control blood glucose.

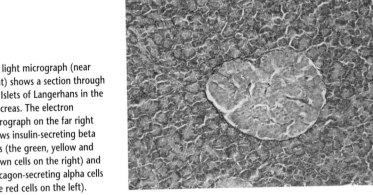
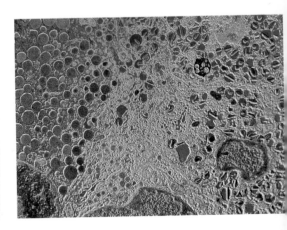

The light micrograph (near right) shows a section through the Islets of Langerhans in the pancreas. The electron micrograph on the far right shows insulin-secreting beta cells (the green, yellow and brown cells on the right) and glucagon-secreting alpha cells (the red cells on the left).

What brings on puberty in girls?

The menstrual cycle in women is controlled by hormones produced by the pituitary gland and by the ovary. During childhood the pituitary gland secretes small amounts of two hormones, FSH and LH, and the ovary secretes small amounts of oestrogen hormones. Puberty begins at about the age of nine when the pituitary gland increases the secretion of FSH. FSH causes oestrogen secretion by the ovaries to increase. The first outward sign of increased oestrogen secretion is the appearance of breast buds and later effects include the growth of pubic hair and of the uterus.

Increased oestrogen secretion between the ages of ten to twelve has a positive feedback effect increasing the production of both FSH and LH. Similarly, the more FSH, the more oestrogen that is produced, so the concentrations of all three hormones in the blood rises sharply between the ages of ten and twelve. However, the positive feedback effect of oestrogen on FSH production is only temporary. As the pituitary gland matures, its sensitivity changes and, by the age of thirteen to fourteen, oestrogen starts to have a negative feedback effect on FSH production (but not on LH production). The effect of this is to kick in the menstrual cycle.

During the course of the menstrual cycle, FSH secretion results in oestrogen secretion, but oestrogen secretion inhibits FSH secretion, so the concentrations of these hormones eventually settle into a monthly cycle of related peaks and troughs. In the menstrual cycle, release of an egg is stimulated when the concentration of LH peaks; this peaking of LH is caused by the positive feedback effect of rising oestrogen concentration.

1 Fertility drugs contain FSH. Birth control pills contain a cocktail of hormones that mimic the effects of oestrogen on FSH production. Suggest how fertility drugs and birth control pills work.

2 Although examples of positive feedback are relatively rare, they are involved in several other aspects of the reproductive process as well as those mentioned in this text – orgasm and the process of labour, for example. Why could these processes not be controlled by negative feedback?

3 What broadly different roles do negative and positive feedback play in the human body?

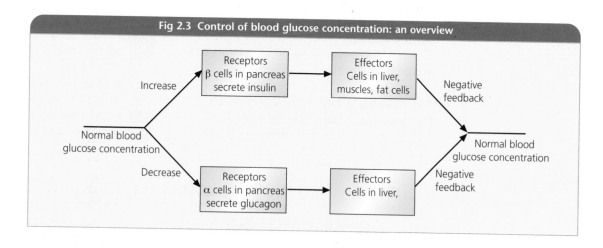

Fig 2.3 Control of blood glucose concentration: an overview

What happens when blood glucose falls?

The alpha cells in the Islets of Langerhans in the pancreas are receptor cells. They detect a *decrease* in blood glucose concentration. When the concentration of glucose in blood flowing through the pancreas falls, the alpha cells respond by secreting the hormone glucagon. Glucagon has its effect mainly on the liver. It activates enzymes inside cells that convert glycogen into glucose, a process called **glycogenolysis**. The glucose then diffuses into the blood, increasing blood glucose concentration towards its normal level. This process is therefore an example of negative feedback.

What happens when blood glucose rises?

The beta cells in the Islets of Langerhans in the pancreas are also receptor cells but they are sensitive to an *increase* in blood glucose concentration. When the concentration of glucose in blood flowing through the pancreas rises, the beta cells respond by secreting the hormone **insulin**. This travels to all parts of the body in the blood, but it mainly affects cells in the muscles, liver and adipose (fat storage) tissue. Insulin increases the rate at which liver cells, muscle cells and fat cells absorb glucose.

Insulin stimulates glucose carrier proteins in the cytoplasm to move to the cell surface membrane. The more carrier molecules that reach the surface, the greater the quantity of glucose that can be absorbed. Insulin also activates enzymes in the liver to convert glucose into glycogen, a process called **glycogenesis**. This decreases the blood glucose concentration of blood passing through the liver. Insulin secretion therefore causes a fall in blood glucose concentration to bring it down to normal level, and is therefore another example of negative feedback.

Fig 2.4 shows the how the rate of glucose intake into the liver is affected by the presence of insulin.

As insulin and glucagon have opposite effects on blood sugar level they are said to be **antagonistic**. Insulin acts to decrease blood glucose concentration, glycogen acts to increase it. Many other hormones that are involved in homeostasis also operate as **antagonistic pairs**.

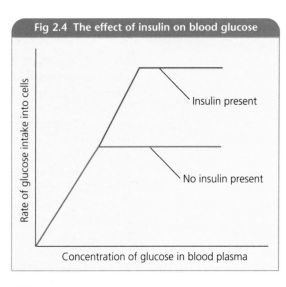

Fig 2.4 The effect of insulin on blood glucose

Rate of glucose intake into cells (vertical axis)

Insulin present

No insulin present

Concentration of glucose in blood plasma (horizontal axis)

3

a What type of carbohydrate is glycogen?

b How is glycogen adapted to this function by its shape?

4

a What type of reaction causes the breakdown of glycogen into glucose?

b What type of reaction converts glucose to glycogen?

5 Glucose enters liver cells by facilitated diffusion.

a What are the main factors that affect the rate of facilitated diffusion of a substance into a cell?

b How does an increase in the number of carrier proteins in the cell surface membrane increase the rate of glucose uptake by cells?

2 Only 2% of cells in the pancreas are involved in blood glucose regulation. What is the function of the other 98%?

2.3 Diabetes: when blood glucose regulation fails

One form of diabetes is called **Type I diabetes**, or early onset diabetes. Symptoms usually appear in young people, under the age of 20. The affected person has a problem with the alpha cells in the pancreas – they may have been damaged or destroyed by an autoimmune response. As a result, the pancreas cannot release insulin when blood glucose rises. Until insulin treatment was developed in the 1930s, this form of diabetes was usually fatal. Since insulin treatment for

diabetes was developed 75 years ago, millions of diabetics have been able to live relatively normal lives - but they have had to inject themselves daily with insulin. The hormone cannot be taken as a pill because it is digested by the enzymes in the gut.

In order to stay healthy, diabetics need to balance what they eat and the amount of insulin they inject very carefully. If they inject too much insulin, or skip a meal, or take too much strenuous exercise, their blood glucose can fall too low. Low blood glucose is known as **hypoglycaemia**, and this is often described by diabetics as 'having a hypo'. The symptoms include sweating, trembling, hunger, blurring of vision, and difficulty in concentration. Eating sugars soon raises the blood sugar concentration and the symptoms disappear. An untreated 'hypo' can lead to unconsciousness.

The opposite can also happen. If the person is not keeping to their diet and eating too much carbohydrate, or if they are taking too little insulin, blood glucose can rise to dangerously high levels. This is called **hyperglycaemia**. The symptoms include feeling sick, drowsiness and stomach pain. It can also lead to unconsciousness if left untreated.

Sugary drinks and foods seem like fun but eating too much of them when you are a child and a young adult is thought to increase your risk of developing diabetes in later life.

6

a Explain why diabetics are encouraged to eat starchy foods rather than sugary foods.

b Suggest an explanation for the symptoms of 'hypo'.

Another form of diabetes is the more common **Type II diabetes**. This accounts for about 90% of all cases of diabetes in the industrialised world. Unlike Type I diabetes, it tends to first appear later in life, typically about the age of 40 in people who are overweight. It is not caused by damage to the islet cells; it occurs because all cells in the body become unable to respond to insulin. When their blood glucose level rises, insulin is released normally, but something goes wrong with the way it is detected by cells. They no longer increase the number of glucose carrier proteins on their cell membranes, and blood glucose can remain higher than normal.

This link between diabetes and obesity has intrigued scientists for years but they could not prove a link between the two. In January 2001, scientists in the USA discovered a new hormone in mice – called *resistin*. This is produced by fat cells and it makes cells in the body resistant to the effects of insulin. Humans also produce resistin, but further research will be needed to find out if it really is the important link between being fat and becoming diabetic.

KEY FACTS

- The pancreas both monitors and controls blood glucose concentration; the brain is *not* involved.

- **Alpha cells** in the pancreas detect a fall in blood glucose concentration and respond by secreting the hormone **glucagon**.

- Glucagon activates enzymes in the liver that convert glycogen to glucose.

- **Beta cells** in the pancreas detect a rise in blood glucose concentration and respond by secreting the hormone **insulin**.

- Insulin increases the rate of uptake of glucose by body cells by stimulating the movement of carrier protein molecules from the cytoplasm to the cell surface membrane. These carrier protein molecules move glucose into the cells by facilitated diffusion.

- Insulin also activates enzymes in the liver that catalyse condensation reactions that convert glucose to glycogen.

- The actions of both insulin and glucagon result in negative feedback, bringing the blood glucose concentration back to normal.

- When control of blood glucose fails, **diabetes** can develop. Type I diabetes occurs when cells in the Islets of Langerhans are damaged and no longer produce insulin. Type II diabetes is a result of cells in the body becoming resistant to the effects of insulin.

APPLICATION

Insulin

The search for ways of producing human insulin began when doctors realised that insulin from animals was not always effective and that it caused side effects in many patients.

Insulin is a protein. It has two peptide chains joined together by sulphur bridges. It is a small molecule and was one of the first proteins to be described in terms of its primary structure. The sequence of amino acids that make up insulin was worked out in 1949. However, although its structure was known, repeated attempts to synthesize insulin gave very poor yields. It didn't seem possible to get the sulphur bridges to form between the two peptide chains to make the functional molecule.

The breakthrough came when a protein called proinsulin was discovered in the pancreas. This longer protein is the molecule from which insulin is formed in the body.

Proinsulin is a relatively simple molecule to synthesise because it consists of single peptide chain. If the 33 amino acids in the C peptide are then chopped of (see the diagram below), the remaining parts of the molecule form insulin using the correct sulphur bridges. This mirrors exactly what happens in the beta cells of the pancreas.

1 a What is a peptide?

b What type of enzyme will remove the C peptide from proinsulin?

c Apart from length, what other differences are there likely to be between the three peptides?

d How many nucleotides are needed to code for proinsulin?

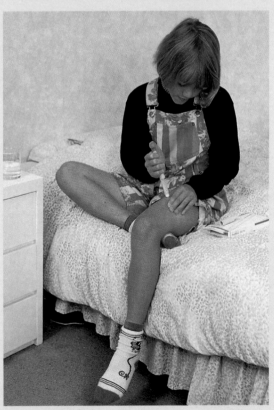

A teenage girl giving herself an insulin injection.

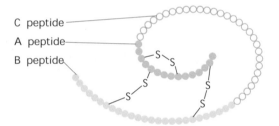

The scientists first produced the whole proinsulin molecule. They then removed 33 amino acids, the C peptide as shown. This left two separate peptides, the A and B peptides joined by sulphur bridges.

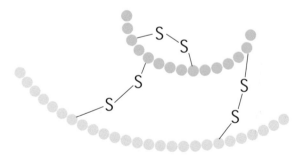

2.4 Temperature regulation

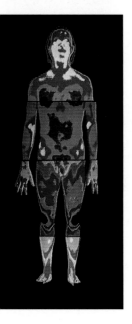

During some illnesses caused by microbes, the body temperature rises as high as 40 °C, causing weakness or exhaustion. Such a temperature is not in itself a serious threat to health so long as it does not persist. However, serious fevers, in which body temperature rises to 42 °C, even for a short time, can result in convulsions and death. Although infection by microbes can be the cause of a severe fever, ironically, many of these infective microbes are extremely susceptible to a rise in body temperature. A fever can therefore be regarded as one of the body's defence mechanisms against microbes.

Body temperature regulation is another good example of homeostasis. Mammals try to keep a high, constant body temperature so that the enzyme-controlled reactions in their bodies always proceed at the optimum temperature. In normal conditions, even when we are exercising, the core temperature of humans does not vary by more than 1 °C, and it does not exceed 37.8 °C. How does the body manage such tight control?

Much of the energy released by respiration in mammals is transferred as thermal energy. It is this thermal energy that keeps body temperature above that of the surroundings. When the surrounding air is warmer than ideal body temperature, a mammal must lose some of is heat to the surroundings. The mechanisms involved are discussed opposite, and on through to page 28. When the surrounding air is cooler than the mammal, the body loses heat, mainly by radiation and convection, and it must conserve heat, or increase its generation of heat, to maintain its body temperature. The mechanisms involved are covered on pages 28-31.

The body's thermostat

The nervous system plays a major part in the homeostatic control of body temperature in mammals. The **hypothalamus**, a region at the base of the brain (Fig 2.5), acts a bit like the thermostat in a central heating system, but with an important difference. A room thermostat simply switches the circulating pump on when the room temperature falls, and switches it off when the room temperature reaches the thermostat setting. It can control the transfer of energy as heat into

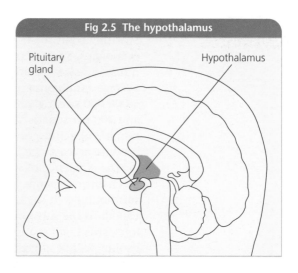

Fig 2.5 The hypothalamus

Pituitary gland

Hypothalamus

a room, but it can do nothing to cool the room down on a hot day. In contrast, the hypothalamus is able to detect an increase or a decrease in body temperature, and respond to both. It has two regions:

- the **heat loss centre**, a group of cells at the front of the hypothalamus, switches on both sweating and increased blood flow to the skin surface if the body temperature rises;

- the **heat gain centre**, a group of cells at the rear of the hypothalamus initiates responses to prevent the body cooling down too much.

What happens when the body needs to cool down?

Inside the hypothalamus, both sets of receptor cells constantly monitor the temperature of the blood. An increase in blood temperature stimulates cells in the heat loss centre. This centre is known as a **coordinator** because it coordinates what happens next. Nerve impulses are sent from the heat loss centre along neurones to effectors. Effectors bring about a change or response. In this case the effectors are the sweat glands in the skin and arterioles that supply the skin capillaries. When the nerve impulses arrive, sweat glands increase their production of sweat and the arterioles increase the supply of blood to capillaries near to the surface of the skin.

Sweating and vasodilation, the two main processes that help the body cool down are both negative feedback mechanisms since they help to restore normal body temperature.

Sweating

Sweating cools the body as the sweat evaporates. Sweat is produced by the body's numerous sweat glands – the skin of the average adult contains between 2 000 000 and 5 000 000 sweat glands. That's between 150 and 300 per square centimetre. With this number of glands, even on a cool day you produce at least one litre of sweat.

The efficiency of sweating as a cooling mechanism depends on the humidity of the surroundings. If there is very little water vapour in the surrounding air (humidity is low), sweat will evaporate more easily and the cooling will be effective. In dry air, humans can tolerate air temperatures of 65 °C for several hours. If, however, the air is saturated with water vapour (humidity is high), the sweat cannot evaporate. In these conditions, sweat simply drips off the body and temperatures of only 35 °C can cause the human body to overheat. Some mammals are adapted for hot conditions, but humidity and high temperature can lead to heat stress in even the best-adapted animal.

Vasodilation

When you exercise on a hot day your skin becomes flushed. This is caused by an increase in the rate at which blood flows through the capillaries in the surface layers of

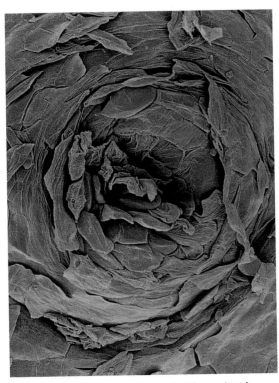

False-colour scanning electron micrograph of the opening of a sweat gland in the surface of human skin.

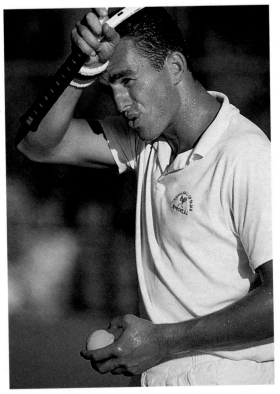

the skin. This transfers more thermal energy from the blood to the surface layers of the skin, which increases the skin temperature and thus the rate of radiant energy loss from the skin. (*Remember not to make the all too common error of stating that blood vessels move towards the surface of the skin!*)

The increase in the rate of blood supply to the capillaries in the surface layers of the skin is brought about by changes to two sets of arterioles in the skin (see Fig 2.6). The arterioles that supply the capillaries **dilate** (become wider), whilst the 'bypass' arterioles, which divert blood away from the capillaries, **constrict** (become narrower). As blood flows through the surface capillaries, it becomes cooler as the effect of radiation is greater. As this cooler blood returns to the core of the body, thermal energy is transferred to it from the tissues by conduction, cooling the tissues.

7

a How does the structure of arterioles enable them to constrict?

b What brings about the dilation of arterioles?

8 Draw a flow chart that shows the sequence of events as the body heats up beyond its normal body temperature.

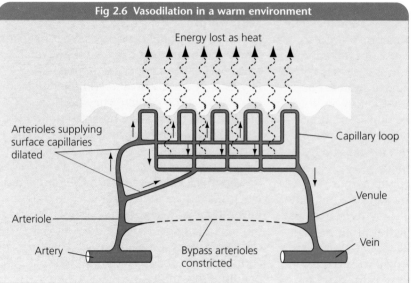

Fig 2.6 Vasodilation in a warm environment

Energy lost as heat

Arterioles supplying surface capillaries dilated

Capillary loop

Arteriole

Venule

Artery

Bypass arterioles constricted

Vein

Special techniques for cooling down

Panting

Some fur-covered mammals like dogs and cats do not possess sweat glands. Fur reduces the rate of evaporation of sweat to such an extent that sweating produces no cooling effect. The sweat glands have therefore been lost during evolution. So what do these animals do to cool down? You have probably noticed dogs panting. To lose thermal energy, they breathe rapidly but shallowly. The rapid passage of air cools the blood in the blood vessels surrounding the mouth and lungs. The correct name for this process is **thermal panting**. A dog may pant up to 300 times a minute on a hot day.

APPLICATION

Football can be a dangerous game

This statement is true – but not not for the reasons you might think. The highest cause of sports-related death amongst American high school football players is not physical injury, but heat stress! About six players die each year from this and many more are made seriously ill.

The problem is mainly due to the padding used to prevent physical injuries. The padding around the chest and shoulders has a mass or about 6 kg. But most types of padding do not allow sweat to evaporate. A typical footballer produces about 5 kJ of heat energy per minute during a game. Without all the padding he would lose about 4.5 kJ of heat energy per minute by the evaporation of sweat. However, if the sweat can't evaporate, his core body temperature may rise by about 1 °C every 5 minutes. If precautions are not taken he will soon be feeling heat-stress symptoms.

To alleviate this problem, scientists have developed a special quilted fabric for padding the footballers. This fabric consists of three layers:

- An inner, porous, good thermal conducting layer
- A sandwiched layer of water-absorbing fibres
- An outer layer of breathable material.

1 Explain how this new material will help the footballers to keep cool.

2 Suggest how the beefy physique of American footballers contributes to heat stress.

Getting wet

Sweat cools the body when it evaporates so it makes sense for animals that don't sweat to find another way to make use of evaporation.

The kangaroo rat lives in hot deserts where water is scarce. These rats have short fur and no sweat glands but to cool themselves down on a hot day they produce saliva that they then lick all over their body. This evaporates, taking thermal energy from the rat's body, and produces a cooling effect.

By comparison, the hippopotamus is a giant compared to the tiny kangaroo rat, but it also lives in a hot environment, in tropical areas of the world. Although it produces sweat, it has a small surface area to volume ratio and must find extra help to keep cool. One of its favourite activities is to spend most of the day wallowing in a pool of water, only coming out at night to graze. This has a dual effect; during the day, when the environment is at its hottest, the hippopotamus transfers thermal energy to the water by conduction. Since water has a higher specific heat capacity than air, this process is much more efficient than trying to cool down in air. At night, when the hippopotamus emerges from its pool, the water evaporates from the surface of its skin, providing an adequate cooling effect in the lower temperatures of the night.

The tiny kangaroo rat (top right) and the huge, wallowing hippopotamus (below right) have very different strategies for keeping cool, but both involve getting wet.

What happens when the body needs to keep warm?

So far we have only considered what happens when large mammals overheat. Most small mammals have the opposite problem: they have a large surface area to volume ratio and can lose heat too rapidly. They need mechanisms to conserve heat and to increase core body temperature when necessary. This is particularly important for small mammals that spend their lives swimming in cool water.

Peripheral cold receptors in the skin detect when the temperature of the surroundings is lower than body temperature and send nerve impulses along neurones to the heat gain centre in the hypothalamus. This then coordinates the body's response to the cold conditions by inhibiting the activity of the heat loss centre and by sending impulses along neurones to a range of effector mechanisms across the body. These bring about:

- vasoconstriction;
- hair erection;
- shivering;
- an increase in metabolic activity in brown fat;
- the release of hormones.

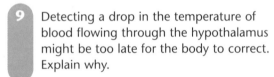

9 Detecting a drop in the temperature of blood flowing through the hypothalamus might be too late for the body to correct. Explain why.

Vasoconstriction

Reducing the amount of heat lost through the skin is achieved by reducing the amount of blood that flows through capillaries near the surface, as shown in Fig 2.7. When detector cells in the heat gain centre are stimulated, they send impulses to the arterioles in the skin. Their action has the opposite effect to impulses coming from the heat loss centre. Heat gain centre impulses force the arterioles that supply the capillaries to constrict, and they cause the 'bypass' arterioles that divert blood away from the capillaries to dilate. This reduces the rate of blood flow through the surface capillaries and consequently reduces heat loss by radiation. In pale-skinned people, the skine becomes emuch whiter, or even bluish, as the blood is no longer visible in the surface layers of the skin, – hence the expression 'to turn blue with cold'.

Fig 2.7 Vasoconstriction in a cold environment

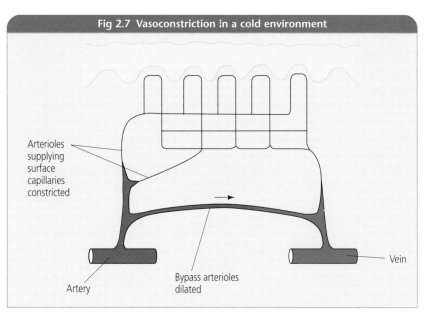

Arterioles supplying surface capillaries constricted

Artery

Bypass arterioles dilated

Vein

Fig 2.8 Hair erection and keeping warm

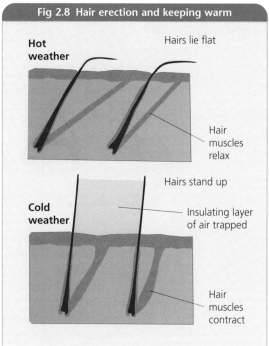

Hot weather

Hairs lie flat

Hair muscles relax

Hairs stand up

Cold weather

Insulating layer of air trapped

Hair muscles contract

Hair erection

Hair erection is another good strategy for conserving body heat – particularly in long-haired mammals (Fig 2.8). In the arctic fox, for example, the insulation provided by the air trapped within its fur is so efficient that the animal does not begin to increase heat production until the external temperature drops to –40 °C.

Each hair in mammalian skin has a muscle attached to a point near its base. When a nerve impulse arrives from the heat gain centre of the hypothalamus, the hair is pulled upright. This process is known as **hair erection**.

You have probably noticed this on your own skin – a 'goose pimple' is a part of the skin where a hair has been pulled upright. The effect of all the hairs in the skin being pulled upright is to trap a layer of air next to the skin. Air is a poor conductor of heat, so the layer of trapped air acts as an insulator, reducing energy transfer by radiation and convection. This method of conserving

energy may be important in fur-covered mammals; it is of little value to humans because we have such short hairs.

Shivering

When we get cold, the brain sends impulses to the skeletal muscles that cause them to contract spasmodically. We call this **shivering**. Shivering muscles have a higher rate of respiration to provide the energy for muscle contraction. Since respiration in muscle cells is very inefficient – up to 80% of the energy released by the oxidation of glucose is transferred as thermal energy –- lots of extra heat is released. This is transferred to the blood passing through the muscles, and then to the tissues and organs.

Brown fat

Some mammals, including some humans, have layers of cells containing 'brown fat', mainly under the skin at the back of the neck. When impulses arrive from the hypothalamus, the cells containing brown fat rapidly oxidise fatty acids to release energy as heat. The position of this tissue means that it acts rather like an electric blanket for the blood supply to the brain. Human babies have an almost complete covering of brown fat, but most of this disappears as we grow up. Babies use brown fat rather than shivering to generate thermal energy when they are cold. Many hibernating mammals can switch on

The arctic fox; happy at temperatures as low as -40 °C, thanks to its furry insulation.

29

APPLICATION   **Treating hypothermia**

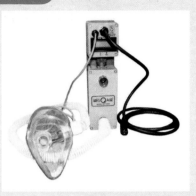

Hypothermia is a fall in core body temperature that occurs when the body remains in a cold environment for too long. Hypothermia can affect anyone, from a child who falls through thin ice into cold water, to a super-fit climbing enthusiast stranded on a mountain during bad weather, to a frail elderly woman whose house is too cold because she can't afford heating bills.

Treating hypothermia is difficult and people have been known to survive long periods of cold, even though they appeared dead when discovered. The basic principles in treating hypothermia are:

- prevention of further heat loss;

- rewarming as soon as is safely possible at a 'successful' rate, i.e. a rate which will not itself produce further damage;

- rewarming the core before the shell, in an attempt to avoid inducing lethal side effects during rewarming.

Hypothermia causes several reactions within the body as it tries to protect itself and retain its heat. The most important of these is vasoconstriction, which halts blood flow to the extremities in order to conserve heat in the critical core area of the body.

When core temperature exceeds 30 °C the major source of heat production is shivering. This maintains peripheral vasoconstriction, which minimises the severity of vascular collapse during rewarming. Induction of vasodilation in these patients may precipitate rewarming shock.

Rapid shunting of cold blood from the periphery to the core as the direct result of vasodilation may cause the core temperature to drop. This phenomenon of a drop in temperature after initiation of therapy is termed core temperature **after-drop**. Prevention of vasodilation is the reason why it is imperative that the patient's extremities should not be rewarmed before the core. If vasodilation occurs, cold blood returning to the heart may be enough to cause ventricular fibrillation (abnormal heartbeat).

The patient must also be handled very gently and not be allowed to exercise, as muscular action can pump cold blood to the heart. One method of treating hypothermia is inhalation rewarming, getting the patient to breathe warmed air. This can be done with equipment such as RES-Q-AIR, which is shown in the photograph above left.

Another method, only to be used if the patient has relatively mild hypothermia, is to place the patient in a warm bath. The graph below left shows the effects of these two treatments on a patient with mild hypothermia, compared with simply leaving the patient to shiver.

1 What is the main way in which the body tries to maintain core body temperature in cold conditions?

2 Why should vasodilation be avoided during recovery from hypothermia?

3 a What is meant by after-drop?
b Why is after-drop dangerous?

4 Explain why placing the patient in a warm bath causes the drop in temperature labelled X on the graph.

5 Explain why inhalation rewarming results in a steady increase in core temperature with no after-drop.

Graph: x-axis "Rewarming time/minutes" (0 to 60); y-axis "Temperature change/°C" (−0.4 to 2.0). Curves labelled "Bath", "Inhalation rewarming", "Shivering only", and "Area shows heart temperature after-drop" with point X.

11 Polar bears live in the arctic. Suggest ways in which the polar bear is adapted for survival in cold conditions.

this 'electric blanket' during particularly cold weather to prevent frostbite or freezing to death.

10 Why can brown fat cells generate much more thermal energy than white fat cells?

Hormones

Several hormones are important in temperature regulation. One is adrenaline, a hormone secreted by the adrenal glands.

Adrenaline acts on the liver in much the same way as glucagon – it brings about the hydrolysis of glycogen to glucose. When adrenaline reaches body tissues it causes an almost immediate, but short-lived, increase in the rate of respiration in the cells. The energy released in respiration is transferred as heat to the blood passing through these tissues. Another is thyroxine, a hormone produced by the thyroid gland. This has the same effect on the rate of respiration as adrenaline, but the effect is slower and more prolonged.

KEY FACTS

- ■ The **hypothalamus** monitors and controls body temperature.

- ■ The principal receptors involved are temperature receptors in the hypothalamus and in the surface layers of the skin. The skin receptors are particularly important in detecting a fall in external temperature.

- ■ Heat loss mechanisms include:
  - **Sweating**; it is the evaporation of sweat that cools the body;
  - **Vasodilation**; the arterioles that supply the capillaries *dilate*, whilst the 'bypass' arterioles that divert blood away from the capillaries *constrict*.

- ■ Heat gain mechanisms include
  - **Vasoconstriction**; the arterioles that supply the capillaries *constrict*, whilst the 'bypass' arterioles that divert blood away from the capillaries *dilate*;
  - Contraction of the hair erector muscles; the erect hairs trap an insulating layer of air;
  - Shivering: skeletal muscles contract releasing thermal energy;
  - High metabolic rate in the brown fat tissue.

- ■ The adrenal and thyroid glands produce hormones that increase the rate of metabolism.

- ■ Remember that blood vessels do NOT move up and down in the skin. Always make clear whether you are referring to arterioles or to capillaries, vasodilation and vasoconstriction refer to arterioles – NOT capillaries.

1 The table shows how the concentrations of insulin and glucose in the plasma vary at different times.

When measurement was taken	Plasma insulin concentration units per cm³	Plasma glucose concentration mg per 100 cm³
During overnight fast	10	60–100
During a meal	70	110–180
After a meal	10	60–100
During prolonged fasting	5	50–70

a Describe the relationship between glucose concentration and insulin concentration in the plasma. (1)

b Explain the rise in plasma glucose and insulin levels that occurs during the meal. (3)

c Use information from the table to explain how the control of insulin production is an example of negative feedback. (2)

d The plasma glucose level is maintained at a minimum of 50 mg per 100 cm³ during prolonged fasting. Suggest how this might be achieved. (2)

Total (8)

BY03 Feb 95 Q4

2 Certain cells in mice have two transmembrane protein systems for the transport of glucose into the cells. The GLUT-1 system transports glucose all the time. The GLUT-4 system is not active all the time and is affected by the presence of insulin.

a
  i Explain why cells need a GLUT-1 system.
  ii Suggest what the effect of insulin on the GLUT-4 system would be. (4)

b Genetically engineered mice have been produced which have many extra GLUT-1 systems in their cell membranes. These mice do not react to insulin, although they have the GLUT-4 system.

Suggest why these genetically engineered mice do not react to insulin. (2)

Total (6)

BY03 Feb 96 Q6

3 Describe the role of the pancreas and the liver in the control of blood sugar concentration. (6)

Total (6)

BY03 March 98 Q9 Part (a)

4 Read the following passage and answer the questions that follow:

Diabetes

Diabetes mellitus is a group of disorders that all lead to an increase in blood glucose concentration (hyperglycaemia). The two major types of diabetes mellitus are Type I and Type II. In Type I diabetes there is a deficiency of insulin. Type I diabetes is also called insulin-dependent diabetes mellitus because regular injections of insulin are essential. It most commonly develops in people younger than age twenty.

Type II diabetes most often occurs in people who are over forty and overweight. Clinical symptoms may be mild, and the high glucose concentrations in the blood can often be controlled by diet and exercise. Some Type II diabetics secrete low amounts of insulin but others have a sufficient amount or even a surplus of insulin in the blood. For these people, diabetes arises not from a shortage of insulin but because target cells become less responsive to it. Type II diabetes is therefore called non-insulin-dependent diabetes mellitus.

a Describe how blood glucose concentration is controlled by hormones in an individual who is not affected by diabetes. (6)

b Suggest how diet and exercise can maintain low glucose concentrations in the blood of type II diabetics. (3)

Total (9)

BY03 June 2000 Q8 Parts (a) and (b)

EXAMINATION QUESTIONS

5 A baboon is a large monkey. It normally regulates its body temperature in the same way as a human.

a When a baboon's blood temperature rises, it is able to detect this rise and produce a coordinated response.
  i Where are the receptors that detect the rise in temperature? (1)
  ii Describe how the response is coordinated. (2)

b Baboons that live in the Kalahari desert in southern Africa have to survive occasional very hot dry periods when no rain falls. During these periods, no drinking water is available. Suggest why the body temperature of a baboon fluctuates much more during a hot dry spell when it cannot get water to drink. (2)

Total (5)

BY01 June 2000 Q7

6 The following observations were made during studies on temperature control in animals.

Use your knowledge of thermoregulation to provide an explanation for each of these observations:

a On a hot day a kangaroo rat produces a lot of saliva which it then licks over its body. (2)

b A mouse exposed to low environmental temperatures
  i lies curled up in a ball; (1)
  ii has pale ears and feet. (3)

Total (6)

BY01 June 97 Q3

7 All living organisms exist in changing external environments and many are able to control their internal environments.

a Explain how the body of a mammal may respond to a rise in the environmental temperature. (8)

b Describe the important differences between the nervous and hormonal co-ordination systems found in a mammal. (4)

Total (12)

BY01 March 99 Q7

3 Regulation by the liver and kidney

Liver failure is one of the most common causes of death in people who have taken an overdose of either medicinal or 'social' drugs. Some drugs may kill large numbers of liver cells. As the normal functions of the liver grind to a halt, metabolic by-products begin to accumulate in the blood. One of these, ammonia, is highly toxic. Other by-products, benzodiazepines, are particularly dangerous if not removed – they poison the brain and they inhibit regeneration of liver cells. The tranquilliser Valium is a benzodiazepine, so an overdose of Valium is particularly bad news for the liver.

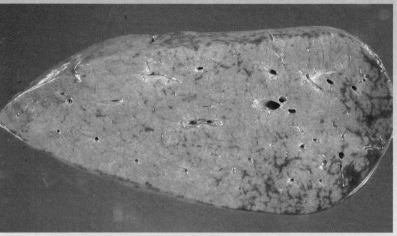

Fortunately, this is a tough organ that fights back. If someone who has taken a drug overdose doesn't die of the initial effects of the poison, their liver cells may grow again naturally. The liver has tremendous powers of regeneration – more than any other part of the body. A surgeon can remove 90% of the liver in a cancer patient, for example, and it will grow back to within 1% of its original size.

Keeping people alive until this happens can be tricky. An early method involved passing the patient's blood through an isolated pig's liver. This worked well for a short time but, after a few days, antibodies produced by the patient's white blood cells started to destroy the pig's liver cells. Today, a more likely treatment is to transplant part of a donor's liver into the overdose patient. The transplanted liver removes ammonia and benzodiazepines from the blood and carries out the liver's other normal functions. When the patient's own liver cells have regenerated, the transplanted liver is removed. The problem with this method is obtaining livers for transplant. To get around this, scientists have been trying for some time now to develop 'liver machines' that contain cultures of human liver cells. The idea is to use this artificial but living structure to carry out most, if not all, normal liver function until the patient's own liver recovers.

3.1 Dealing with waste; some basic principles

In this chapter we consider the roles of the liver and the kidney in removing **metabolic waste** from the body.

Metabolic waste is the unwanted material that is formed as a result of the body's **metabolism** – the huge number of chemical reactions that occur in cells, tissues and organs. You learned at GCSE that the removal of metabolic waste is called **excretion**. Here is a reminder of some of the waste products that the body must get rid of:

- **Carbon dioxide** is the main waste product from cell respiration, the process that releases energy from organic molecules (see this book, Chapter 1). This leaves the body mainly in exhaled air;

- **Urea** is produced by the breakdown of excess amino acids in the liver (Fig 3.1). The body cannot store proteins so it has to break down the proteins it cannot use into their component amino acids. The liver converts amino acids to urea, which goes to the kidneys and then leaves the body in urine.

Fig 3.1 Basic structure of an amino acid

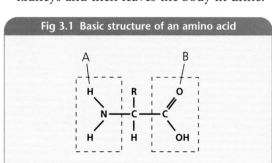

Excess water and salts are also lost in the urine, but these are not waste products and it would be unwise to say this in an exam. The body needs to maintain the correct balance of water and salts and, depending on the conditions, these may be conserved or removed. These levels are controlled by the kidney and an excess of water or salts is removed in the urine.

It is important to realise that the removal of metabolic waste products and excess water and salts are examples of homeostasis (see this book, Chapter 2). This process keeps the conditions in the body within acceptable limits.

APPLICATION   **Artificial livers?**

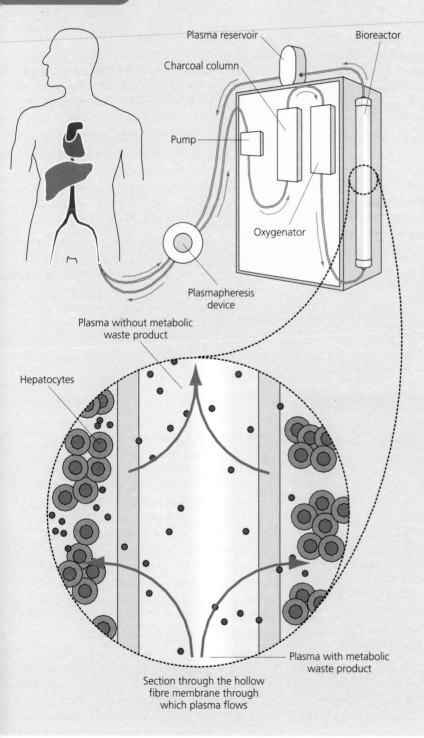

Plasma reservoir

Bioreactor

Charcoal column

Pump

Oxygenator

Plasmapheresis device

Plasma without metabolic waste product

Hepatocytes

Plasma with metabolic waste product

Section through the hollow fibre membrane through which plasma flows

Bioartificial devices are proving increasingly successful in treating liver failure. One such device is shown in the diagram.

The plasmapheresis device separates the patient's plasma from the blood cells. The patient's plasma flows through a bioreactor, a series of hollow fibre membranes surrounded by hepatocytes (liver cells). The cells in this bioreactor are from pigs' livers, but other similar devices use genetically engineered human liver cells. As the plasma flows through the bioreactor, the liver cells remove metabolic waste products that build up as a result of liver failure. These devices have been successfully used to keep patients alive until their own liver regenerates.

1 The plasmapheresis device separates blood cells from blood plasma.
   a What are the main constituents of plasma?
   b Suggest one reason why blood cells are not allowed to flow through the bioreactor.

2 Suggest one function of the charcoal column.

3 The plasma is oxygenated by the device. How is oxygen transported in plasma?

4 Suggest how metabolic waste products enter the hepatocytes.

5 Hepatocytes extracted from the body can be kept alive and functioning in vitro, but they do not divide. A clone of hepatocytes which do divide has been produced by genetic engineering. This is called an immortalised cell line.
   a What is the disadvantage of using hepatocytes which do not divide?
   b Name the type of cell division in dividing hepatocytes.
   c Suggest how the immortalised cell line was genetically engineered.
   d Suggest one possible danger of inserting genes for cell division into cells.

3.2 The liver

The liver is the second largest organ in the body (the largest is the skin). It performs hundreds of different chemical reactions. Many of these reactions are **synthetic**, producing chemicals the body needs. Others are **homeostatic** – regulating the body's internal environment. Still others are **excretory** – breaking down unwanted chemicals into substances that can be safely removed from the body. However, we could define the overall function of the liver as the regulation of blood composition, particularly with respect to the levels of food molecules that have been absorbed from the gut.

More specifically, the liver:

- controls blood glucose concentration;
- controls amino acid levels;
- controls lipid levels;
- removes toxins from the blood;
- removes unwanted proteins, such as hormones, from the blood;
- produces bile;
- synthesises plasma proteins;
- synthesises cholesterol;
- stores vitamins;
- synthesises fetal red blood cells;
- destroys red blood cells when they are no longer needed, or when they are too old.

In this section, we concentrate on how the liver deals with excess proteins by producing urea, which is excreted in the urine, and we see how it processes other waste products for excretion in bile. The role of the liver in controlling blood glucose concentration is covered in Chapter 2, on pages 20-23.

Amino acid metabolism

When we digest the proteins in our diet, amino acids are absorbed into the blood and pass to the liver via the **hepatic portal vein**. Many of the amino acids are used to manufacture **plasma proteins**. These are important blood proteins that have two major functions:

- they are mainly responsible for giving the plasma a low water potential so that water is reabsorbed from tissue fluid;
- they assist in the blood clotting process at wounds.

Other amino acids pass into the general circulation from where they are absorbed by body cells for protein synthesis. However, the body cannot store excess proteins in the same way as it stores excess carbohydrates and excess triglycerides. If more than about 60 g of amino acids – that's the amount in a large egg – are delivered to the liver in a day, excess is broken down.

1 Fig 3.1 shows the structural formula of an amino acid.

a Name the groups labelled A and B.
b What does the 'R' in the structural formula represent?

The liver breaks down excess amino acids into ammonia and organic acids called keto acids (see Fig 3.2). This process is called **deamination** since the amino group is removed from an amino acid, leaving an organic acid. Ammonia is highly toxic, so a series of reactions converts it immediately into urea.

$$2NH_3 + CO_2 \rightarrow NH_2CONH_2 + H_2O$$
$$\text{urea}$$

Urea is less poisonous than ammonia, but it must be removed from the body to prevent ill effects. Urea is transported in the blood from the liver to the kidneys where it forms part of the urine. A person who is deprived of

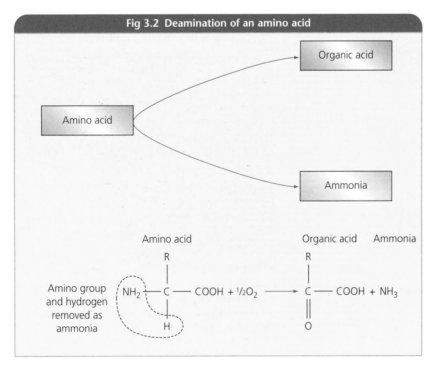

Fig 3.2 Deamination of an amino acid

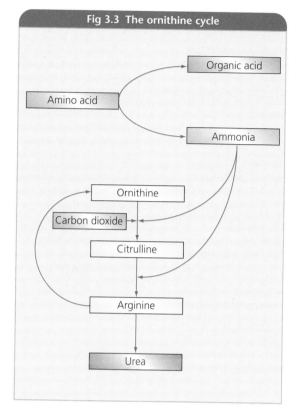

Fig 3.3 The ornithine cycle

Amino acid → Organic acid

Amino acid → Ammonia

Ornithine → Citrulline → Arginine → Urea

Carbon dioxide → Citrulline

Breaking down hormones

As well as deaminating excess amino acids, the liver breaks down many other substances produced by the body. Hormones, for example, are often completely broken down within thirty minutes of being secreted. This is why they have to be made almost continually.

Hormones are broken down in the smooth endoplasmic reticulum of liver cells by a group of enzymes collectively called cytochrome P450. The enzymes in this complex are able to breakdown a wide range of molecules including synthetic drugs and hormones. The breakdown products pass to the kidneys and are then removed in the urine.

Trying to cheat the system

The liver enzymes that break down unwanted substances also help the body to deal with different types of drug. Athletes are now routinely tested for performance enhancing drugs and this is done by analysing their urine for the breakdown products of drugs. The most common urine test is for a substance called *nandrolone*. This is produced from a wide range of bodybuilding drugs called anabolic steroids. The body produces its own anabolic steroids, and then the liver breaks them down into nandrolone. Consequently, when an athlete takes anabolic steroids, the same liver enzymes break the steroids down into nandralone. Traces of nandrolone may remain in the blood for several weeks after taking anabolic steroids – so athletes who cheat stand a good chance of being caught by random drug tests.

water and seriously dehydrated still continues to produce urine to get rid of urea. The organic acids produced by the deamination of amino acids can be used in respiration.

Depending on the nature of the R group organic acids are either converted into acetyl coenzyme A or they enter Krebs cycle directly. The respiration of organic acids provides almost all the resting energy requirements of carnivores such as lions.

The series of reactions that produces urea is called the **ornithine cycle**. This is summarised in Fig 3.3.

2 Why do lions obtain most of their energy requirements from the respiration of organic acids?

3

a Suggest why it is necessary to have several steps in the production of urea.

b From which substance is ornithine regenerated?

4 Explain why a mutation of the gene responsible for the production of the enzyme that converts arginine into citrulline might cause the accumulation of ammonia in the body.

World shotput champion CJ Hunter of the USA, with his wife Olympic sprint champion Marion Jones, at a press conference in September 2000 after it was found he had tested positive for the banned steroid nandrolone 4 times since June 2000. Hunter denied taking the steroid, claiming positive tests had resulted from a contaminated food supplement.

The production of bile

Not all of the waste products produced by the liver enter the bloodstream to be excreted by the kidneys; others are excreted into the gut and pass out with the faeces. The best example of this is a pigment called bilirubin. This brownish-yellow pigment gives faeces their characteristic colour.

Bilirubin is formed by the breakdown of haemoglobin from 'out-of-date' red blood cells. Red blood cells have no nucleus to direct the synthesis of new proteins, so they only live for about 120 days, after which they are destroyed by cells called macrophages. The polypeptide chains of haemoglobin molecules are broken down into amino acids, which are then recycled. The iron from the haemoglobin is re-used to make new haemoglobin molecules. The rest of the haemoglobin molecule is excreted mainly as bilirubin. The liver cells extract bilirubin from blood, then concentrate it about 1000 times before passing it into the gall bladder, a small storage sac sited very close to the liver.

When we eat a meal, the gall bladder contracts, forcing bile into the duodenum. As described in Chapter 5 of the AS book, some constituents of bile are used in fat digestion, but the bilirubin plays no part in digestion. If the liver is diseased its cells cannot remove bilirubin from the blood at the normal rate. The concentration of bilirubin therefore rises and some of it diffuses out of the blood into the tissue fluid of the skin. This gives the skin the yellow colour that is called jaundice. Jaundice is one of the main symptoms of liver malfunction.

 By what route do bile pigments pass out of the body?

KEY FACTS

- The liver produces many **metabolic waste** products.

- Getting rid of metabolic waste materials is called **excretion**.

- Excess amino acids are broken down in the liver into ammonia and keto acids.

- Ammonia is quickly converted into **urea** by the liver.

- Urea is excreted by the kidneys in urine.

- Some of the metabolic waste produced by the liver leaves via bile.

3.3 The kidney

The kidney has two main functions:

- it removes metabolic waste from the body through the process of excretion;

- it regulates the water and ion content of the blood. This keeps the water potential of the blood, and to some extent the pressure of the blood, relatively constant.

The kidneys make up less than 0.5% of the body mass, but the blood flow through the kidneys in a healthy person is 25% of the output of the heart. That's about 1.25 litres per minute when the body is at rest! In this section, we look in detail at why the kidney gets all this blood and we find out what happens to it.

Some basic principles

Before looking at the structure and function of the kidney in detail, you will need to revise some basic information, making sure you are comfortable with all the following points.

You learned at GCSE that:

- the kidneys control the water and ion content of the blood;

- the kidneys produce urine;

- urine consists of urea, excess water and excess ions;

- urine is stored temporarily in the bladder until it leaves the body.

In Chapter 2 of the AS book, you learned about:

- **isotonic solutions** – solutions with the same water potential (ψ);

- **hypotonic solutions** – solutions with a less negative water potential;

- **hypertonic solutions** – a solution with a more negative water potential;

- **active transport** – transport via carrier proteins requiring energy, against a concentration gradient;

- **facilitated diffusion** – diffusion along a concentration gradient through carrier proteins or channel proteins.

You learned in Chapter 11 of the AS book that:

- Tissue fluid is formed by hydrostatic pressure of the blood

- Tissue fluid returns to the blood by osmosis.

Kidney structure and function

Fig 3.4 shows the overall and detailed structure of the kidney. You will need to study it carefully as you read through the text in the section that follows.

Blood entering the kidneys is supplied to thousands of microscopic tubules called **nephrons**, which make up the bulk of the kidney and carry out its work of filtering the blood. It is important to know how the different parts of the nephron are arranged in the kidney.

As you can see from the diagram, the **outer cortex** of the kidney contains the **Bowman's capsules** and the **proximal** and **distal tubules**, while the **medulla** houses the **loops of Henle** and the **collecting ducts**. Bundles of collecting ducts form **pyramids**, which deliver urine into an open space called the **pelvis**. The **ureters** connect the kidneys to the **bladder**.

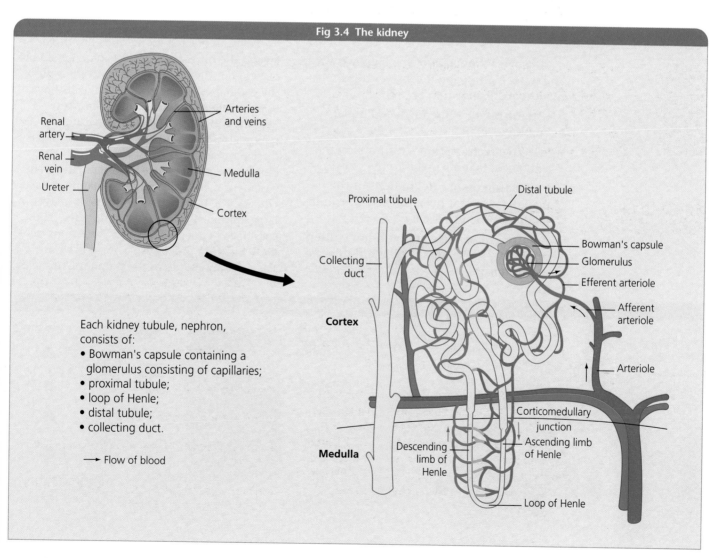

Fig 3.4 The kidney

Each kidney tubule, nephron, consists of:
- Bowman's capsule containing a glomerulus consisting of capillaries;
- proximal tubule;
- loop of Henle;
- distal tubule;
- collecting duct.

→ Flow of blood

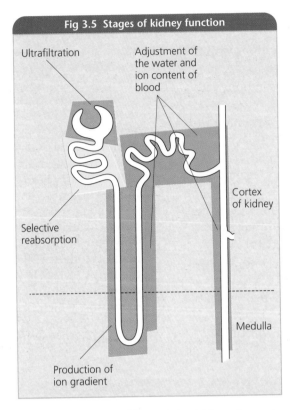

Fig 3.5 Stages of kidney function

Ultrafiltration

Adjustment of the water and ion content of blood

Selective reabsorption

Cortex of kidney

Medulla

Production of ion gradient

The overall function of the kidney is waste and water control and it achieves this in 4 main steps, as shown in Fig 3.5:

- **Ultrafiltration** – filtering blood under pressure;

- **Selective reabsorption** – reabsorbing the substances that are useful to the body;

- **Production of an ion gradient in the medulla** – so that hypertonic urine can be produced when necessary;

- **Adjustment of the water and ion content of blood** – to maintain a constant internal environment.

These stages occur in different regions of the nephron, as we see in the following sections.

Ultrafiltration

Each kidney tubule contains a bunch of capillaries called a **glomerulus**. The **afferent arteriole**, the blood vessel bringing blood into the glomerulus, is wider than the **efferent arteriole**, the vessel taking blood away from the glomerulus. This creates a bottleneck in the capillaries of the glomerulus, which makes the blood pressure in the capillaries rise. The high blood pressure brings about ultrafiltration. Pressure from a liquid is called **hydrostatic pressure** – literally 'pressure from water'. This pressure pushes fluid from the blood in the capillaries of the glomerulus into the capsular space of the Bowman's capsule. Small molecules, such as glucose, pass into the Bowman's capsule but large molecules, such as proteins, do not.

The filtrate is produced rapidly because of the structure of the glomerular capillaries and Bowman's capsule, as shown in Fig 3.6.

The wall of each glomerulus has three layers. The inner layer consists of a membrane of flat endothelial cells that form the wall of the capillaries. These endothelial cells have pores at their junctions called **fenestrae** – literally 'windows'. These fenestrae are 50 – 100 nanometres wide and allow the blood to make direct contact with the second layer – the **basement membrane** of the capillaries. This basement membrane contains mainly collagen. Outside the basement membrane is a layer of large epithelial cells called **podocytes**. These cells have slender cytoplasmic extensions called **pedicels** (foot processes). The pedicels are separated by spaces 20 to 30 nanometres wide.

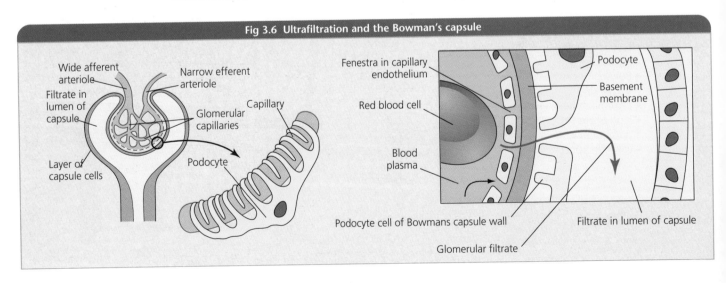

Fig 3.6 Ultrafiltration and the Bowman's capsule

Wide afferent arteriole

Narrow efferent arteriole

Filtrate in lumen of capsule

Glomerular capillaries

Capillary

Layer of capsule cells

Podocyte

Fenestra in capillary endothelium

Red blood cell

Blood plasma

Podocyte

Basement membrane

Podocyte cell of Bowmans capsule wall

Glomerular filtrate

Filtrate in lumen of capsule

Atrial Natriuretic Peptide (ANP)

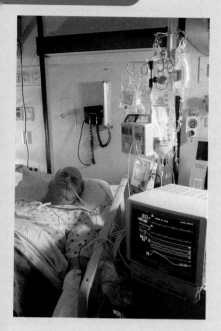

Ultrafiltration is an essential process. If it ceases the body suffers from kidney failure and death occurs rapidly if treatment is not given. This is because ultrafiltration starts the processes that eventually adjust the concentrations of substances in the blood that need to be kept within narrow limits. It also removes poisonous urea from the blood.

The healthy body produces a hormone called atrial natriuretic peptide (ANP). Doctors have discovered that this hormone can be used to kick-start ultrafiltration in some cases of kidney failure.

Injecting ANP causes dilation of the afferent arterioles supplying the glomeruli. In early trials, involving 53 patients, ANP halved the number of deaths compared with a control group who were given the conventional treatment of injecting patients with a solution containing sodium chloride and glucose.

1 Suggest how the conventional treatment increases the rate of ultrafiltration.

2 Suggest how ANP increases the rate of ultrafiltration.

3 ANP is now produced by genetically modified bacteria. These bacteria have been transformed by inserting the gene for ANP. ANP is a peptide consisting of twenty eight amino acids. How many nucleotides will the gene for ANP contain?

Reabsorption – facts and figures

The table below shows the overall amounts of substances filtered, reabsorbed and excreted in the kidneys. (mEq = molar Equivalents)

1 Complete the table by calculating the missing figures.

2 Calculate the glomerular filtration rate per minute.

3 What volume of water is lost as urine in 24 hours?

4 Calculate the concentration of sodium ions in the glomerular filtrate. Give the unit.

5 Suggest why some urea passes back into the blood.

6 Explain how the structure of the proximal tubule cell is adapted for the transport of glucose molecules and sodium ions from the glomerular filtrate into the blood.

7 Many substances are used to treat high blood pressure. One of these is the polysaccharide mannitol. Mannitol appears in the glomerular filtrate but is not reabsorbed by the proximal tubule cells.

a Suggest why mannitol is not reabsorbed.

b Suggest in terms of water potential what effect mannitol has on the amount of water reabsorbed from the proximal tubule.

Substance	Units	Filtered into glomerulus	Excreted in urine	Reabsorbed in nephron	Percentage of filtered load reabsorbed
Water	litres day^{-1}	180	1.5	178.5	99.2
Na$^+$	mEq day^{-1}	25 200	150.0	25 050.0	
K$^+$	mEq day^{-1}	720	100.0	620.0	86.1
Ca^{2+}	mEq day^{-1}	540	10.0	530.0	98.1
HCO$_3^-$	mEq day^{-1}	4320	2.0	4218.0	97.6
Cl$^-$	mEq day^{-1}		150.0	17850.0	99.2
Glucose	mEq day^{-1}	800	0.5	799.5	99.9
Urea	g day^{-1}	56	28.0		50

In effect, the only partially permeable membrane separating the plasma in the capillaries from the lumen of the capsule is the basement membrane of the capillary cells. Once fluid has been forced out through the basement membrane, it flows between the pedicels into the lumen of the capsule. This is the same process that produces tissue fluid (see AS Biology, p 164); glomerular filtrate and tissue fluid have a similar composition.

6 What are the differences in composition between blood and glomerular filtrate? Give the reason for these differences.

Selective reabsorption

The glomeruli produce approximately 180 litres of filtrate in a day, but an adult produces only 1–2 litres of urine every 24 hours. Most of the filtrate is quickly reabsorbed into the blood in the proximal tubule. Here, virtually all filtered glucose and almost 70 per cent of the filtered water and ions are reabsorbed. This occurs no matter what the water potential of the blood. Filtrate that is not reabsorbed continues through the nephron and some of the water and ions are eventually excreted as urine.

How does reabsorption occur? In AS Biology Chapter 2 you learned about some of the mechanisms that move substances into and out of cells. These include diffusion, facilitated diffusion and active transport and all occur in the proximal tubule cells (Fig 3.7).

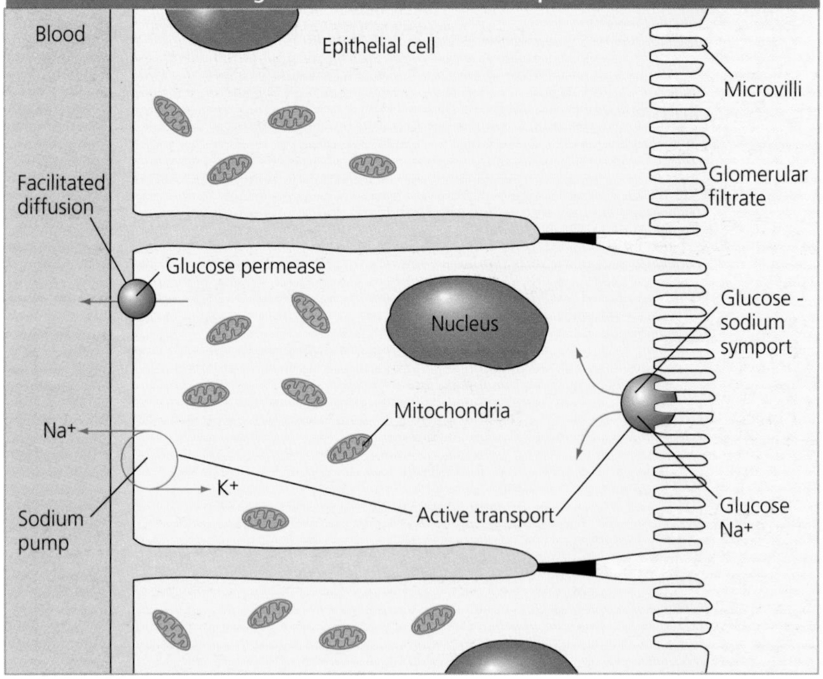

Both sodium ions and glucose molecules are transported from the glomerular filtrate into the proximal tubule cells by active transport. Specialised carrier protein molecules called **symports** transport both glucose molecules and sodium ions at the same time.

Note that the area of the absorbing surface of the proximal tubule cells is increased by microvilli. (Remember that microvilli are parts of a cell, but villi are muticellular structures.) Active transport is, of course, a process that requires energy. The sodium pump needs lots of energy since it transports substances mainly against a concentration gradient. This energy, in the form of ATP, is supplied by abundant mitochondria in the tubule cells.

Glucose is then transported out of the proximal tubule cells and into the blood by facilitated diffusion. The carrier protein responsbile is **glucose permease**. Sodium ions make the same journey via a different route; they are transported into the blood by a sodium pump called Na^+ / K^+ ATPase. This pump actively transports sodium ions into the blood whilst transporting potassium ions in the opposite direction at the same time.

7 How does the process of reabsorption from the glomerular filtrate compare with the processes used to absorb glucose and sodium from the lumen of the intestine into the blood?

The transport of glucose and ions into the blood, together with the presence of plasma proteins makes the water potential of the plasma much more negative than the water potential of the remaining glomerular filtrate. Water therefore moves from the filtrate into the blood by osmosis – from a less negative to a more negative water potential.

Many poisonous substances in the blood are bound onto plasma proteins and are therefore not filtered in the glomerulus. The cells of the proximal tubule actively transport these substances from the blood into the filtrate so that they can be excreted.

Producing an ion gradient in the medulla

When we are short of water we need to reabsorb as much water as possible from the glomerular filtrate rather than lose it in the urine.

In order to reabsorb water from the filtrate there must be a solution with a more negative water potential outside the tubule. The function of the loop of Henle is to produce

Fig 3.7 Mechanisms of reabsorption

Blood

Epithelial cell

Microvilli

Glomerular filtrate

Facilitated diffusion

Glucose permease

Nucleus

Glucose - sodium symport

Mitochondria

Na⁺

K⁺

Active transport

Sodium pump

Glucose Na⁺

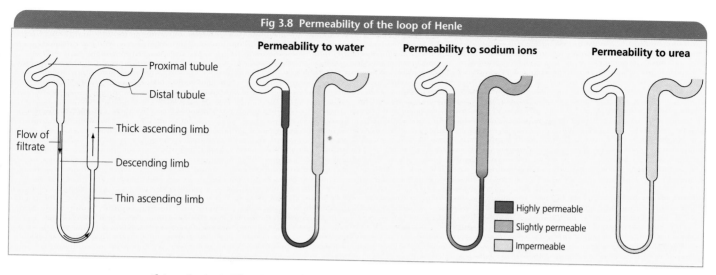

Fig 3.8 Permeability of the loop of Henle

Proximal tubule

Distal tubule

Flow of filtrate

Thick ascending limb

Descending limb

Thin ascending limb

Permeability to water

Permeability to sodium ions

Permeability to urea

Highly permeable

Slightly permeable

Impermeable

this solution. The different regions of the loop of Henle have different permeabilities to water, sodium ions and urea, as Fig 3.8 shows.

- The **descending limb** is highly permeable to water but only slightly permeable to sodium ions;

- The **ascending limb** is impermeable to water, but its narrow region is highly permeable to sodium ions and its wide region actively pumps sodium from the filtrate into the surrounding tissue fluid;

- The whole loop is relatively impermeable to urea. This means that most urea molecules remain within the filtrate.

The filtrate that enters the loop of Henle has urea and ion concentrations similar to those in blood plasma. This means that the two fluids have roughly the same water potential.

The events that produce an ion gradient in the medulla are summarised in Fig 3.9 and in the flow chart below.

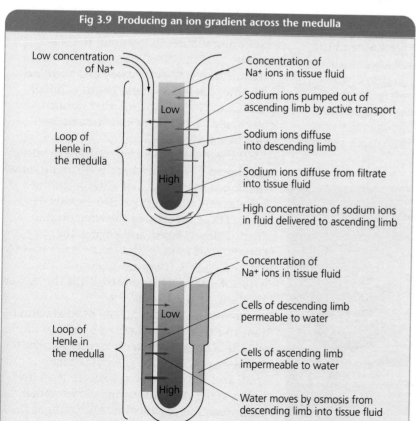

Fig 3.9 Producing an ion gradient across the medulla

Low concentration of Na+

Loop of Henle in the medulla

Low

High

Concentration of Na+ ions in tissue fluid

Sodium ions pumped out of ascending limb by active transport

Sodium ions diffuse into descending limb

Sodium ions diffuse from filtrate into tissue fluid

High concentration of sodium ions in fluid delivered to ascending limb

Loop of Henle in the medulla

Low

High

Concentration of Na+ ions in tissue fluid

Cells of descending limb permeable to water

Cells of ascending limb impermeable to water

Water moves by osmosis from descending limb into tissue fluid

Sodium ions are pumped from the filtrate into the tissue fluid of the medulla by the cells of the wide region of the ascending limb.

This produces a higher concentration of sodium ions in the tissue fluid in the upper region of the medulla than in the filtrate flowing down the descending limb.

Sodium ions therefore diffuse from the tissue fluid into the filtrate in the descending limb.

Because sodium ions diffuse into the filtrate at this point, fluid delivered to the ascending limb has a high concentration of sodium ions.

Because of their high concentration in the filtrate, sodium ions diffuse from the narrow region of the ascending limb into the tissue fluid in the lower region of the medulla.

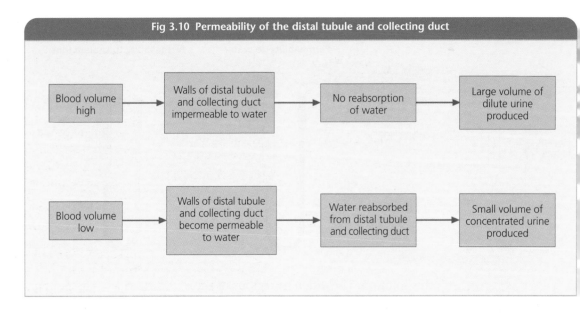

Fig 3.10 Permeability of the distal tubule and collecting duct

The high concentration of sodium ions in the tissue fluid of the medulla causes water to diffuse from the filtrate in the descending limb into the tissue fluid. Approximately 20 per cent of the water in the original filtrate leaves the tubule in this way. Having this gradient also enables water reabsorption into the blood when the water potential of the blood becomes too negative, as we shall see in the next section

Adjusting the water content of the blood

The amount of urine you produce and the concentration of this urine vary considerably according to how much you drink, where you are and what you are doing. You have probably noticed that when your body is dehydrated, e.g. after a long day on a hot beach, you produce very little urine and this urine is concentrated.

A long day on the beach can leave you feeling dehydrated.

8 Through what type of protein molecule do sodium ions diffuse into and out of the tubule?

9 Explain in terms of water potential why water diffuses out of the descending limb.

However, if you have drunk a lot of liquid you produce large quantities of very dilute urine. The volume and concentration of urine are adjusted by the distal tubules and the collecting tubules to maintain the water potential of the blood plasma, the total volume of blood in the body and the blood pressure. These are controlled to maintain homeostasis and, as with other homeostatic mechanisms, receptors, coordinator and effectors are involved.

The permeability of the walls of the distal tubules and the collecting ducts can be varied to control the amount of water reabsorbed from the tubules in these two regions (Fig 3.10). These tubules are the effectors, but what is the receptor, and what is the coordinator?

The role of ADH in controlling the water content of the blood

Receptors in the right atrium of the heart are sensitive to a change in blood pressure or blood volume. These receptors send impulses to the hypothalamus. The hypothalamus itself also has receptors that detect a change in the water potential of the blood. When the hypothalamus receives information that the blood pressure, blood volume or water

Fig 3.11 Overview of the role of ADH

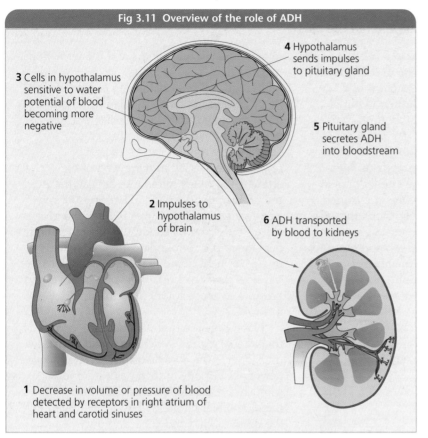

3 Cells in hypothalamus sensitive to water potential of blood becoming more negative

4 Hypothalamus sends impulses to pituitary gland

5 Pituitary gland secretes ADH into bloodstream

2 Impulses to hypothalamus of brain

6 ADH transported by blood to kidneys

1 Decrease in volume or pressure of blood detected by receptors in right atrium of heart and carotid sinuses

potential of the blood has changed, it sends impulses to the pituitary gland. In response, the pituitary gland secretes a hormone called anti-diuretic hormone (ADH), which is transported to the kidneys by the blood. ADH controls the permeability of the distal tubules and the collecting ducts. The role of ADH is summarised in Fig 3.11.

The effect of low and high blood ADH is shown in Fig 3.12. When blood volume is

low, ADH secretion increases. When ADH reaches the kidneys it increases the permeability of the distal tubule and the collecting duct to water. Because there is a high concentration of sodium ions in the tissue fluid of the medulla, its water potential is more negative than that of the filtrate. Water therefore diffuses out of the tubules into the tissue fluid of the medulla. This both decreases the volume of urine produced and increases the concentration of the dissolved substances in the urine. The urine produced when ADH acts on the kidneys is therefore **hypertonic** to blood plasma.

Increasing the amount of water reabsorbed from the filtrate makes the water potential of the blood less negative.

When blood volume is high, ADH secretion is low, so the walls of the collecting ducts become less permeable to water. This results in reduced reabsorption of water. Urine hypotonic to blood plasma is produced – there is a large volume of urine with a low concentration of dissolved substances.

Decreasing the amount of water reabsorbed from the filtrate makes the water potential of the blood more negative.

10 The control of the production of ADH is an example of negative feedback. Copy and complete the diagram to show how negative feedback operates to stop ADH production.

Water potential of blood becomes more negative

↓

Change in water potential detected by hypothalamus

↓

Impulses from hypothalamus to pituitary gland increase ADH production

↓

ADH causes increased water absorption by distal tubules and collecting ducts.

↓

Water potential of blood becomes less negative

11 There are many treatments for high blood pressure. Doctors usually advise patients to reduce the amount of salt in the diet. Explain in terms of water potential how this reduces blood pressure.

Fig 3.12 The effect of ADH on the distal tubule

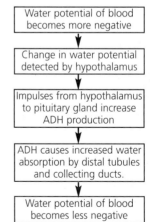

Low blood ADH

High blood ADH

Hypertonic tissue fluid

Walls of distal tubule and collecting duct impermeable to water

Walls of distal tubule and collecting duct permeable to water

Hypotonic urine

Hypertonic urine

APPLICATION

Adjusting the ion concentration of the blood

Every beat of the left ventricle drives blood into the arteries, creating pressure in the blood. This pressure is known as systolic blood pressure and is usually measured in mm mercury. A healthy systolic blood pressure for an adult is about 140 mm Hg. The force of the blood causes the elastic tissue in arterial walls to stretch. Recoil of the elastic tissue keeps the pressure of the blood in the arteries high in between contractions. The pressure caused by elastic recoil is called diastolic blood pressure, and the healthy adult value for this is about 80 mm Hg. Whilst we need a blood pressure higher than 80 mm Hg to maintain ultrafiltration in the kidneys and the formation of tissue fluid in other tissues, values just a bit higher this can have damaging consequences.

High blood pressure is called hypertension. It is also known as the 'silent killer' because people can have it without suspecting anything is wrong. It can be caused by physical effects such as narrowing of the arteries. Too much salt in the diet can make the problem worse. High blood pressure can lead to a stroke. This happens when blood vessels burst and bleed into the brain, causing damage in the surrounding area of brain tissue. So, high blood pressure is dangerous – but how does the body normally control blood pressure to protect itself from the risk of strokes?

Blood pressure is partly under the control of the adrenal glands, which are found just above the kidneys. The adrenal glands secrete many hormones but one of them, aldosterone, stimulates reabsorption of sodium ions from the glomerular filtrate by cells in the walls of the distal tubules and collecting ducts. Aldosterone secretion is brought about by the hormone renin, which is secreted by the walls of the afferent arterioles supplying the glomeruli in response to a fall in blood pressure.

Adrenal gland secretes aldosterone - transported by blood to kidneys

Hormone (renin) secreted - transported by blood to adrenal gland

Pressure receptors in wall of arterioles supplying glomeruli detect fall in blood pressure

Cells in wall of distal tubules and collecting ducts pump sodium ions into blood

1 Use information from the diagram to explain how secretion of aldosterone results in an increase in blood pressure.

KEY FACTS

- Ultrafiltration is rapid filtration caused by high blood pressure.

- The filtrate is blood plasma minus large molecular mass proteins.

- In the proximal tubules reabsorption of most of the water and selective reabsorption of all the sugars and most of the ions takes place.

- Reabsorption of sugars and ions is mainly by active transport.

- Differences in permeability of the parts of the loop of Henle result in a gradient of sodium ions developing in the tissue fluid of the medulla, the highest concentration being towards the base.

- The importance of this high concentration of ions is that it is hypertonic to the filtrate and will cause reabsorption of water from the filtrate.

- The hormone ADH increases the permeability of the walls of the distal tubules and collecting ducts, resulting in greater reabsorption of water and hypertonic urine.

- ADH is secreted by the pituitary gland.

- Receptors in the hypothalamus are sensitive to a fall in water potential of the blood, resulting in increased secretion of ADH.

- Urine consists mainly of excess water, excess ions and urea.

1 The diagram below shows the process by which urea is formed from an amino acid:

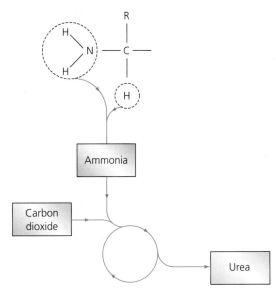

Fig 3.Q1

a
i Complete the diagram to show the chemical structure of the amino acid. (1)
ii Name the cycle of reactions in which urea is produced from ammonia. (1)

b In a mammalian kidney, the concentration of urea in the filtrate at the beginning of the collecting duct is approximately thirty times that of urea in the blood plasma. At the end of the collecting duct it is approximately fifty times that of the blood. Explain what causes the change in urea concentration along the collecting duct. (2)

Total (4)

BY03 June 97 Q6 Parts (a) and (c)

2 The diagram shows a cell from the proximal (first) convoluted tubule of a mammalian kidney as seen with an electron microscope.

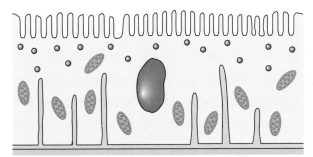

Fig 3.Q2

a Explain how two features shown in the diagram adapt the kidney tubule for the reabsorption of substances. (4)

b Ageing affects the efficiency of the kidneys. One method of assessing the efficiency of the working of the kidneys is by calculating the renal: plasma ratio for urea.
i The table shows how this was calculated for a 30-year-old man. Complete the table to show the missing value for the 70-year-old man. (1)

Man's age /years	Urea conc. urine/g dm^{-3}	Urea conc. blood/g dm^{-3}	Renal:plasma ratio for urea
30	0.63	0.42	1.5:1
70	0.59	0.76	

ii Explain how the renal : plasma ratio for urea indicates the efficiency of the kidney in removing urea. (2)

Total (7)

BY03 March 2000 Q 4

3 Read the extract about the drug Ecstasy and then answer the questions that follow.

A few deaths have been due to drinking too much water. This occurred either because people thought that water was an antidote to Ecstasy (it is only an antidote to dehydration) or because the drug induced repetitive behaviour. Under the influence of Ecstasy people have been known to drink 20 litres of fluid and smoke 100 cigarettes within three hours. Drinking pure water to replace the fluid lost in sweating is dangerous because it does not put back the sodium ions and so dilutes the blood. This makes the cells of the body swell up, which is particularly lethal in the brain which can expand and be crushed against the skull. The centres in the brain that regulate breathing and the heart can be irreversibly damaged, and the person dies. Ecstasy increases the risk of brain damage by triggering the release of antidiuretic hormone (ADH).

Reproduced by permission of The Guardian.

a i Explain in terms of water potential why the drinking of large amounts of pure water after copious sweating may lead to swelling of cells in the brain. (4)
ii Explain how 'Ecstasy increases the risk of brain damage by triggering the release of antidiuretic hormone (ADH)'. (4)

Total (8)

BY03 June 98 Q8 Part (a) only

4 Coordination and the nervous system

Christopher Reeve as superman (above) and making his directorial debut for his film 'In the Gloaming' in 1997 (right).

As Superman, Christopher Reeve performed stunts that tested his muscles and nerves to the limit. In 1995 his lifestyle was shattered by a riding injury that left him a quadriplegic – unable to move any of his four limbs by himself.

Nerve fibres in Christopher Reeve's spinal cord have been damaged. The fibres, called axons, are long, thin strings of cytoplasm inside a plasma membrane that carry electrical impulses along the spinal cord. The axons are assembled in bundles. Some axons carry sensory information about touch, temperature and pain, to the brain; if these are damaged the victim cannot feel any of these sensations. Other axons run downward from the brain to control the voluntary movements of the body; if these are damaged the muscles they serve will be paralysed.

Part of Christopher's treatment involves the use of a 'shocker-cycle' – a contraption that looks like a cross between an exercise bicycle and a sort of interrogation device. Electrodes pasted to his thighs and calves deliver a series of 50 volt shocks, making the muscles contract in sequenced spasms that bring his legs back to life and send the pedals flying. It preserves his muscle tone, moves the blood and stops the flesh from withering on the bone.

Christopher puts up with this treatment because he believes science will find a way to reconnect the shattered nerves in his spine. And when the cure comes, he wants his body to be fit. Regeneration of nerves in the spinal cord was thought to be impossible, but recent scientific discoveries hold out great hope that nerve cells can be encouraged to regenerate and make new connections in shattered human spinal cords.

4.1 The nervous system

The nervous system is a complex network of specialised cells that allow us to sense our surroundings and to react to it. In this chapter, we take a brief look at the structure of **the central nervous system**, and then we look in detail at an individual nerve cell, a **neurone**. The text introduces the main features of the cell, and later in the chapter we see how nerve impulses are transmitted along a neurone, and between different neurones.

Back to basics
First, some basic terms:

- **Central nervous system** The brain and the spinal cord.
- **Stimulus** A change inside or outside an organism that brings about a response in that organism. Examples of stimuli include light, sound, chemicals and pressure.

- **Receptor** A structure that detects a stimulus and initiates a nerve impulse. Examples of receptors include rod cells in the retina, chemoreceptors on the tongue and in the nose, pressure receptors in the skin.

- **Effector** A structure which responds to the arrival of a nerve impulse. Effectors are usually muscles or glands.

- **Sensory neurone** A nerve cell that carries impulses from a receptor to the central nervous system.

- **Motor neurone** A nerve cell that carries impulses from the central nervous system to an effector.

- **Reflex action** A rapid, automatic response to a stimulus, for example, the pain withdrawal reflex that makes you pull your hand away quickly when you touch something very hot.

Repairing nerves

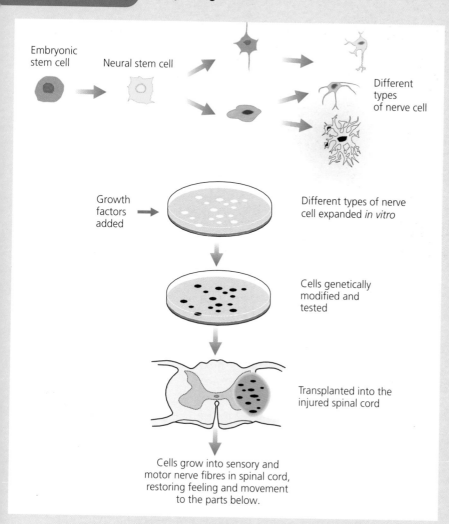

Embryonic stem cell   Neural stem cell

Different types of nerve cell

Growth factors added

Different types of nerve cell expanded *in vitro*

Cells genetically modified and tested

Transplanted into the injured spinal cord

Cells grow into sensory and motor nerve fibres in spinal cord, restoring feeling and movement to the parts below.

It has recently been discovered that cells from human embryos can be persuaded to grow into nerve cells. These cells, called stem cells, are obtained from human fetuses that have been aborted. The technique that may one day lead to stem cells being used to treat spinal injuries is shown in the diagram. Note that this is not yet possible; this scheme just shows how it may be done:

1 Suggest why the neural stem cell is able to grow into several different types of neurone.

2 Suggest how the neural stem cells are genetically modified to produce motor neurones.

3 Great controversy surrounds research into this method of treating spinal injuries. There are those who think that it is justified to bring relief to people like Christopher Reeve. Others consider that cells from human embryos should not be used in this way. What do you think – and why?

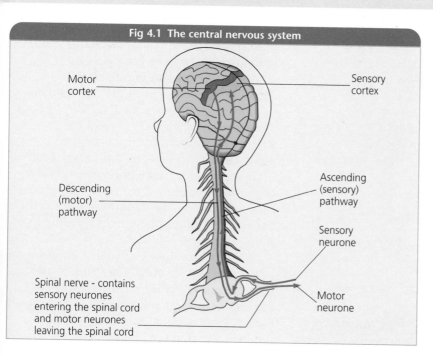

Fig 4.1 The central nervous system

Motor cortex

Sensory cortex

Descending (motor) pathway

Ascending (sensory) pathway

Sensory neurone

Spinal nerve - contains sensory neurones entering the spinal cord and motor neurones leaving the spinal cord

Motor neurone

Overview of the central nervous system

The nervous system consists of two regions, the **central nervous system** and the **peripheral nervous system**. The central nervous system consists of the brain and the spinal cord. The peripheral nervous system consists of nerves made up of neurones that carry information to and from the central nervous system. There are two regions in the central nervous system called **white matter** and **grey matter**. Grey matter consists of nerve cells – you have countless billions of these in the grey matter of your brain and these control most of your body's activities. Grey matter is also where nerve cells meet and pass information to one another. White matter consists of the fibres of long nerve cells that carry information within the brain and up and down the spinal cord as shown in Fig 4.1.

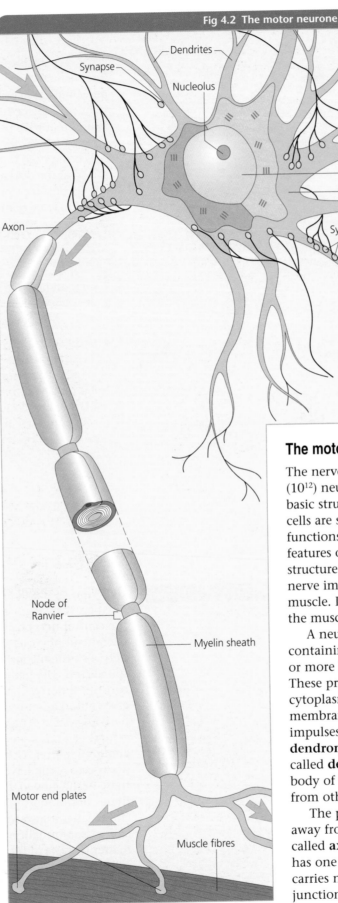

Fig 4.2 The motor neurone

The motor neurone

The nervous system contains about 10 billion (10^{12}) neurones. Neurones all have the same basic structure, but the different types of nerve cells are specialised for their particular functions. Motor neurones show typical features of neurones. Fig 4.2 shows the structure of a motor neurone that carries a nerve impulse from the spinal cord to a muscle. If impulses do not reach this neurone, the muscle it serves will be paralysed.

A neurone consists of a cell body, containing the nucleus of the cell, with one or more long, thin structures called processes. These processes are extensions of the cytoplasm, surrounded by a plasma membrane. The processes that conduct nerve impulses towards the cell body are called **dendrons**. Dendrons have very fine processes called **dendrites**. The dendrites on the cell body of this motor neurone receive impulses from other neurones in the spinal cord.

The processes that carry nerve impulses away from the cell body of a neurone are called **axons**. The motor neurone in Fig 4.2 has one long axon, called a nerve fibre, which carries nerve impulses to a muscle. At the junction between the neurone and the muscle is the **motor end plate**. You will notice that this motor neurone has an insulating cover over the axon called a **myelinated sheath**. This sheath is formed by **Schwann cells**, which twist round the axon several times as they grow, as Fig 4.3 shows. Most of the myelinated sheath is composed of the cell membranes of Schwann cells. The junctions between adjacent Schwann cells are called **nodes of Ranvier**.

1 The myelinated sheath is made up mainly of the membranes of Schwann cells. These membranes contain phospholipid molecules that have long fatty acids. These fatty acids prevent the movement of charged water-soluble ions. There are several layers of membranes in the sheath. Suggest the function of the sheath.

Fig 4.3 Schwann cell growing round an axon

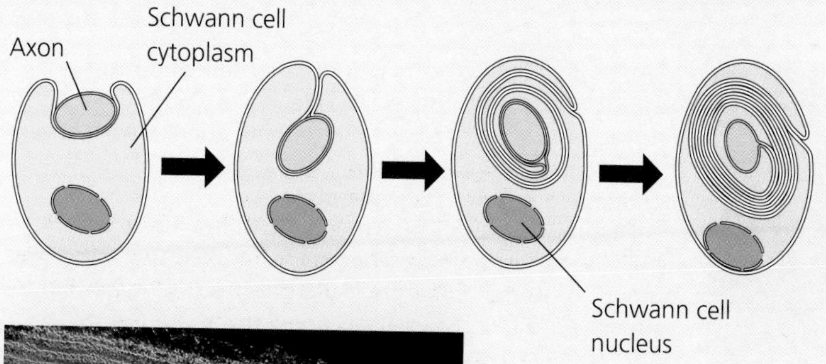

Axon

Schwann cell cytoplasm

Schwann cell nucleus

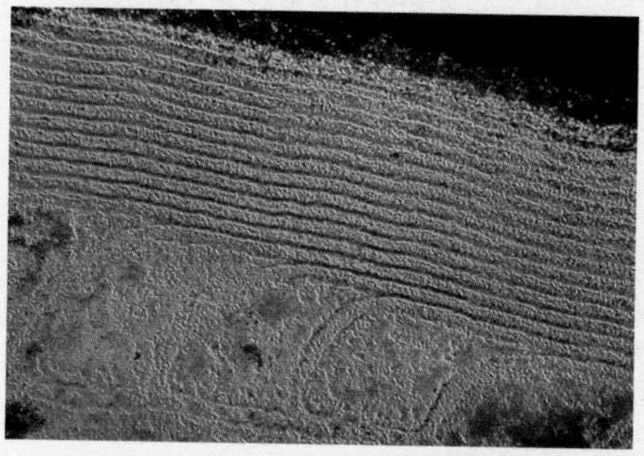

False-colour transmission electron micrograph of part of the myelin sheath (orange and green layers) of the human auditory nerve.

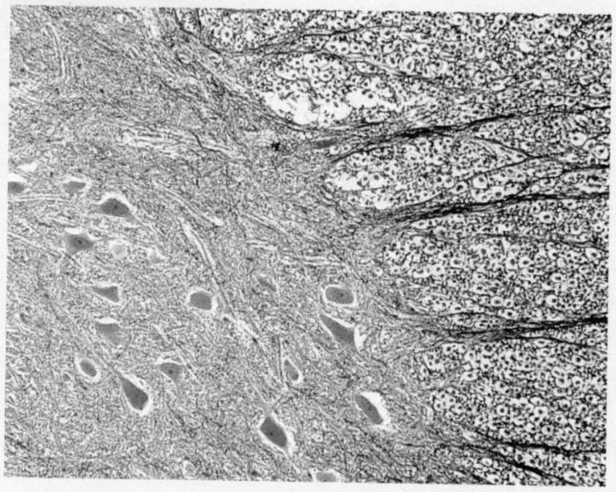

Light micrograph of normal human spinal cord. This cross section shows the junction between the grey matter (bottom, orange) and the white matter (top). Grey matter contains the cell bodies of the neurones; the white matter consists of axons that form nerve fibres.

Where neurone meets neurone

A junction between two neurones is called a **synapse**. At this junction there is a very narrow gap, only about 20 nm wide. Transmission across this gap is by movement of chemical substances, as we see later in this chapter, on page 60-61.

Nerves

Nerves are bundles of nerve fibres, as Fig 4.4 shows.

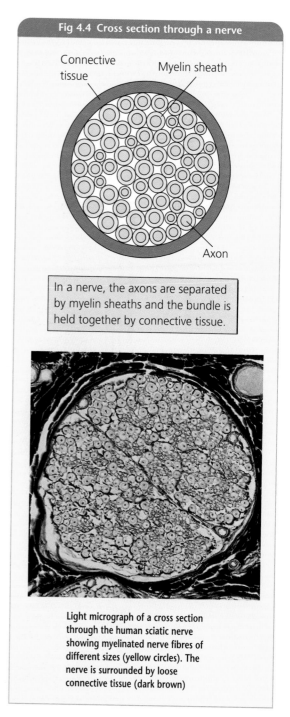

Fig 4.4 Cross section through a nerve

Connective tissue

Myelin sheath

Axon

In a nerve, the axons are separated by myelin sheaths and the bundle is held together by connective tissue.

Light micrograph of a cross section through the human sciatic nerve showing myelinated nerve fibres of different sizes (yellow circles). The nerve is surrounded by loose connective tissue (dark brown)

Myelinated and non-myelinated nerves

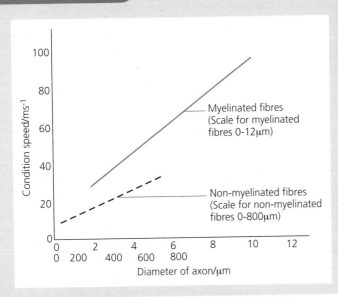

The graph shows the relationship between nerve impulse conduction speed, axon diameter and the presence of a myelinated sheath.

1 What is the maximum conduction speed of a non-myelinated nerve fibre?

2 Calculate the percentage increase in conduction speed when the diameter of a non-myelinated fibre increases from 2 to 4 μm.

3 How much thicker is the myelinated fibre conducting at maximum speed than the non-myelinated fibre transmitting at maximum speed?

4 Vertebrate animals possess myelinated fibres in many parts of the nervous system, but invertebrates do not have myelinated nerve fibres. Apart from conduction speed give two advantages to vertebrates of possessing myelinated nerve fibres.

Posture reflexes

A newborn baby cannot sit up and may take a year to learn to walk.

Sitting, standing and walking all involve reflex arcs. As you sit and read this book you are unaware of the hundreds of reflex arcs continually in operation to keep you in the sitting position. The reflexes involved are called **posture reflexes**. These posture reflexes are mainly spinal reflex arcs – the brain need not be involved. Posture reflexes develop as sensory and motor neurones develop synapses with each other in the spinal cord and in the brain. Since posture reflexes develop during childhood they are known as conditioned reflexes. Very complicated sets of posture reflexes allow us do things like ride a bike. A top flight tennis player doesn't have time to think about where to put the racket to return a ball travelling at 100 km per hour – conditioned reflexes take care of it.

Posture reflexes involve muscle spindles. These are specialised muscle fibres. They act as receptors to the amount of stretch in a muscle. As they become stretched, spindles send impulses via sensory neurones to the spinal cord. These synapse with motor neurones that lead back to the muscles. The motor neurones supply several muscles. There impulses cause some of these muscles to contract, but inhibit the contraction of others. Posture is achieved by regulating the state of contraction of dozens of opposing sets of muscles in this way. You didn't realise that sitting up was so complicated, did you!

The diagram below shows a very simple posture reflex:

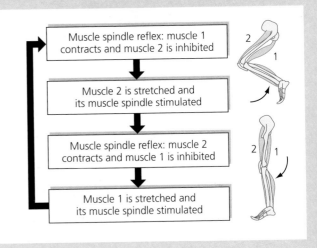

Muscle spindle reflex: muscle 1 contracts and muscle 2 is inhibited

Muscle 2 is stretched and its muscle spindle stimulated

Muscle spindle reflex: muscle 2 contracts and muscle 1 is inhibited

Muscle 1 is stretched and its muscle spindle stimulated

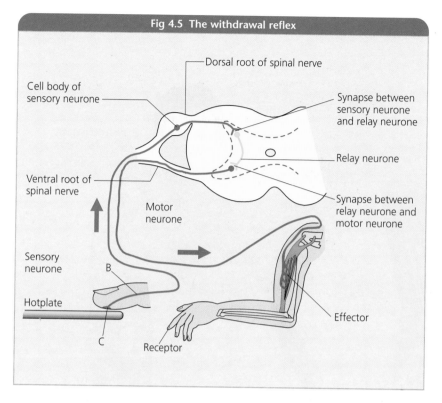

Fig 4.5 The withdrawal reflex

Dorsal root of spinal nerve

Cell body of sensory neurone

Synapse between sensory neurone and relay neurone

Relay neurone

Ventral root of spinal nerve

Motor neurone

Synapse between relay neurone and motor neurone

Sensory neurone

B

Hotplate

C

Receptor

Effector

Types of nerve

A spinal nerve usually contains both sensory neurones and motor nerve fibres. Myelinated sheaths insulate the plasma membrane of the fibres from tissue fluid. We shall see later that this enables them to transmit impulses much faster. The outside of a nerve is made up of connective tissue – a tissue adapted for binding structures together.

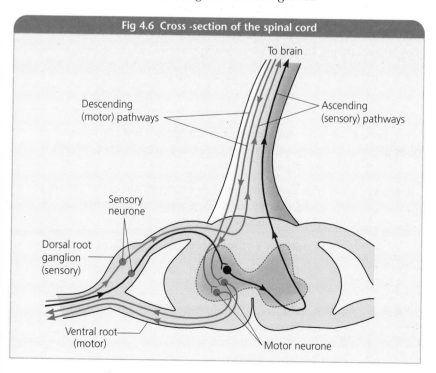

Fig 4.6 Cross-section of the spinal cord

To brain

Descending (motor) pathways

Ascending (sensory) pathways

Sensory neurone

Dorsal root ganglion (sensory)

Ventral root (motor)

Motor neurone

2

a What is the difference between a nerve and a neurone?

b Which type of neurone in a spinal nerve is damaged when

  i a person cannot feel a pin prick on the leg?

  ii a person cannot move a leg?

The reflex arc

The simplest responses to stimuli are **reflex actions**. A reflex action is a rapid, automatic response to a stimulus. Reflex actions are rapid because there is a direct link between the receptor and the effector; the nerve impulses do not need to be processed by the higher centres of the brain to bring about a response. The shortest route between a receptor and an effector is called the **reflex arc**.

The nerve pathway of a reflex arc can go through the brain, for example, widening and narrowing the pupil, or sneezing. Or it can go through the spinal cord, for example the pain withdrawal reflex shown in Fig 4.5, or the knee jerk reflex.

Usually three neurones make up a reflex arc, but in the knee jerk reflex there are just two, the sensory neurone and the motor neurone. A spinal nerve contains both sensory neurones and motor neurones.

As Fig 4.5 shows, a spinal nerve has two roots where it joins the spinal cord. The fibres of sensory neurones enter the spinal cord via the **dorsal root** of the spinal nerve. The cell bodies of the sensory neurones are found in this dorsal root. The motor neurones leave via the **ventral root** of the spinal nerve.

3 Look at Fig 4.5. Which part of the sensory neurone is the axon? Give the reason for your answer.

Reflexes do not have to be learned: the nerve pathways are built into the nervous system under genetic control. They control simple responses needed for survival or avoiding danger. Neither do reflex actions need conscious thought. When we stand on a pin, or touch something hot or cold, the response occurs before we are aware of the pain. The fact that we *later* become aware of pain shows that the neurones in reflex arcs also have connections to the brain.

Fig 4.6 shows some of the pathways that can be taken by nerve impulses.

APPLICATION   Reversing paralysis?

In 1981, Roger Fenn fell and broke his neck. The accident damaged his spinal cord above the point where spinal nerves branch off to the arms. Nerve tissue, unlike bone, cannot repair itself easily, so Roger's arms and legs are permanently paralysed. Fortunately, he can still move the muscles in his shoulders normally and this has given him the chance to be much less dependent on the help of others.

In the early 1990s, electronics and biology came together and, using a thorough understanding of the structure of the nervous system, designers came up with the electronic grip system, shown in the diagram, right. The electronics mimic the natural signals that pass along nerve cells to operate the muscles. In 1995, Roger had an operation to implant the system in his right arm. After 14 years of living without the use of his hands, Roger now uses his shoulder muscles to operate his lower arms and hands and he can feed himself, clean his teeth, comb his hair, and let himself in and out of his house using an ordinary door key.

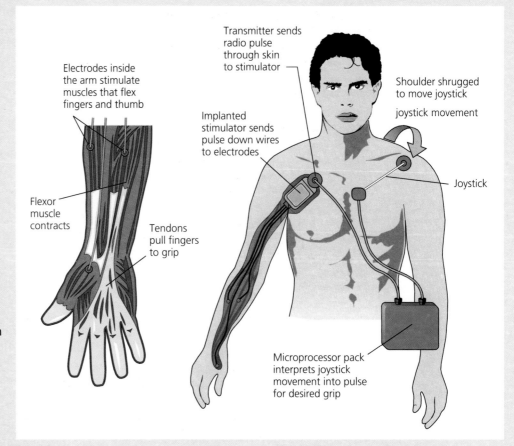

1 In what form is the electric current carried along the wires in the electronic grip system?

2 What structure in the nervous system does the joystick mimic?

3 What type of neurone has the same function as the wires that take electronic signals to Roger's muscles?

KEY FACTS

- There are three types of **neurone** in most **reflex arcs**: **sensory neurones**, **relay neurones** and **motor neurones**.

- These neurones have the same basic structure:
  - A **cell body** containing the nucleus.
  - **Dendrons** which carry impulses towards the cell body.
  - An **axon** which carries impulses away from the cell body.

- A **myelin sheath**, made up from **Schwann cells**, acts as an insulator of nerve fibres.

- The **white matter** of the spinal cord consists of myelinated nerve fibres; the **grey matter** consists mainly of cell bodies.

- The junctions between neurones are called **synapses**; transmission across synapses is by movement of chemical substances.

- A **nerve** is a collection of the nerve fibres of neurones.

- A reflex action is a rapid, automatic response to a stimulus.

- A reflex arc is the shortest route from a receptor to an effector.

4.2 Nerve impulses

In this section we see how nerve impulses are transmitted down the axon of a neurone. Before we see how this happens, it is important to find out what is happening inside a nerve cell at rest, when no impulse is being transmitted.

The resting potential

To describe a neurone as 'resting' is a bit misleading as it gives the impression that the cell is inactive. In fact, it is using energy to maintain a difference in electrical charge between the inside and the outside of the axon. Fluid on the inside of the axon is negative, compared with the fluid that bathes the outside. This bathing fluid has the same concentration of ions as tissue fluid. The difference in charge is called the **resting potential** of the neurone. It gives the *resting* neurone the *potential* to transmit a nerve impulse.

Measuring potential differences

But how do we know this about nerve cells? Scientists first observed electrical activity in nerves over two hundred years ago, but it is only in the last 50 years that the underlying mechanisms have been understood.

During the 1950s, scientists developed micropipettes with points as narrow as 0.5 μm. (You would have to split a human hair at least a hundred times before it would fit into this pipette.) These can be used to insert micro-electrodes into individual axons. Two electrodes are needed to measure the potential difference (the voltage) between the outside and inside of an axon; one in the neurone and one immersed in the fluid outside the axon.

4　Which ions occur at the highest concentrations in tissue fluid? (Refer to Fig 12 on page 164 of the AS book.)

5　Non-myelinated fibres are usually used in experiments that investigate electrical activity in neurones. Suggest why.

Figs 4.7a and 4.7b show how electrodes can be used to investigate electrical activity in a giant squid axon. When both electrodes are positioned in the bathing fluid there is no potential difference between them (Fig 4.7a). When the micropipette is inserted into the axon there is a potential difference of –70 mV between the inside of the axon and the outside (Fig 4.7b). This difference in potential is called the resting potential.

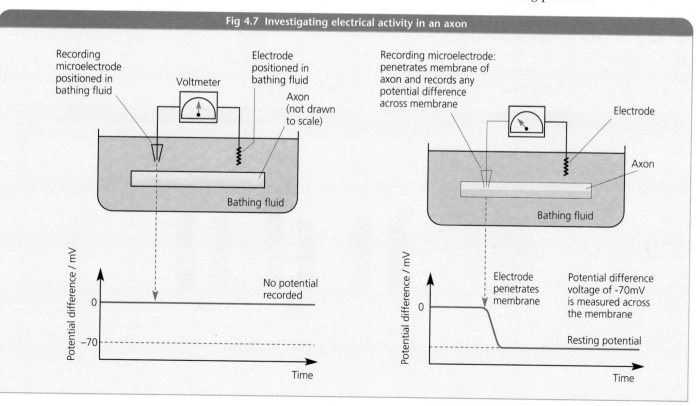

Fig 4.7 Investigating electrical activity in an axon

Positively charged ions such as sodium (Na⁺) are called cations (because they move towards a negative electrode called a cathode); negatively charged ions such as chloride (Cl⁻) are called anions (because they move towards an anode). The resting potential is caused by the movement of cations through the cell membrane of the axon. Since the inside of the axon is negatively charged with respect to the outside, the net movement of cations required to produce a resting potential is *outwards* through the cell membrane.

How is the resting potential produced?

Fig 4.8 shows the mechanisms that produce the resting potential across the membrane of the axon. There are two mechanisms involved in producing the resting potential:

- Active transport by Na⁺ / K⁺ pumps – specialised carrier protein molecules;
- Facilitated diffusion that occurs through channel protein molecules.

The Na⁺ / K⁺ pump consists of the enzyme **ATPase**, which is also a carrier protein. For this reason, the pump is known as the Na⁺ / K⁺ ATPase pump. It pumps ions in exactly the same way as the pumps that operate in the cell membranes of cells in the kidney tubules (see Chapter 3, page 43). Every square micrometre of the axon membrane contains up to 200 of these pumps and each one moves about 200 Na⁺ ions out of the axon and about 130 K⁺ ions inwards every second – a ratio of approximately 3 Na⁺ ions outwards for every 2 K⁺ ions inwards.

The two ions also move through the axon membrane by facilitated diffusion through channel proteins. However, the channel proteins move ions in the opposite direction to the Na⁺ / K⁺ ATPase pump; Na⁺ ions diffuse in through the membrane and K⁺ ions diffuse out.

So what is the net result of all this ion transport in different directions? There are two important facts to note:

- The channel proteins that carry K⁺ ions outnumber those that carry Na⁺ ions, so more K⁺ ions diffuse out than Na⁺ ions diffuse in;
- The Na⁺ / K⁺ ATPase pump moves more ions than are moved by facilitated diffusion.

The net result is therefore that there are more sodium ions outside the membrane than potassium ions inside. This gives a net positive charge outside the membrane – and therefore a net negative charge inside. This gives the potential difference that is the resting potential.

6 Why do the Na⁺ ions and K⁺ ions move in opposite directions through the channel proteins?

7 Dinitrophenol (DNP) is a metabolic poison that inhibits respiration. If DNP is added to the solution bathing an axon, the axon does not develop a resting potential. Explain why.

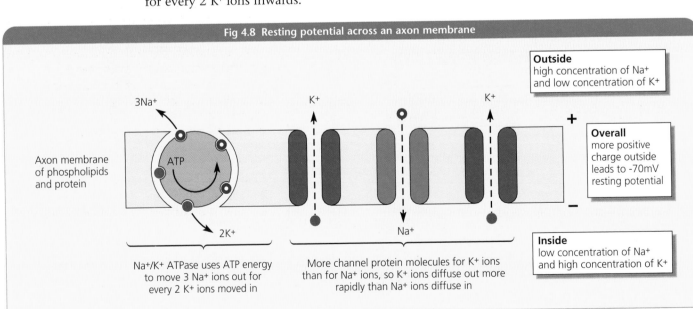

Fig 4.8 Resting potential across an axon membrane

3Na⁺

K⁺   K⁺

Outside
high concentration of Na⁺ and low concentration of K⁺

Axon membrane of phospholipids and protein

ATP

+

Overall
more positive charge outside leads to -70mV resting potential

−

2K⁺

Na⁺

Inside
low concentration of Na⁺ and high concentration of K⁺

Na⁺/K⁺ ATPase uses ATP energy to move 3 Na⁺ ions out for every 2 K⁺ ions moved in

More channel protein molecules for K⁺ ions than for Na⁺ ions, so K⁺ ions diffuse out more rapidly than Na⁺ ions diffuse in

The action potential

When a neurone is stimulated, a message passes down the length of its axon. This message takes the form of a wave of **depolarisation** – instead of having a negative resting potential, one small stretch of axon after the next develops a positive charge with respect to the fluid outside it. Depolarisation happens because of channels in the membrane of the axon that can change shape. In the 'open' position, they allow ions to pass through; in the 'closed' position, they block ion movement (Fig 4.9). Because they can be open or closed, these protein channels are called **gated ion channels**.

If an action potential is generated in a neurone it is always the same size. The size of the action potential does NOT depend on the size of the stimulus. This is known as the **all-or-nothing principle**.

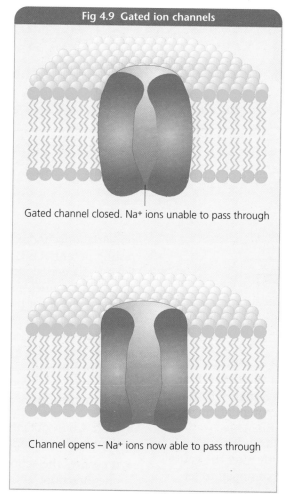

Fig 4.9 Gated ion channels

Gated channel closed. Na⁺ ions unable to pass through

Channel opens – Na⁺ ions now able to pass through

Depolarisation

Fig 4.10 shows the movements of ions during the depolarisation and repolarisation that occurs during an action potential. The gated channels for sodium ions are normally closed in the resting neurone. If the neurone is stimulated, these gated channels open. Since there is a higher concentration of sodium ions outside the axon membrane than inside, sodium ions move along their concentration gradient and rush in through the membrane. This movement results in a higher concentration of cations inside the membrane than outside, giving the inside of the axon a positive charge. This part of the axon membrane is depolarised. This change of potential from negative to positive, which travels down the axon membrane, is known as the **action potential**.

A stimulus can set up an action potential only if it is greater than a minimum level known as the **threshold level**. If a stimulus exceeds the threshold level the gated sodium channels in the axon membrane open. If the stimulus is below the threshold level, they remain closed and no depolarisation occurs.

Depolarisation of the membrane takes only a few milliseconds but it can be studied by attaching microelectrodes to an axon then connecting them to an oscilloscope (Fig 4.11). The oscilloscope can record, then 'freeze' events that occur in each tiny fraction of a second.

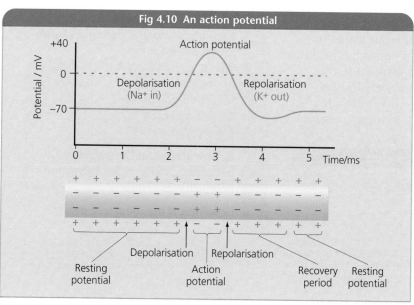

Fig 4.10 An action potential

57

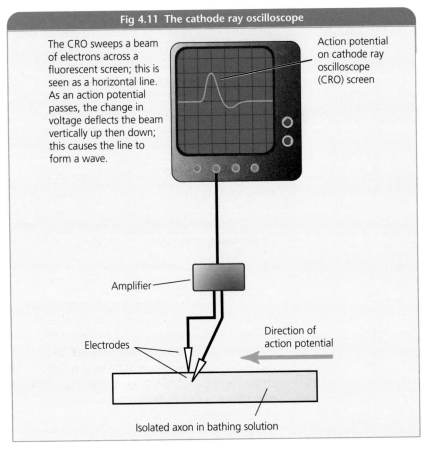

Fig 4.11 The cathode ray oscilloscope

The CRO sweeps a beam of electrons across a fluorescent screen; this is seen as a horizontal line. As an action potential passes, the change in voltage deflects the beam vertically up then down; this causes the line to form a wave.

Action potential on cathode ray oscilloscope (CRO) screen

Amplifier

Electrodes

Direction of action potential

Isolated axon in bathing solution

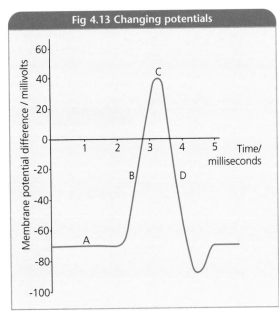

Fig 4.13 Changing potentials

Repolarisation

Depolarisation occurs in a short stretch of membrane, and then this recovers its resting potential, and the action potential moves on down the axon. The membrane recovers its negative resting potential because of gated potassium channels. Shortly after the gated sodium channels in the axon open to let sodium ions in, thus depolarising the membrane, gated potassium channels also open (Fig 4.12). Because there is a greater concentration of potassium ions inside the membrane than outside, potassium ions move along their concentration gradient to the outside. This movement of potassium ions results in the net positive charge outside the membrane being restored, forming a resting

potential once more. The restoration of the resting potential is called **repolarisation**. For a short period after repolarisation both the gated channels for sodium ions and the gated channels for potassium ions remain closed. During this period the membrane cannot be depolarised and therefore no impulse can pass. This period is known as the **refractory period**.

The refractory period is important for the following reasons:

- Each action potential is kept discrete – there is no overlapping of potentials;
- It ensures the action potentials pass in only one direction.

8 Fig 4.13 shows changes in potential across an axon membrane during and after an action potential.

a Which of the letters A to D labels:
  i   repolarisation?
  ii action potential?
  iii resting potential?
  iv depolarisation?

b By how much did the potential difference change when the action potential was produced?

c How long is the refractory period?

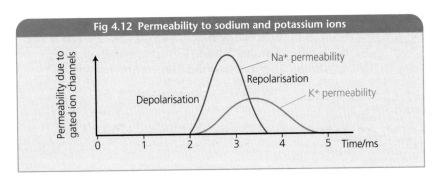

Fig 4.12 Permeability to sodium and potassium ions

Fig 4.14 Myelin and conduction speed

Non-myelinated axon

The impulse passes along the nerve fibre by each section of membrane depolarising the next, so transmission is relatively slow.

Myelinated axon

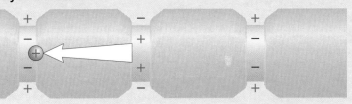

The impulse jumps from one node to the next, so only the membrane at the nodes is depolarised. This leads to rapid transmission.

The myelin sheath, then, is an adaptation for rapid transmission of nerve impulses. Non-myelinated fibres are not adapted in this way and therefore transmit impulses much more slowly.

Transmission of impulses along nerve fibres

In non-myelinated fibres, the impulse is transmitted along the fibre when each tiny segment of the membrane causes the next segment to depolarise. Transmission is relatively slow since the whole of the membrane must be depolarised, in successive sections.

Depolarisation in myelinated fibres occurs only at the nodes of Ranvier since the sheath cells are pressed tightly against the axon (Fig 4.14). In these myelinated nerve fibres, the impulse 'jumps' from one node of Ranvier to the next, missing out sections of membrane, thus leading to rapid transmission.

EXTENSION More than you think

In the introduction to his book *The Astonishing Hypothesis*, Francis Crick writes:

"The Astonishing Hypothesis is that 'You', your joys and your sorrows, your memories and your ambitions, your sense of personal identity and free will, are in fact no more than the behaviour of a vast assembly of nerve cells. One of the most difficult aspects of the nervous system to explain is: how can ion movements in neurones give us consciousness and self-awareness? Yet we accept that certain other complex structures have qualities that we would not predict by looking at their component parts. For example, the components of a motorcar do very little until they are fitted together – but then the whole assembly can be driven down the motorway at 70 mph."

KEY FACTS

- A resting potential gives a neurone the potential to transmit a nerve impulse.

- The resting potential is produced mainly by the active transport of sodium ions to the outside of the nerve fibre. This makes the outside of the membrane positively charged. The membrane in this state is said to be polarised.

- The pump that does this consists of the enzyme ATPase which is also a carrier protein in the cell membrane.

- As sodium ions are pumped out of the cell potassium ions are pumped in, but at a slower rate.

- Depolarisation occurs when closed sodium channels in the membrane suddenly open. Because there is a higher concentration of sodium ions outside than inside, sodium ions move into the cell by facilitated diffusion

- This movement of sodium ions into the cell gives the inside of the membrane a higher positive charge than the outside – the membrane is said to be depolarised.

- This change in potential of the membrane is called the action potential.

- After depolarisation, the membrane is repolarised by the pumping out again of the sodium ions.

- Whilst the membrane is being repolarised, the membrane cannot be depolarised. The period when this happens is called the refractory period.

4.3 Synapses

The junction that occurs where two neurones meet is called a synapse. In all but the most powerful electron micrographs, neurones appear to be actually touching, but there is, in fact, a very narrow gap between them called the **synaptic cleft**. Information is carried across the synaptic cleft by chemicals called **transmitters**. Some drugs interfere with this chemical transmission and it is by studying their effects on synapses that we have obtained much of our understanding of how synapses work.

The photograph on this page shows an electron micrograph of several nerve fibres forming synapses with a cell body. A neurone may have synapses that connect with up to ten thousand other neurones!

Transmission of an impulse across a synapse

Transmitters are stored at nerve endings in tiny bags of membrane called **synaptic vesicles**. Fig 4.15 shows the main stages in the transmission of impulses across the junction between two neurones and these are described below:

- An action potential arrives at the end of the presynaptic neurone.
- This action potential causes calcium-gated channels in the membrane to open, resulting in an influx of calcium ions.

- The calcium ions cause the synaptic vesicles to move to the membrane and release the transmitter substance into the synaptic cleft. At cholinergic synapses the transmitter substance is acetylcholine.
- The transmitter substance diffuses across the synaptic cleft to the postsynaptic membrane.
- The transmitter substance molecules bind to protein molecules in the postsynaptic membrane.
- This causes depolarisation of the postsynaptic membrane, starting a nerve impulse in the postsynaptic neurone
- There is a delay of about half a millisecond at a synapse. This is the time needed for the transmitter to diffuse across the gap, bind to a receptor protein and so activate or inhibit the next cell.

The different ways in which synapses connect neurones to other neurones or to muscle cells is used to produce a whole range of responses. The response can also be affected by the type of transmitter substance -transmitters can be either excitatory (they increase the activity of the next cell) or inhibitory (they decrease the activity of the next cell), enabling synapses to either pass signals onward or to block signals.

Synapses can become fatigued. This happens when so many action potentials arrive in so short a time that the cell runs out of transmitter (or its components). The impulse can no longer cross the synapse. This loss of response at a synapse is known as **adaptation** and it means that animals ignore stimuli that go on for a long time. For example, we do not notice stimuli such as the tick of a clock or the feel of our clothes brushing against our skin, once we are used to them. Such stimuli are irrelevant to our survival. Sudden changes in our environment, like the unexpected approach of a car in a quiet lane, are more important.

Synapses between neurones might direct an impulse to just one other neurone, or spread it out to several. Synapses also occur at the junctions between nerve and muscle, where they are called **neuromuscular junctions**. Besides their role in controlling deliberate movement such as writing or lifting a cup, synapses are just as important in regulating involuntary movement such as heartbeat.

False-colour scanning electron micrograph of the junction sites (synapses) between nerve fibres (purple) and a neurone cell body (yellow).

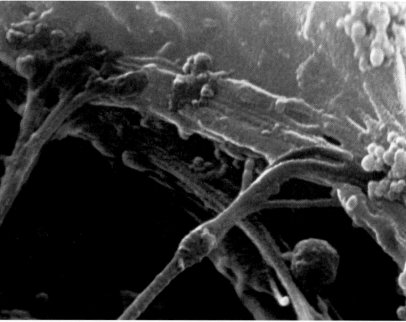

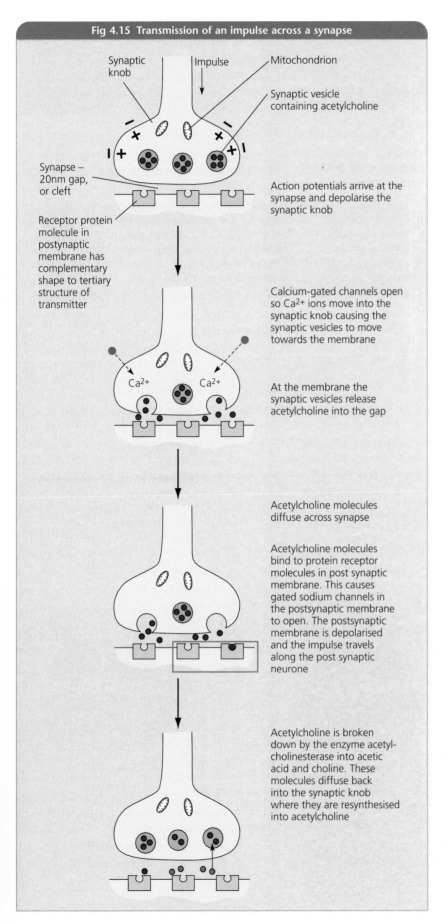

Fig 4.15 Transmission of an impulse across a synapse

Synaptic knob

Impulse

Mitochondrion

Synaptic vesicle containing acetylcholine

Synapse – 20nm gap, or cleft

Receptor protein molecule in postsynaptic membrane has complementary shape to tertiary structure of transmitter

Action potentials arrive at the synapse and depolarise the synaptic knob

Calcium-gated channels open so Ca²⁺ ions move into the synaptic knob causing the synaptic vesicles to move towards the membrane

At the membrane the synaptic vesicles release acetylcholine into the gap

Acetylcholine molecules diffuse across synapse

Acetylcholine molecules bind to protein receptor molecules in post synaptic membrane. This causes gated sodium channels in the postsynaptic membrane to open. The postsynaptic membrane is depolarised and the impulse travels along the post synaptic neurone

Acetylcholine is broken down by the enzyme acetylcholinesterase into acetic acid and choline. These molecules diffuse back into the synaptic knob where they are resynthesised into acetylcholine

Cholinergic synapses

Over 40 transmitters have now been identified. One of the commonest transmitters in voluntary nerves is **acetylcholine**. Synapses that have acetylcholine as their transmitter are called **cholinergic synapses**.

Once the nerve impulse has been passed on to the next neurone, transmitters are quickly removed from the synaptic cleft. If they were not, neurones would keep on firing uncontrollably. A very fast-acting enzyme called **acetylcholinesterase** breaks down acetylcholine into acetic acid and choline. These substances are reabsorbed through the presynaptic membrane. ATP energy from mitochondria is used to provide the energy to resynthesise acetylcholine, which is then returned to the vesicles.

9 Eserine is a drug used after eye surgery. It helps to prevent swelling of the eye caused by fluid accumulation. Muscle contractions help to remove excess fluid from the eye. Eserine works by inhibiting acetylcholinesterase. What is the effect of eserine at a cholinergic synapse?

Synapses that use noradrenaline

Synapses that use noradrenaline affect heart rate, breathing rate and brain activity. This is similar to the effect of the hormone adrenaline, which prepares the body for emergencies.

In AS Biology, you learned that noradrenaline speeds up the rate of heartbeat when it is released by nerve fibres. In some people, release of too much noradrenaline causes the heart to race. One way of treating this is to use drugs known as beta-blockers. These drugs have molecular shapes similar to noradrenaline.

10
a Which part of the heart is directly affected by the release of noradrenaline?
b Suggest how beta-blockers work.

EXTENSION

Summation

Sometimes, the amount of transmitter substance resulting from one impulse in the presynaptic neurone is not sufficient to cause depolarisation of the postsynaptic membrane. This may be because the transmitter substance at a synapse is removed almost as quickly as it is released. To produce depolarisation, several action potentials might be needed to produce enough transmitter to overcome the threshold of the postsynaptic membrane. This can be done in two ways:

- By ensuring that several action potentials from different neurones arrive at the postsynaptic membrane at the same time. This is called **spatial summation**. Spatial summation occurs in the retina of the eye. In dim light an

individual receptor cell might not produce sufficient transmitter substance to depolarise a sensory neurone, but several receptors will produce enough transmitter, thus enabling us to see.

- By ensuring that the action potentials from one presynaptic neurone arrive in rapid succession. This is known as **temporal summation**.

Summation is important for the brain to work properly. For example, it might be better to ignore a weak stimulus, such as mild pressure on the skin, but a stronger stimulus might cause injury and so require a response. A strong stimulus sends a high frequency of nerve impulses to the brain.

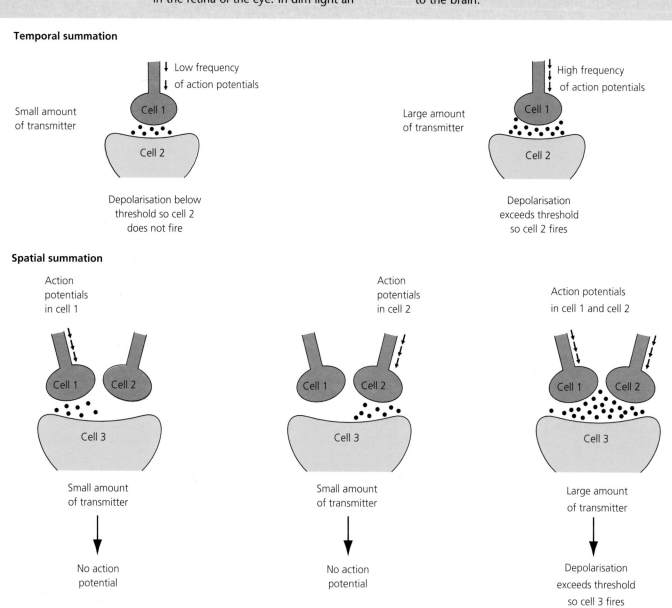

Temporal summation

Low frequency of action potentials

Small amount of transmitter

Cell 1

Cell 2

Depolarisation below threshold so cell 2 does not fire

High frequency of action potentials

Large amount of transmitter

Cell 1

Cell 2

Depolarisation exceeds threshold so cell 2 fires

Spatial summation

Action potentials in cell 1

Cell 1   Cell 2

Cell 3

Small amount of transmitter

No action potential

Action potentials in cell 2

Cell 1   Cell 2

Cell 3

Small amount of transmitter

No action potential

Action potentials in cell 1 and cell 2

Cell 1   Cell 2

Cell 3

Large amount of transmitter

Depolarisation exceeds threshold so cell 3 fires

The neuromuscular junction

Fig 4.16 shows a drawing of an electron micrograph of the junction between a motor neurone and a muscle fibre.

Exactly the same sequence of events happens at this synapse as when two neurones connect, but in this case the postsynaptic membrane is the muscle fibre membrane, the **sarcolemma**. The sarcolemma is depolarised when acetylcholine, released by the presynaptic membrane of the neurone, diffuses across the synapse and binds to protein receptors. Depolarisation sets in motion a sequence of events that lead to contraction of the muscle fibre. These events will be described in Chapter 6.

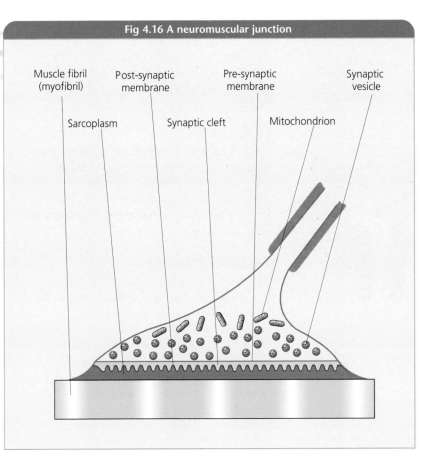

Fig 4.16 A neuromuscular junction

Muscle fibril (myofibril)
Post-synaptic membrane
Pre-synaptic membrane
Synaptic vesicle
Sarcoplasm
Synaptic cleft
Mitochondrion

- The sequence of events at cholinergic synapses and neuromuscular junctions is:
  - Action potential arrives at presynaptic membrane;
  - Ca^{2+} channels open and Ca^{2+} ions enter presynaptic membrane;
  - Vesicles containing acetylcholine move towards presynaptic membrane;
  - Acetylcholine is released from synaptic vesicles into synaptic cleft;
  - Acetylcholine diffuses across synaptic cleft to postsynaptic membrane;
  - Acetylcholine binds with specific receptor protein of postsynaptic membrane.

- Depolarisation of postsynaptic membrane results in:
  - an action potential in the postsynaptic neurone;
  - or depolarisation of the sarcolemma leading to contraction of the muscle fibre.

4.4 Drugs and synapses

Transmitters are released in tiny amounts, only 500–1000 molecules from each synaptic knob are required to transmit an impulse. So, drugs that affect transmitters or their binding sites can have powerful effects when given in fairly small doses. Some chemicals, many of them from plants, have a dramatic effect on the nervous system.

The effect of nicotine

The nicotine molecule is a similar shape to acetylcholine, so it can bind with acetylcholine receptors and open sodium channels as shown in Fig 4.17.

Nicotine receptors are found throughout the nervous system and there are at least five different types. Some of these are more sensitive to nicotine than others. Some activate quickly, then turn off. Others stay

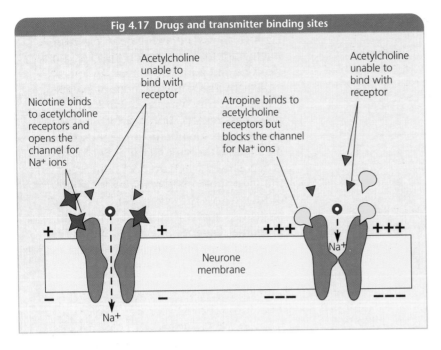

Fig 4.17 Drugs and transmitter binding sites

Nicotine binds to acetylcholine receptors and opens the channel for Na⁺ ions

Acetylcholine unable to bind with receptor

Atropine binds to acetylcholine receptors but blocks the channel for Na⁺ ions

Acetylcholine unable to bind with receptor

Neurone membrane

active as long as nicotine is present. Nicotine is, of course, a major component of tobacco and is the main reason for smokers becoming addicted to their habit. Once the nervous system gets used to nicotine, doing without it creates unpleasant symptoms such as depression and anxiety. The average smoker inhales smoke from about 20 cigarettes per day, which averages at about 200 puffs per day or 80 000 puffs per year. This delivers a constant supply of nicotine to their nervous system – a smoker has to puff on a cigarette every 5 minutes during waking hours to

Deadly nightshade (*Atropa belladonna*) is very poisonous. It contains the alkaloids atropine, solanine and hyoscyamine. It was called 'belladonna' because sixteenth-century Italian women used it to dilate their pupils – which they thought made them more attractive.

maintain nicotine levels that will keep the nicotine receptors active.

There is a powerful correlation rate between smoking and depression. Do people learn to smoke to relieve an underlying depression or anxiety?

11

a A caffeine molecule has a similar shape to a molecule of an excitatory brain transmitter called adenosine. How does caffeine increase alertness?

b How could someone become addicted to caffeine?

The effect of atropine

Atropine also binds to acetylcholine receptors, but does not open the sodium channels. It blocks the receptors, and prevents acetylcholine binding to them as shown in Fig 4.17. When this happens in motor neurones, it causes muscle paralysis.

Atropine is extracted from the plant *Atropa belladonna*. 'Atropa' comes from the Greek Fate, Atropa, who severs the strand of life; 'belladonna' means 'beautiful woman' in Italian. The latter alludes to the Renaissance when a 'doe-eyed' expression was considered to be the utmost of beauty. Ladies would drop juice from deadly nightshade leaves into their eyes, dilating their pupils and giving them the desired look.

Drugs and noradrenaline

Beta-blockers have a similar shape to noradrenaline and so compete with it for receptors on the postsynaptic membrane. Amphetamines and cocaine also affect noradrenaline synapses, but they work in a different way. They prevent the reabsorption of noradrenaline from the synaptic gap. So, noradrenaline remains in the gap and the neurone keeps on firing. One of the effects of amphetamines is to make a person feel energetic and carefree, which is why they are often known as speed. Before the harmful effects were known, amphetamines were given to pupils with poor attention spans, to help them concentrate.

Amphetamines are psychologically addictive. Users become dependent on the drug to avoid the 'down' feeling they often experience when the drug's effect wears off. This dependence can lead a user to turn to stronger stimulants such as cocaine, or to larger doses of amphetamines to maintain a 'high'.

People who stop using amphetamines abruptly often experience the physical signs of addiction, such as fatigue, long periods of sleep, irritability, and depression. How severe and prolonged these withdrawal symptoms are depends on the degree of abuse.

Curare

Curare is used as a muscle relaxant in abdominal surgery. It competes with acetylcholine at the neuromuscular junctions, preventing nerve impulses causing the abdominal muscles to contract. South American Indians first used curare as a poison. They used it mainly to catch animals for food by smearing arrow tips with it. In a poisoned animal it first affects the muscles of the toes, ears, and eyes, then those of the neck and limbs, and, finally, those involved in respiration. The leads to death caused by respiratory paralysis.

 12 Suggest why it is important that the muscles of the abdominal walls are relaxed during abdominal surgery.

Prozac and tranquillizers

Serotonin is a neurotransmitter normally active in the brain. Some forms of depression are caused by a reduced concentration of serotonin in the brain. The antidepressant drug Prozac is a known as a serotonin re-uptake inhibitor. Prozac alleviates depression because it competes with serotonin for the 'active' sites on the proteins that reabsorb serotonin, leading to a higher concentration of serotonin at synapses in the brain. It also competes for the active sites on the enzymes that break down serotonin at synapses.

Tranquillisers are drugs that reduce tension. Benzodiazepine tranquillisers, such as valium, work by increasing the binding of inhibitory transmitters in the brain. Inhibitory transmitters hyperpolarise rather than depolarise the membrane of the next neurone. This makes the next neurone less excitable. Valium reduces stress and anxiety, but it can be addictive.

EXAMINATION QUESTIONS

1 When the back of the hand accidentally touches a hot surface, the biceps muscle contracts and the hand is rapidly removed. This is one example of a reflex action and involves three neurones.

a

  i Explain what is meant by a reflex action. (2)
  ii Name the effector involved in the above reflex action. (1)

b The diagram opposite shows a cross-section through the spinal cord. Copy and complete the diagram by drawing and labelling the neurones involved in this reflex action. (3)

Total (6)

BY04 Feb 97 Q1

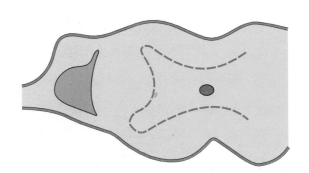

Fig 4.Q1

2 The graph below shows the change in potential difference at a point in a neurone during the propagation of a nerve impulse.

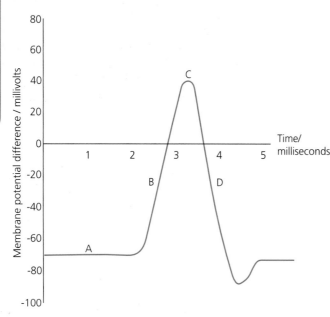

Fig 4.Q2

a From this graph give the value of:
  i the resting potential of the neurone;
  ii the maximum change which occurs in the potential difference across the membrane. (2)

b Explain, in terms of ion movements, the change in potential difference which takes place between
  i points A and B;
  ii points C and D. (4)

c An action potential is sometimes referred to as an 'all or nothing' process.
  i Explain what is meant by describing an action potential as an 'all or nothing' process. (1)
  ii Explain how this property relates to the way in which a nerve impulse conveys information about the strength of a stimulus. (1)

Total (8)

BT04 June 96 Q6

3 The graph in Fig 4.Q3 shows changes in concentration of sodium ions inside the axon of a large neurone. The axon was stimulated at the points indicated on the graph.
Between A and B on the graph the neurone was treated with dinitrophenol. This prevents the production of ATP.

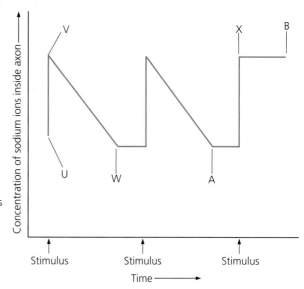

Fig 4.Q3

a Explain the changes in sodium ion concentration
  i between U and V; (2)
  ii between V and W. (2)

b Explain why the concentration of sodium ions did not change between X and B. (2)

Total (6)

BY04 June 2000 Q5

4 The membrane potential of a neurone leading from a stretch receptor in a muscle was measured before, during and after a period in which the muscle was stretched. The results are shown in the graph below.

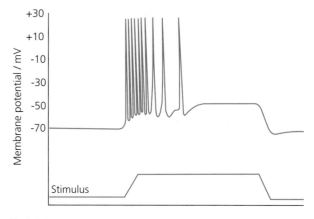

Fig 4.Q4

a Explain what causes the initial increase in membrane potential. (2)

b How do these results illustrate the 'all-or-nothing' principle? (1)

c
i For how long was the muscle stretched? (1)
ii Describe and explain the effect on the neurone of keeping the muscle stretched for this period. (2)
iii Suggest one biological advantage of this effect on the neurone. (1)

Total (7)

BY04 March 99 Q6

5 Read the following passage.

Cone snails extend a long, whippy tube tipped with a poisonous barb disguised as food. Fish that swallow the bait are instantly harpooned, their fate sealed by a dose of paralysing toxins squirted through the barb.

Research at Stanford University has shown that some of the toxins block the tiny channels that allow sodium ions through the membranes of the nerve and muscle cells. Other toxins paralyse fish by blocking the receptors for acetylcholine at neuromuscular junctions.

Cone snails produce many different toxins. These toxins are very small; they are protein fragments seldom longer than 30 amino acids or shorter than 10.

a Describe the structure of the channels that allow sodium ions through membranes. (2)

b Explain how each of the following leads to paralysis of fish:
i blocking of sodium channels in nerve cells;
ii blocking of receptors for acetylcholine in nerve cells. (6)

c Different species of cone snails produce different types of toxins.
Explain in terms of natural selection how this may lead to different cone snail species living in the same habitat. (4)

Total (12)

BY04 March 2000 Q8

6
a What happens in a neurone membrane when an action potential passes? (3)

b The neurotransmitter serotonin is involved in controlling appetite. The increase in blood sugar concentration after a meal causes certain cells in the brain to release serotonin. This binds to neurones which then inform the appetite centre in the brain that enough food has been eaten.

Fig 4.Q6a shows the normal events involving serotonin.

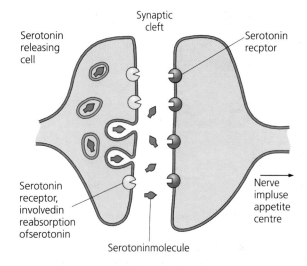

Fig 4.Q6a

i Serotonin is a neurotransmitter. Use the diagram and your knowledge of synapses to explain how information is transmitted across this synapse. (5)
ii Adifax is a drug which can be used to affect people's eating habits. Fig 4.Q6b represents a serotonin molecule and an Adifax molecule.

Fig 4.Q6b

Explain how Adifax might affect the action of serotonin and the appetite of the person. (4)

Total (12)

BY04 March 98 Q8

5 Senses and sensibility

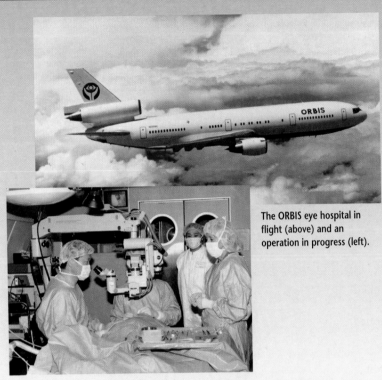

The ORBIS eye hospital in flight (above) and an operation in progress (left).

but in Africa there is only one eye specialist for every million people.

In the mid-1970s, Dr. David Paton, an American ophthalmologist, conceived the idea of an airborne, ophthalmological teaching hospital. Dr. Paton's solution was ORBIS, a mobile teaching eye hospital. At the invitation of local doctors, ORBIS flies into a new country. ORBIS's aim is to share and transfer knowledge between eye surgeons, nurses, anaesthetists and biomedical engineers around the world. Commercial pilots give up their holidays to fly ORBIS to its next destination. Everybody in the crew helps to unpack and set up the operating theatre and recovery area – and everybody, irrespective of rank, receives the same salary.

The problem for many who seek help from the ORBIS team is a cataract – cloudiness of the lens. Cataracts cause more than 50 per cent of the blindness in many countries; around the world 17 million people suffer from this eye disease. Usually, cataracts occur in older people, but they can also occur in babies (perhaps as a result of the mother suffering from rubella during pregnancy) and can be caused by injury or infection.

About 80 per cent of the 42 million blind people in the world live in poor countries. The majority of these people are unnecessarily blind. With medical care, their sight could be restored or their blindness prevented. In the UK and the USA there is one eye specialist for every thousand people,

Most of us will need artificial help with vision at some stage in our life. In this chapter you will learn about the structure and functioning of the eye, and how this is related to common eye defects.

5.1 Sight

A human being has five senses; sight, hearing, touch, smell and taste. In this course, it is important to know the details of sight only. However, before you start to study sight in more detail, you need to revise the structure of the eye.

Basic structure of the eye

Fig 5.1 shows the eye's main components and how they fit together.

The human eye is a sphere about 2.5 cm in diameter. The wall of the eye is composed of three layers:

- the outer **sclera**, the white of the eye, which has a transparent window – the **cornea** at the front;

- the inner **retina** which contains receptor cells that are sensitive to light;

- the **choroid**, a layer between the sclera and the retina, consists of the blood vessels that supply the eye and contains cells that contain black pigment. This pigment prevents reflection of light inside the eye.

Inside, the eye is divided into two chambers by the **lens**. The chamber in front of the lens is filled with a watery fluid called the **aqueous humour**; the chamber behind the eye with **vitreous humour**, which is jelly-like. These two fluids exert a pressure on the wall of the eyeball. This pressure has an important role in the focusing mechanism of the eye. It also keeps the shape of the retina smooth so that the image that the eye sees is always focused sharply.

Fine focusing is brought about by changing the shape of the lens. This is done

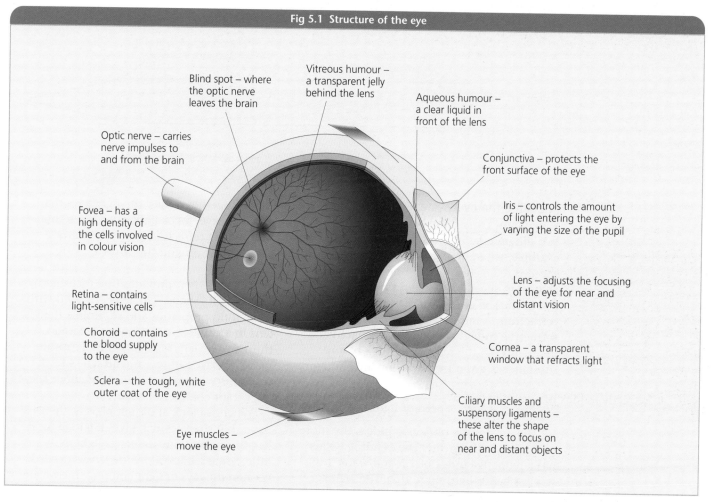

Fig 5.1 Structure of the eye

Blind spot – where the optic nerve leaves the brain

Vitreous humour – a transparent jelly behind the lens

Aqueous humour – a clear liquid in front of the lens

Optic nerve – carries nerve impulses to and from the brain

Conjunctiva – protects the front surface of the eye

Iris – controls the amount of light entering the eye by varying the size of the pupil

Fovea – has a high density of the cells involved in colour vision

Lens – adjusts the focusing of the eye for near and distant vision

Retina – contains light-sensitive cells

Choroid – contains the blood supply to the eye

Cornea – a transparent window that refracts light

Sclera – the tough, white outer coat of the eye

Ciliary muscles and suspensory ligaments – these alter the shape of the lens to focus on near and distant objects

Eye muscles – move the eye

by the action of the **ciliary muscles** and **suspensory ligaments**, and by the pressure of the eye fluids. The iris consists of **involuntary muscles** that contract to control the size of the pupil and thus the amount of light entering the eye.

Fig 5.2 The iris and light

Pupil

Circular muscles

Radial muscles

In bright light
The circular muscles contract and reduce the size of the pupil. The radial muscles are relaxed

In dim light
The pupil widens as the radial muscles contract and pull the edges of the iris away from the centre. The circular muscles are relaxed

The iris

The eye accurately controls the amount of light that falls on the retina. This is quite a fine balancing act – too much light would damage the light-sensitive cells in the retina, too little light and the cells would not be stimulated. Light entering the eye passes first through the **cornea** and then through the **pupil** on its way to the lens and eventually the retina. The **iris** muscles control the size of the pupil. There are two sets of muscles in the iris, **circular** and **radial**. These have opposite effects: contraction of the radial muscles causes the pupil to dilate; contraction of the circular muscles causes the pupil to constrict (Fig 5.2). Muscles that have opposite effects are said to be **antagonistic**.

The changes in size of the pupil are brought about by a reflex arc. The light receptors in this arc are located in the retina. The sensory neurones carry impulses to the grey matter of the brain via the optic nerve. Impulses from the brain to the iris muscles are transmitted by nerve fibres of the autonomic nervous system (see page 81).

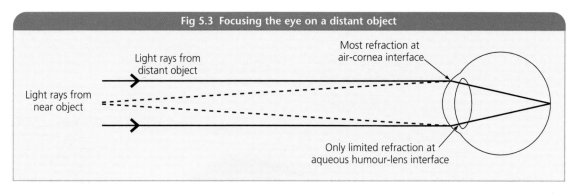

Fig 5.3 Focusing the eye on a distant object

Most refraction at air-cornea interface

Light rays from distant object

Light rays from near object

Only limited refraction at aqueous humour-lens interface

Focusing the eye

When light crosses the boundary between two different substances, it changes speed. For example, when light enters glass from air, its speed is reduced by about one third. This change in speed brings about a change in direction. The change of direction is called **refraction**. A measure of refraction is **refractive index**. Air is given a refractive index of 1, so the refractive index of any substance is given by the following equation:

$$\text{Refractive index of a substance} = \frac{\text{Speed of light in air}}{\text{Speed of light in substance}}$$

The greater the refractive index, the more refraction so the greater the bending. Glass has a refractive index of 1.5 and water 1.33, so glass bends light more than the water.

1 When you are swimming under water there is no refraction of light as it passes from water into the cornea. Explain why.

When the eye is at rest it focuses on distant objects. The cornea and the lens, which together refract the light rays that enter the eye, focus light onto the retina. Most of the refraction is at the interface between the air and the cornea, as Fig 5.3 shows.

The lens then provides fine focusing by changing its shape. The lens is a solid with some fluid properties and so, unlike the glass lens in a camera, it can be made fatter or thinner. The lens is enclosed in a capsule, made of elastic fibres, and attached to the suspensory ligaments that bring about these important changes in shape.

When we look at distant objects, the lens has a thin shape, which gives it a long focal length. In this state, it refracts light, but only a little. Some refraction by the lens is needed because the rays of light entering the eye are almost parallel and if they were not refracted at all, focusing would be impossible. The lens is pulled into this thin shape by tension in the suspensory ligament pulling on the lens capsules (Fig 5.4). This tension is caused by the outward pressure of the eye fluids on the wall of the eyeball. The suspensory ligaments can be put under tension because the ciliary muscles, to which they are attached, are relaxed.

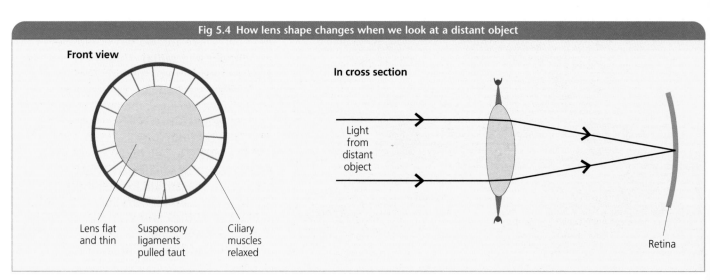

Fig 5.4 How lens shape changes when we look at a distant object

Front view

Lens flat and thin

Suspensory ligaments pulled taut

Ciliary muscles relaxed

In cross section

Light from distant object

Retina

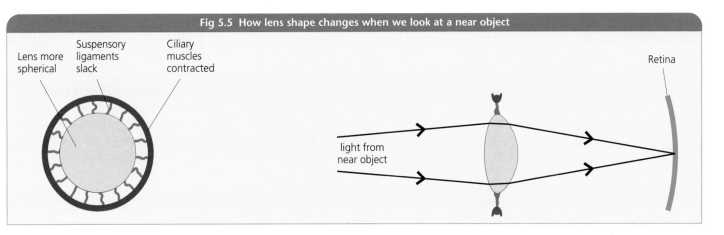

Fig 5.5 How lens shape changes when we look at a near object

Lens more spherical

Suspensory ligaments slack

Ciliary muscles contracted

Retina

light from near object

Focusing the eye on near objects, for example to read a book, is known as **accommodation**. To do this the focal length of the lens has to shorten since the rays of light entering the eye are diverging (Fig 5.5). The ciliary muscles are arranged in a ring. When the ciliary muscles contract the diameter of the ring is reduced. This reduction reduces the pull on the suspensory ligaments and so on the lens capsule. The elastic fibres in the capsule contract, forcing the lens into a more round shape. The lens now has a shorter focal length, so it will refract the light more.

KEY FACTS

- Light is refracted mainly at the **cornea** but also by the **lens**.

- Contraction of the circular muscles constricts the pupil, reducing the amount of light entering the eye.

- Contraction of the radial muscles dilates the pupil, allowing more light to enter the eye.

- Pressure of fluid in the eye causes tension in the **suspensory ligaments** which pull the lens capsule, including the lens, into a thinner shape with a longer focal length to focus distant objects.

- Accommodation is altering the shape of the lens to focus near objects.

- Contraction of the **ciliary muscles** reduces tension in the suspensory ligaments. Reducing the tension on the elastic lens capsule allows the elastic fibres in the lens capsule to transform the lens into a more spherical shape with a shorter focal length to focus on near objects.

- Antagonistic muscle action in the iris controls the diameter of the pupil.

5.2   The retina

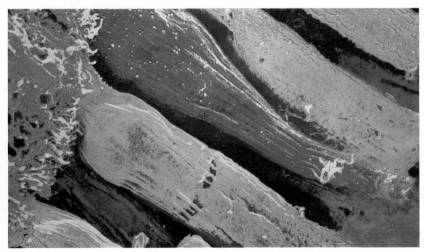

False-colour scanning electron micrograph of rod cells (orange) and cone cells (blue).

There are two types of light-sensitive cells in the human retina: **rods** and **cones**. The photograph (left) shows how rods and cones appear under the scanning electron microscope. Fig 5.6 on page 73 shows the detailed structure of these two specialised cells.

Rods and cones have the same basic structure, but they differ in shape and in the pigment they contain. Rod cells contain **rhodopsin**, cone cells have **iodopsin**. Rhodopsin and iodopsin are bleached by light, as are many pigments. This is why curtains in a sunny window fade. A similar change happens to the pigments in rods and cones, but here the bleaching is rapid and reversible.

APPLICATION

Repairing eye defects

Replacing the lens

To improve the sight of patients with a cataract, the whole lens can be replaced with an artificial one. The anaesthetised eye is held open, and a small flap of conjunctiva folded back. A cut is then made along the edge of the cornea, and the lens is very carefully removed, first through the dilated pupil, and then through the cut in the cornea. The most modern technique is to remove the central part of the lens, leaving a section of the lens capsule, like an open bag, to hold the implant. The lens implant has two curved, hair-like projections to hold it in place inside the lens capsule.

Lens implants like this enabled Haiam to see again. This implant is drawn actual size. Implants are made from an inert material called polymethyl methacrylate (PMMA) and are made in one piece so the hairs can't fall off.

This is Haiam, age 9, before her operation. Both her eyes were affected by cataracts, so she couldn't see. Apart from cloudy lenses, her eyes were healthy. After the operation, Haiam needed glasses because lens implants cannot change shape to accommodate objects at differing distances.

Haiam was selected for treatment in order to demonstrate the techniques involved. One eye was treated by the ORBIS surgeons while 50 Sudanese surgeons watched the operation in the ORBIS classroom. One of them later operated on Haiam's second eye. The operations were very successful. The transfer of skills and knowledge will benefit many other Sudanese people.

Folding lenses have recently been developed for use in some patients. These can be inserted into a very small cut in the eye, and spring open when put in position. In the future, lens cells grown by tissue culture might be used as implants, but animal trials have found that when cultured lenses are used, the lens capsule may become opaque. This

problem must be overcome before human trials can begin.

Lens replacement surgery gives the patient much clearer vision, and the world will seem more vividly coloured. However, a replacement lens lacks the slight yellow colouring of the natural lens, so colour vision is not restored to its exact natural state.

Replacing the cornea

The cornea has a very poor blood supply, as blood vessels crossing the cornea would obscure vision. Any serious damage to the cornea is therefore not repaired by the body and can lead to permanent blindness. Fortunately, the lack of blood supply also means that corneas can be transplanted with little risk of rejection.

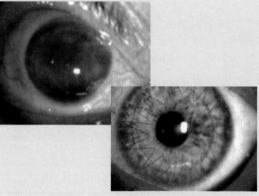

The ORBIS surgeons use a round cutting disc for corneal transplants. The surgeon places the disc on the surface of the eye and twists to make a circular cut in the damaged cornea. A round piece of cornea is then lifted out and replaced by a donor cornea that has been trimmed to the exact size in advance. Given the role of the cornea, it is important that no scar tissue forms and that the corneal surface does not become distorted.

1 Why does lack of a blood supply to the cornea lessen the risk of rejection of a corneal transplant?

2 How does a cataract affect vision?

3 Give two reasons why an artificial lens is not as good as a healthy real one.

4 Why is it important not to distort the cornea during a corneal transplant?

Fig 5.6 Rods and cones

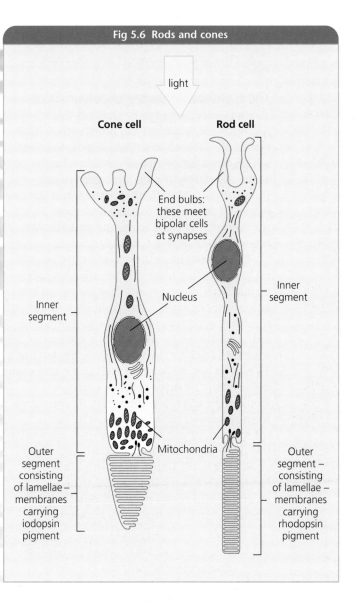

light

Cone cell   Rod cell

End bulbs: these meet bipolar cells at synapses

Nucleus

Inner segment

Inner segment

Mitochondria

Inner segment

Outer segment consisting of lamellae – membranes carrying iodopsin pigment

Outer segment – consisting of lamellae – membranes carrying rhodopsin pigment

Fig 5.7 Rod cells in the dark and in the light

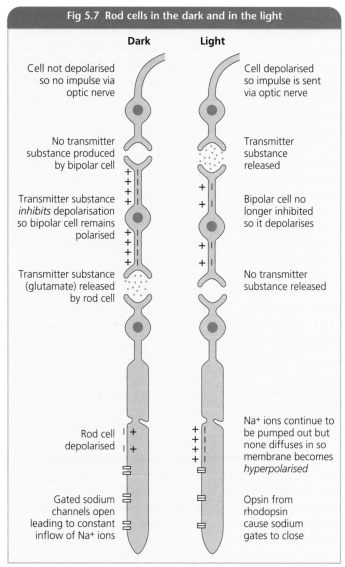

Dark   Light

Cell not depolarised so no impulse via optic nerve

Cell depolarised so impulse is sent via optic nerve

No transmitter substance produced by bipolar cell

Transmitter substance released

Transmitter substance *inhibits* depolarisation so bipolar cell remains polarised

Bipolar cell no longer inhibited so it depolarises

Transmitter substance (glutamate) released by rod cell

No transmitter substance released

Rod cell depolarised

Na^+ ions continue to be pumped out but none diffuses in so membrane becomes *hyperpolarised*

Gated sodium channels open leading to constant inflow of Na^+ ions

Opsin from rhodopsin cause sodium gates to close

Rods

Each rod is packed with about 180 molecules of the light-sensitive pigment rhodopsin arranged in discs called **lamellae**. The rhodopsin molecule breaks down when exposed to light into a pigment called **retinal** and the protein **opsin**. The breakdown of rhodopsin into opsinbegins a series of chemical reactions that result in the release of a transmitter substance by the rod cell. The transmitter substance stimulates a chain of events that may eventually result in an impulse being passed to the brain along a nerve fibre in the optic nerve.

When we enter a dark room, the light-bleached pigment is restored to its unbleached form, rhodopsin. This effect is called **dark adaptation** and explains why we are gradually able to see more as we 'get used to' the lack of light. In the dark, it takes about 30 minutes to resynthesise all the rhodopsin from the retinal and opsin.

In complete darkness, rhodopsin is very stable. If rhodopsin were not so stable, rods might send impulses to the brain when no light was falling on them. In strong light, rhodopsin is broken down quicker than it can be reformed, so the rods are not of much value. In dim light breakdown of rhodopsin is much slower so production keeps up with breakdown.

Rod cells are connected to **bipolar cells**. The rod cell and its bipolar cell work in a different way to most other receptors. Other receptors produce transmitter substance only when they are stimulated. But a rod cell produces a transmitter substance when it is not being stimulated, and stops production when it is stimulated (Fig 5.7).

In the dark, the gated sodium channels of

rod cells are open, so sodium ions constantly diffuse in causing the cell to be constantly depolarised. Depolarised rod cells produce the transmitter substance glutamate. Glutamate is an inhibitory transmitter substance. Rather than causing depolarisation of the bipolar cell, it prevents it so that the bipolar cell does not produce a transmitter substance. Consequently no impulses are transmitted to the nerve fibres in the optic nerve.

When a rod cell absorbs light, rhodopsin breaks down, producing opsin. Opsin causes the gated sodium channels to close. The membrane continues to pump out sodium ions and so becomes hyperpolarized and stops producing the glutamate transmitter. The bipolar cell is not inhibited, so it now produces a transmitter substance, causing an impulse to be produced in the optic nerve fibre.

Cones

Cones work on the same principle as rods except that their pigment is iodopsin. Cones have a high threshold; the pigment is only broken down by high intensity light, so they operate in daylight. Most of the impulses passing to the brain in bright light come from the cones, where iodopsin is resynthesised much more quickly than rhodopsin in the rods.

2 Why can't we see very well when we first enter a poorly lit room from a brightly lit area?

3 It is often very sunny in winter in ski resorts. Skiers wear dark goggles to prevent snow 'blindness'. Explain what causes snow 'blindness'.

 4 Suggest the advantage to rod cells of having large numbers of mitochondria.

The trichromatic theory of colour vision

There is only one type of rod and this responds most strongly to bluish-green light. Cones are divided into three types, each of which has a different sensitivity to light. There are red-light receptors, green-light receptors and blue-light receptors, but the ranges of sensitivity overlap and most wavelengths of light stimulate at least two types of cone, as Fig 5.8 shows.

The discovery of three types of cone, supports the trichromatic theory of colour vision. This theory states that we see all the colours of the visible spectrum by a mixing of the three primary colours – blue, green and red. A white wall reflects all the colours of the spectrum back to the eye; the white parts of a TV screen are made up of red, green and blue dots. When all three types of cone are stimulated, the brain interprets the impulses from the cones as white light. The brain interprets any combination of messages from the three types of cone as a particular colour. Look at Fig 5.8. Yellow light stimulates the red-light receptors and the green-light receptors and the brain interprets the impulses from the receptors as yellow.

5 Which cones are stimulated by light of wavelength 600 nm?

6 Why do you see an orange colour when light of 600 nm stimulates the cones?

7 Which cones are stimulated by the white paper and black letters of this page?

Colour-blindness

About 8 per cent of men and less than 1 per cent of women have faulty colour vision. The genes for making the cone receptor pigments (cone opsins) in green-sensitive and red-sensitive cones (but not the blue-sensitive cone) are on the X chromosome. Because men have only one X chromosome and women have two, a defective gene for cone pigment is more likely to be expressed in men. Many colour-blind men lack either the red-sensitive cones or the green-sensitive ones and so confuse red, blue-green and grey. For example, bright red roses can look the same colour as the leaves, and scarlet clothes may look dark grey.

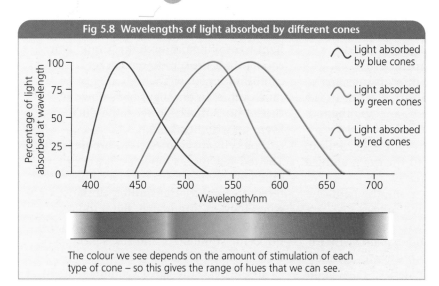

Fig 5.8 Wavelengths of light absorbed by different cones

Light absorbed by blue cones

Light absorbed by green cones

Light absorbed by red cones

Percentage of light absorbed at wavelength

Wavelength/nm

The colour we see depends on the amount of stimulation of each type of cone – so this gives the range of hues that we can see.

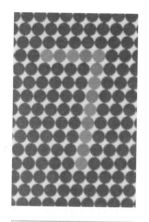

Complete colour blindness in which all cone pigments are absent is very rare.

The genes for the cone opsins have now been cloned. Their base pair sequences show that the three cone opsins differ only slightly from each other. Since the cone opsins are also similar to rhodopsin, it seems that cone opsins were derived from a modified form of rhodopsin during evolution.

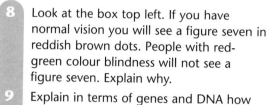

8 Look at the box top left. If you have normal vision you will see a figure seven in reddish brown dots. People with red-green colour blindness will not see a figure seven. Explain why.

9 Explain in terms of genes and DNA how opsins might have been derived from rhodopsin.

10 Stare at the shape on the left for 20 seconds then look at a white surface. What colours do you see? This is called an after-image. How does the trichromatic theory explain after-images?

Sensitivity and acuity

Fig 5.9 shows a section through the retina. The retina is said to be **inverted** since light has to pass between several layers of cells before it reaches the rods and cones. The rod and cones form synapses with cells called bipolar cells. The bipolar cells in turn synapse with ganglion cells, which synapse with the sensory neurone fibres. These transmit impulses to the brain via the optic nerve.

Cone cells give colour vision and also allow us to see in detail – they give good **acuity**. There is maximum acuity at the **fovea** because here there are many densely packed cones and each bipolar cell is stimulated by a single cone cell. Elsewhere in the retina there are fewer cones and each bipolar cell is stimulated by several cones (Fig 5.10).

Bright light is needed for cones to work well. On the other hand, rods are more effective in dim light, because up to 45 rods synapse with each bipolar cell. Dim light only results in the production of a small amount of transmitter substance by each rod. Individually, this is insufficient to overcome the threshold of the bipolar cell, but the total amount of transmitter substance produced by several rods is sufficient to overcome the threshold and depolarise the rod cell. The result of several rods causing depolarisation of one bipolar cell is to give less acuity, but better **sensitivity**.

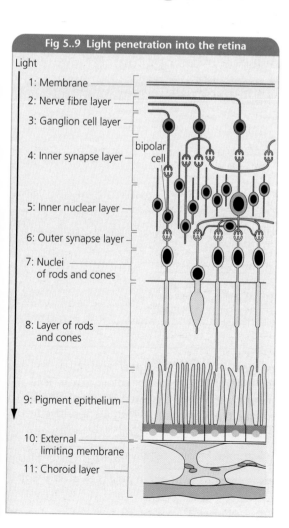

Fig 5..9 Light penetration into the retina

Light

1: Membrane
2: Nerve fibre layer
3: Ganglion cell layer
bipolar cell
4: Inner synapse layer
5: Inner nuclear layer
6: Outer synapse layer
7: Nuclei of rods and cones
8: Layer of rods and cones
9: Pigment epithelium
10: External limiting membrane
11: Choroid layer

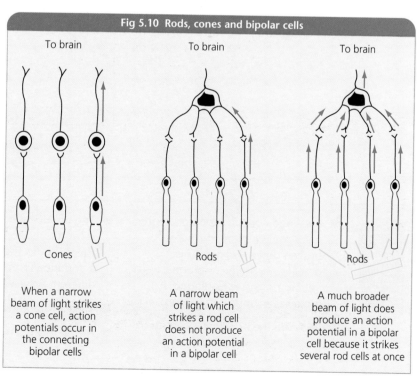

Fig 5.10 Rods, cones and bipolar cells

To brain

To brain

To brain

Cones

When a narrow beam of light strikes a cone cell, action potentials occur in the connecting bipolar cells

Rods

A narrow beam of light which strikes a rod cell does not produce an action potential in a bipolar cell

Rods

A much broader beam of light does produce an action potential in a bipolar cell because it strikes several rod cells at once

A comparison of rods and cones is given in Table 5.1.

When we look directly at something in bright light, light from it is focused on the fovea, and we see it clearly. But when there is not much light, for example when we look at a faint star, we can see the object a bit more easily if we look slightly to one side of it. This is because light is then focused to one side of the eye where there are more rods, rather than on the fovea where there are more cones.

Fig 5.11 shows how the relative numbers of rods and cones varies in different parts of the retina.

Table 5.1 Rods and cones compared

	Rods	Cones
Number per eye / millions	120	6
Absorption peak wavelength / nm	500 (green)	420 (blue) 531 (green) 558 (red)
Retinal convergence	15–45 rods to 1 bipolar cell	in fovea, 1 cone to 1 bipolar cell
Sensitivity	good: 1 photon gives response	poor: several hundred photons needed
Acuity	poor	good

11

a Why can't we see colours in dim light?

b Why do rods give us greater sensitivity in dim light?

c Why do cones give us greater acuity in bright light?

d Light from the centre of our field of vision is focused on the cones at the fovea. What evidence is there, from what we see, that we have cones in other parts of the retina?

12

a In Fig 5.11, which region, A to D, is the fovea? Give the reason for your answer.

b Which regions would be most sensitive to dim light?

c What would we see of an image focused at B? Give the reason for your answer.

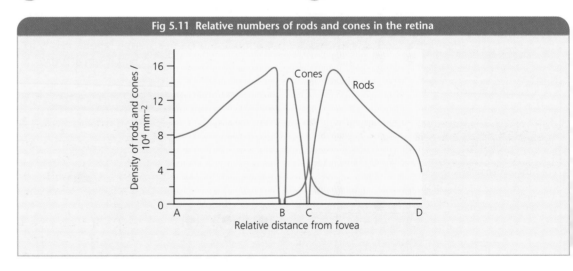

Fig 5.11 Relative numbers of rods and cones in the retina

KEY FACTS

- Rods and cones are photoreceptors. They contain pigment that is broken down by light. This breakdown produces products that initiate processes leading to impulses in optic nerve fibres.

- Rods are the principal receptors in dim light, cones in bright light.

- The discovery of three types of cone, blue, green and red-receptors, supports the trichromatic theory of colour vision. This theory states that different colours are the result of stimulation of a combination of the three types of cones, which are sensitive to different wavelengths of light.

- 15–45 rods converge with one bipolar cell giving low visual acuity.

- At the fovea, one cone converges with one bipolar cell giving high visual acuity.

5.3 The brain and sensory perception

Fig 5.12 The human brain

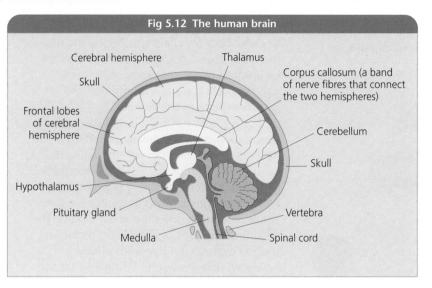

Cerebral hemisphere
Thalamus
Corpus callosum (a band of nerve fibres that connect the two hemispheres)
Skull
Frontal lobes of cerebral hemisphere
Cerebellum
Skull
Hypothalamus
Pituitary gland
Vertebra
Medulla
Spinal cord

Fig 5.13 The cerebral cortex

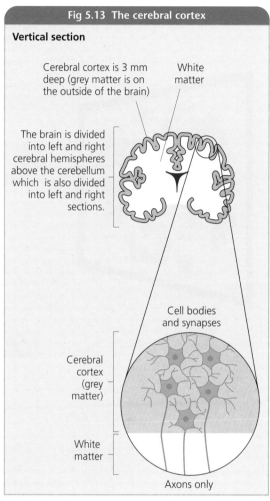

Vertical section

Cerebral cortex is 3 mm deep (grey matter is on the outside of the brain)

White matter

The brain is divided into left and right cerebral hemispheres above the cerebellum which is also divided into left and right sections.

Cerebral cortex (grey matter)

White matter

Cell bodies and synapses

Axons only

Structure of the brain

Fig 5.12 shows the main regions of the brain. You have already met the medulla, the hypothalamus and the pituitary body in your study of homeostasis. In this chapter we shall be mainly concerned with the **cerebral hemispheres**. The other main region of the brain, the **cerebellum** coordinates the contractions of the skeletal muscles.

The **cerebrum** is divided into left and right cerebral hemispheres, connected by the nerve fibres of the **corpus callosum**. The cerebrum is greatly enlarged in mammals, particularly primates (monkeys and apes). The folded surface of the cerebral hemispheres is covered with a thin layer of neurone cell bodies, sometimes known as grey matter or the **cerebral cortex** (Fig 5.13)

13 How does the arrangement of white and grey matter in the brain compare with that in the spinal cord?

The cerebral cortex contains sensory areas, association areas and motor areas. These are shown in Fig 5.14.

Sensory areas of the cerebral cortex

The sensory areas receive impulses via sensory neurons from receptors that detect the stimuli reaching the body. Each part of the skin surface connects with a different part of the touch sensory area. The skin has more receptors in

Fig 5.14 Areas of the cerebral cortex

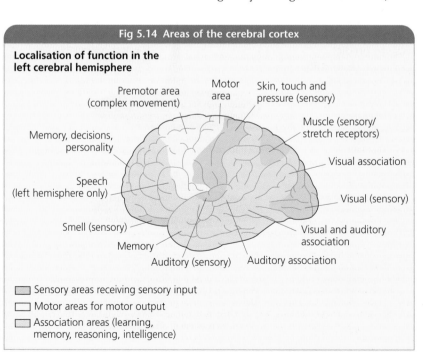

Localisation of function in the left cerebral hemisphere

Premotor area (complex movement)
Motor area
Skin, touch and pressure (sensory)
Muscle (sensory/ stretch receptors)
Memory, decisions, personality
Visual association
Speech (left hemisphere only)
Visual (sensory)
Smell (sensory)
Visual and auditory association
Memory
Auditory (sensory)
Auditory association

☐ Sensory areas receiving sensory input
☐ Motor areas for motor output
☐ Association areas (learning, memory, reasoning, intelligence)

APPLICATION   New techniques for diagnosing eye disease

The patient views a projected image of hundreds of tiny hexagons that flash up to 75 times a second. Each targets a different part of the retina and responses are recorded by an electrode on the lower lid.

Adapted from an article in the Sunday Times 'Culture' p54–55 August 27 2000

The MFERG technique can now map the function of the retina and can detect disorders before symptoms appear.

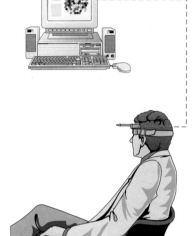

A new technique has been developed that can diagnose eye disease by observing electrical signals from the retina. Current tests and treatments for many eye disorders are far from ideal, particularly if you have a suspected problem with your retina. If tests reveal signs of glaucoma, there is no way to predict whether you will be unlucky enough to suffer serious damage until it happens. Glaucoma is caused by excess aqueous humour that does not drain away as normal. It can cause macular degeneration – a condition that destroys the centre of the retina. Glaucoma damages the ganglion cells in the third layer of the retina and is normally very hard to monitor. At the moment, patients who show certain symptoms, such as high pressure in the eye, are told that it is not yet serious and

to come back for check-ups but by the time that the ophthalmologists can say definitely they've got glaucoma, about 40% of the ganglion cells have been destroyed and treatment options are limited.

But this may not be the case for long – a new testing device is already providing detailed reports on how well the retina is functioning. A multifocal electroretinogram (MFERG) can tell if anything is wrong long before any signs of signs of trouble become visible, even to a skilled ophthalmologist. The patient sits in front of a flickering projection screen covered with hundreds of tiny hexagons that flash up to 75 times a second. Each flash targets a slightly different part of the retina and all the responses are recorded by a tiny gold-foil electrode attached to the lower lid.

Scientists analyse the wave patterns to show if there is a problem, and where it is. For instance, damage in the lower layers will show up later than data coming from the surface. MFERG has the greatest potential application for people developing glaucoma as it may reveal problems with ganglion cells long before glaucoma starts, allowing earlier treatment.

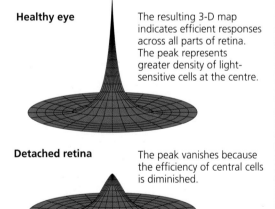

Healthy eye

The resulting 3-D map indicates efficient responses across all parts of retina. The peak represents greater density of light-sensitive cells at the centre.

Detached retina

The peak vanishes because the efficiency of central cells is diminished.

1 Look again at Fig 5.9. Why are ganglion cells difficult to monitor by conventional techniques?

2 In the second diagram above,
  a Why does the MFERG record a large 'pointed peak' at the centre of the map?
  b How would the vision of a person with a detached retina be affected?

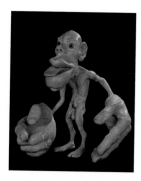

some parts of the body than in others, so these are represented by a greater portion of the sensory area. The photograph (left) of the homunculus represents the relative amount of sensation that the brain gains from skin receptors in different parts of the body.

14

a Which parts of the skin contain the greatest number of receptors per unit area?

b Suggest an advantage for the differences in the distribution of receptors.

c The sensory area for the eyes is larger than the sensory areas for the rest of the body combined. Suggest an explanation for this.

Association areas of the cerebral cortex

The association areas receive impulses from the sensory areas, make decisions, and send out impulses through the motor areas. When we see a familiar face, our visual association areas piece together the image of the face and compare it with faces we know; recognition is relayed to the frontal lobes; the frontal lobes make a decision to call a greeting and send out nerve impulses to the motor areas.

The visual association area is the region of grey matter where the information from the optic nerves is transformed into perception. Fig 5.15 shows the paths taken by nerve impulses from the eyes to the visual association areas.

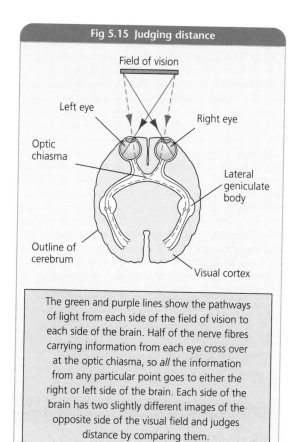

Fig 5.15 Judging distance

The green and purple lines show the pathways of light from each side of the field of vision to each side of the brain. Half of the nerve fibres carrying information from each eye cross over at the optic chiasma, so *all* the information from any particular point goes to either the right or left side of the brain. Each side of the brain has two slightly different images of the opposite side of the visual field and judges distance by comparing them.

The brain puts together the 'electrical storm' of information from the eyes and perceives objects. Information about colour, movement and form are analysed separately by the brain, and finally combined (Fig 5.16).

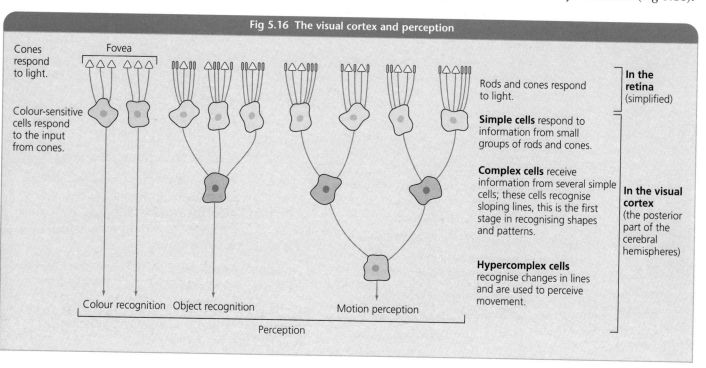

Fig 5.16 The visual cortex and perception

Fig 5.17 What shape do you think you are?

What shape do you think you are?

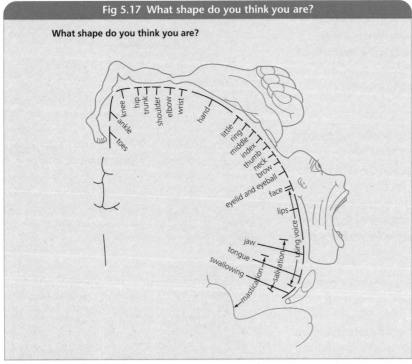

Fig 5.18 Motor pathways and the cerebral cortex

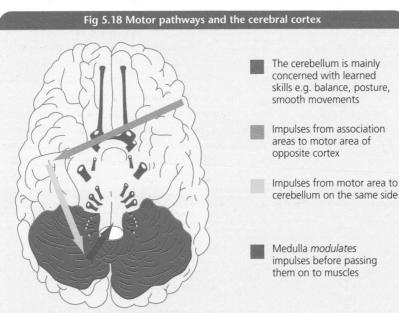

- The cerebellum is mainly concerned with learned skills e.g. balance, posture, smooth movements

- Impulses from association areas to motor area of opposite cortex

- Impulses from motor area to cerebellum on the same side

- Medulla *modulates* impulses before passing them on to muscles

What we see is not simply a pattern of dots, one from each receptor. The association areas analyse and modify the visual stimuli they receive. Unimportant messages are screened out, and relevant details are enhanced. The brain also uses past experience to interpret visual images.

Motor areas of the cerebral cortex

Motor areas send impulses to skeletal muscles along nerve fibres passing down the brain stem and spinal cord. As with the sensory areas, each part of the body is represented by an area of the motor cortex (Fig 5.17).

15 Why is the area of the motor cortex controlling the fingers so large in comparison to the area serving the legs?

Motor pathways

The left side of the cerebral cortex controls the right side of the body, and vice versa (Fig 5.18). The motor cortex is mainly concerned with learned skills such as balance. When we decide to do something involving our voluntary muscles, impulses pass from the association areas in the cortex on one side of the brain to the motor area of the opposite cortex. Impulses then pass from the motor area to the cerebellum on the same side. The medulla *modulates* impulses before passing them on to muscles.

Much of the information about motor pathways comes from careful examination of the brains of stroke victims. In a stroke, part of the brain dies due to shortage of blood, and injury to the right side of the brain often causes paralysis in the left side of the body.

KEY FACTS

- The **sensory areas** of the **cerebral hemispheres** receive impulses from the sense organs and transmit them to the **association areas**.

- The association areas of the cerebral hemispheres receive impulses, analyse them then pass them on to the appropriate **motor area**.

- The motor areas of the cerebral hemispheres transmit impulses to the appropriate effectors.

- The size of each region of the sensory and motor areas is related to the number of receptors or effectors associated with that area, e.g. the regions relating to the fingertips and the lips are by far the largest in the sensory areas.

- The right cerebral hemisphere controls the left side of the body and vice versa.

- In the **visual association area**, language is recognised in one area; another area controls the muscles that produce speech.

5.4 The autonomic nervous system

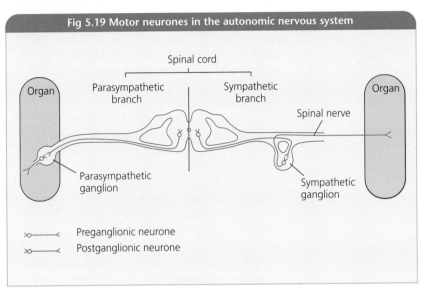

Fig 5.19 Motor neurones in the autonomic nervous system

Preganglionic neurone
Postganglionic neurone

The medulla of the brain, situated at the top of the spinal cord, controls all the non-skeletal muscles (those which are not attached to bones). These muscles are of two types, **cardiac muscle** in the heart and **smooth muscle** surrounding the many internal tubes and ducts such as the bronchioles, the blood vessels and the gut. We are usually unaware of these internal movements, and unable to control them consciously. For example, we cannot decide to make our stomach muscles begin contracting; this happens automatically when food stretches the stomach wall.

The motor neurones controlling cardiac and smooth muscles make up the **autonomic nervous system**. The autonomic nervous system consists of two parts:

- the **sympathetic nervous system**;
- the **parasympathetic nervous system**.

The sympathetic system has opposite effects to the parasympathetic system.

16 You learned in Chapter 12 of the AS book that the medulla contains a cardiovascular centre and a respiratory centre that control the heart rate and the breathing rate.

a The medulla contains receptors concerned with monitoring the composition of blood. What are these receptors sensitive to?

b Name the receptors in other parts of the body that send information to the medulla concerned with the regulation of breathing rate and rate of heartbeat.

Autonomic neurones do not go directly from the spinal cord or brain to an organ. Along the route there is a synapse in a ganglion. A ganglion is a place outside the central nervous system where cell bodies and synapses occur in a small region of grey matter (Fig 5.19).

Sympathetic and parasympathetic postganglionic neurones have opposite effects on organs because they secrete different transmitters. They are said to be **antagonistic**.

- Sympathetic postganglionic neurones secrete the transmitter **noradrenaline** and the effects of the sympathetic system are similar to those of the hormone adrenaline. Both expand the bronchioles, stimulate the heart and increase blood pressure. In this condition, the body is ready to flee from danger or attack an enemy. The sympathetic nervous system acts more quickly than adrenaline; the hormone travels in the blood stream and maintains the 'ready-for-danger' state after the sympathetic nervous system has done its job.

- Parasympathetic postganglionic neurones secrete the transmitter **acetylcholine**. This counteracts the effects of the sympathetic system by the constriction of some muscles, and the relaxation of others.

Table 5.2 shows the effects of the autonomic nervous system on controlling the pupil, tear production and emptying of the bladder.

17 Which neurotransmitter is released at the neuromuscular junction:

a in the radial muscles of the iris;

b in the circular muscles of the iris?

Table 5.2 Effects of the autonomic nervous system		
	Effect of sympathetic nervous system	**Effect of parasympathetic nervous system**
Pupil	Pupil dilates	Pupil constricts
Tear production	None	Stimulates secretion of tears
Emptying of the bladder	Contracts sphincter of bladder Relaxes muscle in wall of bladder	Relaxes sphincter of bladder Muscles in wall of bladder contract

APPLICATION   Split brain experiments

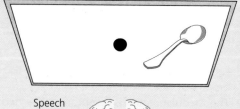

Picture of spoon flashed to right of dot

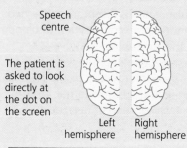

Speech centre

The patient is asked to look directly at the dot on the screen

Left hemisphere   Right hemisphere

When asked what the picture was the patient says 'spoon'. Visual information from the right eye crosses to the left hemisphere where the speech centre is

Picture of spoon flashed to left of dot

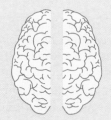

The patient will say nothing was seen because the information passes from the left eye to the right hemisphere, and there is no speech centre in the right hemisphere. However, if the person is asked to touch the object with the left hand, they will immediately do so. This is because the touch information from the left hand crosses to the right hemisphere that saw the spoon. But if asked again what object they have just touched, the patient will be unable to say as the speech area is in the left hemisphere

How many brains do you have – one or two? The answer is of course one, but the largest part of the brain, the cerebrum, is divided into two halves called cerebral hemispheres. The hemispheres are connected by the corpus callosum, which contains about 250 million nerve fibres.

Much of what we know about the two hemispheres comes from studies of people who have had the corpus callosum partially split. This operation is performed on some patients who have a life-threatening form of epilepsy. One symptom of epilepsy is seizures. The corpus callosum is partially split to prevent seizures passing from one hemisphere to the other.

After surgery the patients appear to be able to perform every-day activities normally. But careful studies by two neurosurgeons, Roger Sperry and Michael Gazzaniga, showed that the surgery had done more than prevent the spreading of seizures.

Dr Sperry used a tachistoscope, an instrument which can present a visual stimulus to one hemisphere or the other. The diagram on the left shows the results of one of the experiments.

The results of experiments like this and observations of the effects of brain injuries have led to an understanding of the functions of the different regions of the brain.

APPLICATION   Brain imaging

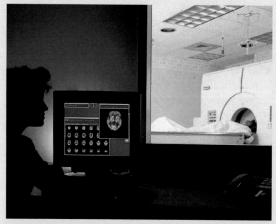

Data from the PET scanner's detectors identify the brain area from which the gamma rays came. The brain images on the computer screen show which areas of the brain are active at the time of the scan.

Brain areas used for particular activities have been mapped by positron emission tomography (PET). Radioactive fluorine attached to glucose molecules is injected into the bloodstream. The glucose collects in active areas of the brain where the radioactive fluorine decays and emits a subatomic particle called a positron.

1 Which brain areas would you expect to be active in someone listening and taking notes?

Memory

Many of the decisions we make depend on memory. We have a working memory, which we use when we hold a telephone number in our head before writing it down, or when we keep track of the flow of a conversation. Such things are usually soon forgotten, but there is also a long-term memory with which we remember things about our past lives. Some of these memories can be called to the conscious mind, for example the image of the house where we live, or a familiar tune.

How PET scanning is done
Positron annihilation

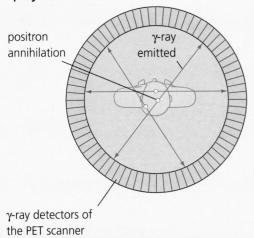

positron with positive charge

electron with negative charge

γ-ray

γ-ray

In the body, a positron travels only about 1 mm before being annihilated and producing two γ-rays that travel in opposite directions.

γ-ray detection

positron annihilation

γ-ray emitted

γ-ray detectors of the PET scanner

Other memories are for motor skills, such as being able to type quickly or ride a bicycle. The cerebral cortex holds most of our memories but other regions, including the cerebellum, are needed in order to store and retrieve them.

Speech
Some functions are controlled by one side of the brain only. The left side of the brain is used for understanding, speech, written language, mathematics and reasoning. The right has a greater role in understanding three-dimensional shapes and music.

Patients with speech problems gave the first clues about how the brain controls language. Inability to talk is called aphasia. In 1861 a doctor called Paul Broca described a patient who could only say one word 'tan'. When the patient died, Broca examined his brain and found that there was damage to part of the left cerebral hemisphere. This part of the brain is now known as 'Broca's area (see the diagram below right).

In 1867 Karl Wernicke noticed that damage to another region of the cortex, further back and lower down in the brain, also caused language problems. This area is now known as Wernicke's area. The two areas are connected by a bundle of nerve fibres called the arcuate fasciculus. If these are damaged the patient can understand language, but cannot repeat words.

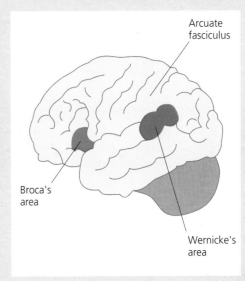

Arcuate fasciculus

Broca's area

Wernicke's area

Wernicke's area is mainly concerned with understanding language – both spoken and written. Broca's area is mainly concerned with controlling the muscles that produce speech. In 95% of people these areas are in the left cerebral hemisphere. The diagram on the right shows drawings of PET scans that reveal the parts of the brain that are active when someone is speaking a written word and speaking a heard word.

2 In what order will impulse pass through the active parts of the brain when speaking:
   a the written word;
   b the heard word?

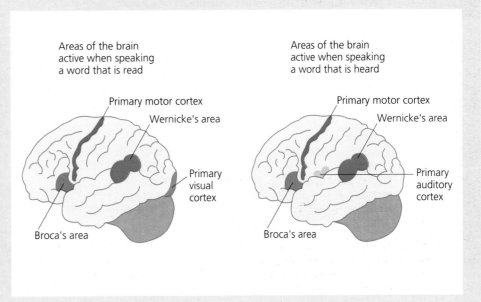

Areas of the brain active when speaking a word that is read

Primary motor cortex

Wernicke's area

Primary visual cortex

Broca's area

Areas of the brain active when speaking a word that is heard

Primary motor cortex

Wernicke's area

Primary auditory cortex

Broca's area

18 It is possible to gain control of some parts of the autonomic system. For example, we learn at an early age to control the sphincter muscles of bladder and anus. In the control of urination, when receptors are stimulated acetylcholine is released at the bladder sphincter and the bladder walls. Suggest which type of receptors are stimulated and explain how control of urination is achieved.

19 Suggest the advantage of the autonomic system being divided into two antagonistic parts.

EXAMINATION QUESTIONS

1 The retinas of some mammals that are active in the daytime contain a high proportion of cones; in mammals active at night there are many rods and very few cones.

a Give two ways in which the relative number and distribution of rods and cones in the retina can affect how mammals see objects. (2)

b Explain how the relative number of rods and cones in the retina is related to the activity pattern of the mammal. (2)

c Cats are usually active at night. The pupils of a cat are reduced to slits in daylight.
  i Give the receptor and effector which are involved in this reflex action. (2)
  ii Suggest how the cat benefits from very narrow pupils in daylight. (2)

Total (8)

BY04 June 97 Q1

2

a In the retina of a human eye there are about 125 million rod cells but only about 7 million cone cells. Give two reasons why, despite this difference, colour vision is much better for seeing detail. (2)

b The flow chart in Fig 5.Q2a shows some of the events that occur in a rod cell in the dark, and the diagram in Fig 5.Q2b shows the flow of sodium ions in a rod cell in the dark.

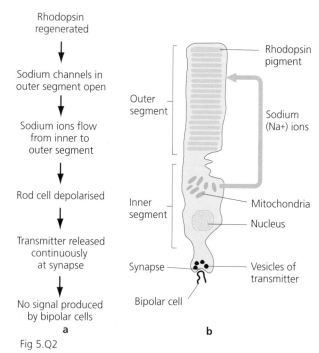

Fig 5.Q2

Rod cells differ from other receptors in that they are depolarised when they are not being stimulated.
  i Explain what is meant by depolarisation. (2)
  ii Suggest why rod cells require a large number of mitochondria. (2)

c A bipolar cell generates a signal to the brain when the amount of transmitter reaching it from a rod cell falls. When illuminated the rhodopsin molecules change shape. This produces a series of reactions that cause the sodium channels in the outer segment to close.

Explain how illumination will result in the generation of a signal by a bipolar cell. (2)

Total (8)

BY04 June 99 Q6

3 The diagram shows the distribution of rod cells and cone cells across the retina of a human eye.

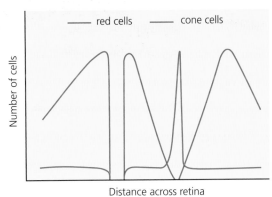

Fig 5.Q3

a Describe and explain how the distribution of the rod cells and cone cells relates to variation in sensitivity and visual acuity in different parts of the retina. (6)

b Describe:
   i how a rod cell converts light energy into a nerve impulse; (3)
   ii how cone cells allow us to see colours. (3)

Total (12)

BY04 June 96 Q8

4
a A person, who has been watching a distant view from a window, looks down and starts to read. Describe how a clear image is formed on the retina of this person's eye, and explain the changes that take place in the eye in order to produce a clear image when the person starts to read. (6)

b Explain the roles of the eye and brain in enabling humans to distinguish colours in a picture. (6)

Total (12)

BY04 March 99 Q8

5
a A student was asked to stare intently at a brightly illuminated blue cross for several minutes. After this time the teacher replaced the cross with a plain white screen at which the student continued to stare. The student then saw an image of a yellow cross on the white paper.
Explain why the student saw
   i the cross as blue in colour;
   ii an image of a yellow cross when staring at the plain white screen. (6)

Total (6)

BY10 March 99 Q8 (b only)

6 The diagram shows the human brain as seen from below.

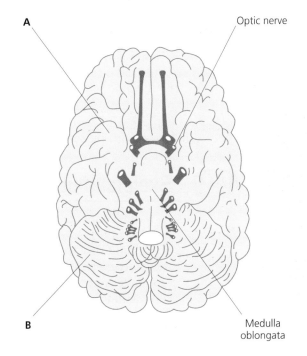

Fig 5.Q6

a Name the regions of the brain labelled A and B. (2)

b Give one function of the medulla oblongata. (1)

c The optic nerve transmits impulses to the brain.
   i Which part of the brain receives these impulses? (2)
   ii Describe how the brain might process the information contained in the impulses. (2)

Total (7)

BY04 Feb 97 Q2

6 Muscle power

On 9 November 1992, Sir Ranulph Fiennes and Dr Mike Stroud began their attempt at the first unassisted crossing of the Antarctic continent. Ninety-five days later, more dead than alive, they achieved their aim. They had pulled their 220 kg sledges across 2300 km of ice and snow. The energy used was more than the equivalent of running a marathon every day. No pack dogs or food depots supported them: they achieved everything using human muscle power.

To drag their sledges all this way, they planned to eat a diet that contained twice the energy level of an average individual. Because fat is energy dense and lighter to carry, their diet was very high in fat (57% energy from fat as against the recommended 35%). Breakfast was porridge with butter, lunch soup with butter, tea flapjack with butter and supper a freeze-dried meal with butter. Four chocolate

bars and a hot chocolate drink provided the extras.

Even this amount of food turned out to be inadequate for their physical needs and they lost weight. Interestingly, in spite the huge intake of saturated fat, their blood cholesterol concentration stayed the same, showing that exercise is obviously a very important factor in controlling blood cholesterol concentrations.

6.1 Skeletal muscle

How did Fiennes and Stroud's muscles transfer all this energy into movement? To understand this, in this chapter we consider the structure of muscle fibres, the mechanism of muscle contraction and how muscle contraction moves parts of the body.

There are three types of muscle tissue in the body: **involuntary muscle** – also called **unstriped muscle; cardiac muscle** and **voluntary muscle** – also called **striped muscle** or **skeletal muscle**. You have already met unstriped muscle: it is the muscle that brings about peristalsis in the gut and it is also found in the iris and the ciliary bodies of the eye. The muscles attached to the skeleton are voluntary muscles – you can decide whether or not to lift your arm, but you have no control over your iris.

The structure of skeletal muscle
Skeletal muscles are made up of overlapping striped muscle fibres. These are held together by **connective tissue**, with a **tendon** at each end. The tendons attach the muscle to bones.

When the fibres contract, the muscle shortens, pulls the tendons and moves the bones.

The stripes on skeletal muscle fibres can be seen through a light microscope as Fig 6.1 shows.

Striped muscles are very different from the rest of the cells in the body. Like other cells, a striped muscle fibre has cytoplasm, called **sarcoplasm**, and is surrounded by a plasma membrane, called a **sarcolemma**. However, there is an important difference: striped muscle fibres have many nuclei in the cytoplasm, and these lie near the surface of the fibre.

The central part of a striped muscle fibre consists mainly of much thinner fibre-like structures called **myofibrils**, which are composed mainly of protein molecules. It is these myofibrils that transfer chemical energy from food into movement.

1 List the main differences between a striped muscle fibre and a typical animal cell.

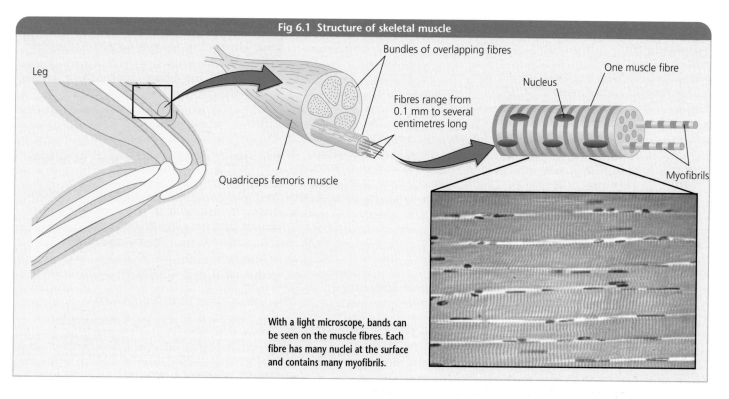

Fig 6.1 Structure of skeletal muscle

Leg

Bundles of overlapping fibres

Fibres range from 0.1 mm to several centimetres long

Quadriceps femoris muscle

Nucleus

One muscle fibre

Myofibrils

With a light microscope, bands can be seen on the muscle fibres. Each fibre has many nuclei at the surface and contains many myofibrils.

Ultrastructure of skeletal muscle

Although it is possible to see the stripes in skeletal muscle with a light microscope, it is only when we look at muscle fibres with an electron microscope that it becomes clear what the stripes actually are. Each myofibril is made up protein filaments of two types – thick filaments composed of the protein **myosin** and thin filaments composed of the protein **actin**.

Fig 6.2 shows the structure of a myofibril as determined by early electron microscopes. The light bands consist of actin filaments only. The dark bands consist of overlapping actin and myosin filaments. Discs hold the groups of actin filaments together.

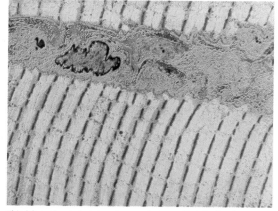

This false-colour electron micrograph shows that the bands on the myofibrils are lined up to give a banded appearance to the whole fibre.

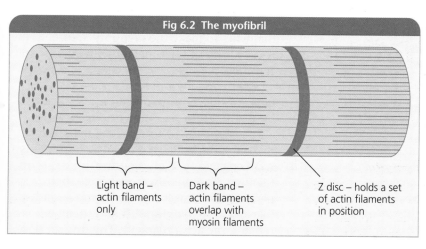

Fig 6.2 The myofibril

Light band – actin filaments only

Dark band – actin filaments overlap with myosin filaments

Z disc – holds a set of actin filaments in position

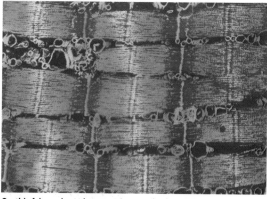

On this false-colour electron micrograph, the straight green lines are the Z discs, the myosin filaments are orange-pink and the actin filaments are blue. The green bubble-like structures are sarcoplasmic reticulum.

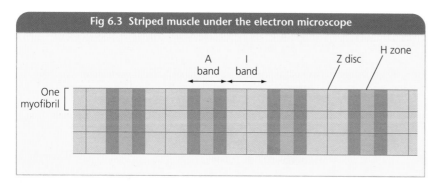

Fig 6.3 Striped muscle under the electron microscope

As the resolving power of electron microscopes increased, more detail could be seen in the myofibril:

- Where the two sets of filaments overlap the myofibril appears dark;

- The region where there are only myosin filaments is slightly lighter;

- The region where there are only actin filaments appears lighter still;

- In the centre of each light band is the Z disc, which holds actin filaments in position. Similarly, M discs hold myosin filaments in position.

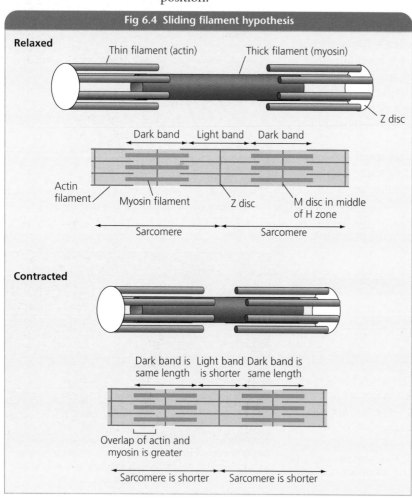

Fig 6.4 Sliding filament hypothesis

2 Scientists use the letters A, H, I and Z to identify the different parts of a myofibril. Look at Fig 6.3.

a Why do the A bands look dark?

b What is found:
   in the H zone?
   in the I band?

The sliding filament hypothesis of muscle contraction.

Now that you know the structure of skeletal muscle it is possible to go on to look at how muscle fibres are able to contract to bring about movement. When a myofibril contracts:

- the sarcomeres become shorter;

- the light bands become shorter;

- the dark bands stay the same length.

In the 1950s, Jean Hanson and Hugh Huxley at London University put forward the **sliding filament hypothesis of muscle contraction**, which suggested that muscular contraction comes about by the actin filaments sliding between the myosin filaments, using energy from ATP. This theory is still accepted. In the region of overlap, six actin filaments are arranged neatly around each myosin filament, as Fig 6.4 shows.

3
a Do either the actin or the myosin filaments change their length when a sarcomere shortens?

b Why does the A band widen and the H zone shorten when a sarcomere contracts?

Electron micrographs of the dark bands show cross-bridges between the myosin and actin filaments. These bridges are part of the myosin molecules, and push on the actin filaments to make the myofibril shorten. This is called the **ratchet mechanism** because the actin molecules are moved along one step at a time by the myosin heads. Fig 6.5 shows how this mechanism operates. Myosin cross-bridges point in six different directions and are arranged in the form of a spiral. Each myosin cross bridge has a wider 'head'. This head engages in a 'binding site' on the actin filament. The myosin cross-bridge then performs its 'power stroke' – it moves rather like an oar, remaining stiff and therefore moving the actin filament. The myosin head

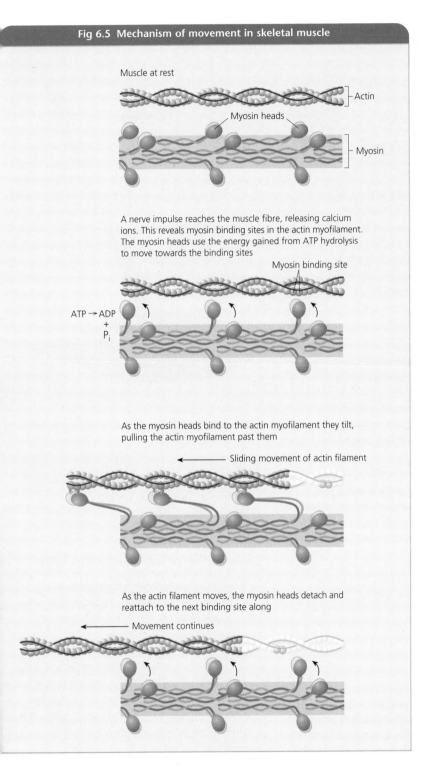

Fig 6.5 Mechanism of movement in skeletal muscle

Muscle at rest

Actin

Myosin heads

Myosin

A nerve impulse reaches the muscle fibre, releasing calcium ions. This reveals myosin binding sites in the actin myofilament. The myosin heads use the energy gained from ATP hydrolysis to move towards the binding sites

Myosin binding site

ATP → ADP + P_i

As the myosin heads bind to the actin myofilament they tilt, pulling the actin myofilament past them

Sliding movement of actin filament

As the actin filament moves, the myosin heads detach and reattach to the next binding site along

Movement continues

then disengages and moves through a 'recovery stroke', rather like returning an oar to the starting position, to engage with the next binding site. The cycle is then repeated. Because of their spiral arrangement, cross-bridges will be at different positions in the power stroke / recovery stroke cycle, so muscle contraction is smooth rather than jerky.

The role of tropomyosin, calcium ions and ATP in muscle contraction

Muscle contraction is turned on and off by a calcium switch. When a nerve impulse arrives at the muscle fibre, calcium channels open and calcium ions diffuse in. This allows actin and myosin to bind. Each myosin cross-bridge can bind to, push against and release an actin filament many times a second. Each swing of a cross-bridge uses the energy from one molecule of ATP. Many thousands of cross-bridges working together create the power of the muscle.

Why don't cross-bridges form in resting muscle? Although the actin filaments have myosin binding sites, these are blocked by protein molecules called tropomyosin, as shown in Fig 6.6.

When calcium ions bind to tropomyosin molecules, this alters the shape of the protein and it can no longer block the binding site, so the fibre is ready to start the process of muscle contraction. The calcium ions also activate the myosin molecules to breakdown ATP to release the energy needed to bring about contraction.

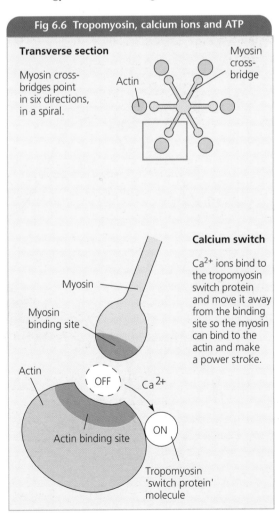

Fig 6.6 Tropomyosin, calcium ions and ATP

Transverse section

Myosin cross-bridges point in six directions, in a spiral.

Actin

Myosin cross-bridge

Calcium switch

Myosin

Myosin binding site

Actin

OFF

Ca^{2+}

ON

Actin binding site

Tropomyosin 'switch protein' molecule

Ca^{2+} ions bind to the tropomyosin switch protein and move it away from the binding site so the myosin can bind to the actin and make a power stroke.

Controlling muscle contraction

In order to control movement, the brain can control how strongly a muscle contracts. It does this by changing:

● how much each fibre contracts;

● how many fibres contract.

When one action potential arrives at a neuromuscular junction it causes one brief contraction or twitch of the fibre. If a second action potential arrives before the fibre has fully relaxed, the second twitch adds to the effect of the first, and a greater contraction occurs. The 'adding' of the effects of action potentials is called summation.

1 In Chapter 4, you learned that there are two types of summation possible at neurone–neurone synapses: spatial summation and temporal summation. Which of these types of summation is occurring in a muscle fibre to cause increased contraction?

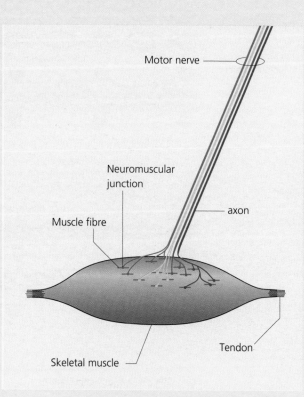

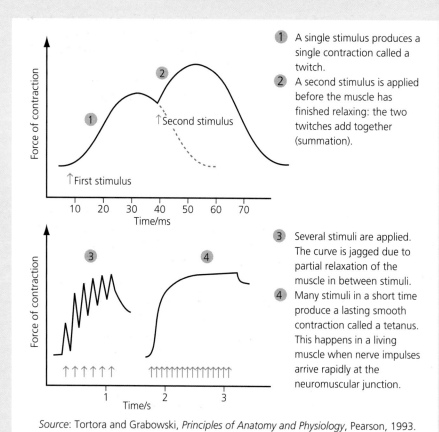

1 A single stimulus produces a single contraction called a twitch.

2 A second stimulus is applied before the muscle has finished relaxing: the two twitches add together (summation).

3 Several stimuli are applied. The curve is jagged due to partial relaxation of the muscle in between stimuli.

4 Many stimuli in a short time produce a lasting smooth contraction called a tetanus. This happens in a living muscle when nerve impulses arrive rapidly at the neuromuscular junction.

Source: Tortora and Grabowski, *Principles of Anatomy and Physiology*, Pearson, 1993.

A rapid sequence of action potentials causes a continuous strong contraction of the fibre called a tetanus. The more nerve impulses there are per second in a motor nerve, the stronger the contraction of each muscle fibre will be.

2 What are the main differences in behaviour between a muscle fibre and a neurone on receiving impulses at increasing frequencies?

Each motor neurone serves about 150 muscle fibres. One motor neurone and its associated muscle fibres are together called a motor unit. Action potentials in a motor neurone cause all the muscle fibres in its motor unit to contract together. If a stronger contraction is needed, the brain recruits more motor units by sending action potentials along more motor neurones within the motor nerve.

3 Which parts of the brain are involved in sending impulses down motor neurones to skeletal muscles?

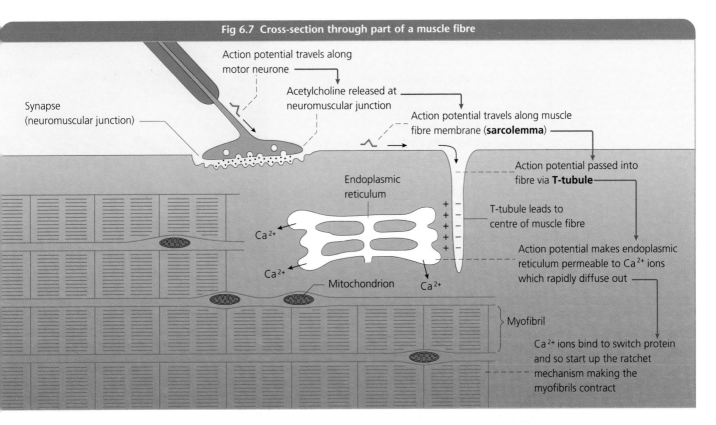

Fig 6.7 Cross-section through part of a muscle fibre

Action potential travels along motor neurone

Acetylcholine released at neuromuscular junction

Action potential travels along muscle fibre membrane (**sarcolemma**)

Synapse (neuromuscular junction)

Action potential passed into fibre via **T-tubule**

Endoplasmic reticulum

T-tubule leads to centre of muscle fibre

Ca²⁺

Action potential makes endoplasmic reticulum permeable to Ca²⁺ ions which rapidly diffuse out

Ca²⁺

Mitochondrion

Ca²⁺

Myofibril

Ca²⁺ ions bind to switch protein and so start up the ratchet mechanism making the myofibrils contract

The neuromuscular junction

In muscles, calcium ions (Ca²⁺) are stored in the endoplasmic reticulum of the cytoplasm that surrounds each myofibril. When the muscle is resting, Ca²⁺ ions are pumped into the endoplasmic reticulum by active transport. The arrival of an action potential at a neuromuscular junction sets off the chain of events leading to the contraction of myofibrils shown in Fig 6.7.

4

a Look at Fig 6.7. Draw a flow chart to show how a nerve impulse arriving at a neuromuscular junction causes a muscle fibre to contract.

b Why are there large numbers of mitochondria in the muscle fibre?

KEY FACTS

- There are three types of muscle tissue in the body: voluntary (skeletal) muscle which we mainly use to move our limbs; cardiac muscle which makes up most of the heart; and involuntary (unstriped) muscle which is found in organs such as the intestines, ureters and blood vessels.

- Skeletal muscle is composed of bundles of striped fibres which have features distinguishing them from typical body cells.

- Each fibre contains thick **myosin filaments** and thinner **actin filaments**.

- The **sliding filament hypothesis** states that contraction of myofibrils is brought about by a ratchet mechanism in which processes from the myosin filaments bind to the actin filaments and move the actin filaments.

- The sequence of events causing contraction of myofibrils is
  - nerve impulse arrives at neuromuscular junction
  - acetylcholine released into synaptic cleft
  - action potential produced in plasma membrane
  - action potential transmitted down T-tubules
  - calcium ions released from endoplasmic reticulum
  - calcium ions bind to tropomyosin switch proteins
  - binding sites on actin filaments exposed
  - myosin processes bind to exposed sites on actin filaments
  - energy from ATP used to move actin filaments.

6.2 Muscle action

Muscles attached to bones are known skeletal muscles. Muscles can pull but not push. They pull on the bones to which they are attached by tendons. Fig 6.8 shows some of the muscles involved in walking.

The biceps femoris and quadriceps femoris act as one antagonistic muscle pair, bending and straightening the leg at the knee. The biceps femoris is known as the flexor muscle since it causes bending of the leg at the knee. The quadriceps femoris is known as the extensor because it straightens the leg at the knee.

Fig 6.8 Muscles involved in walking

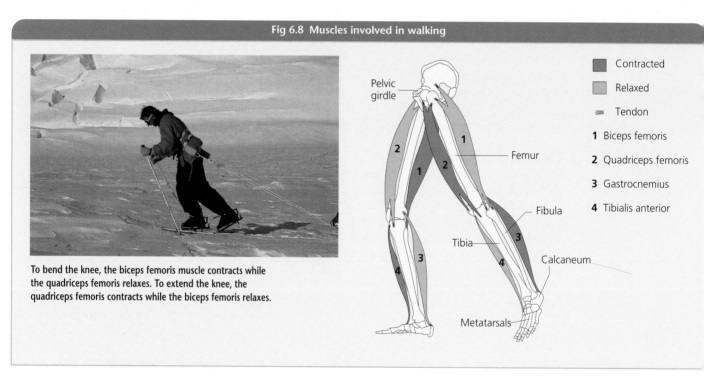

To bend the knee, the biceps femoris muscle contracts while the quadriceps femoris relaxes. To extend the knee, the quadriceps femoris contracts while the biceps femoris relaxes.

Contracted
Relaxed
⇌ Tendon
1 Biceps femoris
2 Quadriceps femoris
3 Gastrocnemius
4 Tibialis anterior

Pelvic girdle
Femur
Fibula
Tibia
Calcaneum
Metatarsals

5 How do the gastrocnemius and tibialis anterior muscles work as an antagonistic pair to bend the ankle joint?

During walking, the muscles that are being stretched are relaxed, but not completely. They provide some resistance so the legs do not move too suddenly. Other leg muscles (not shown in Fig 6.8) are used to keep the body balanced, as weight is transferred from leg to leg. As muscles contract, tendons pull on the bones. Tendons do not stretch or break because of the presence of the fibrous protein, **collagen**. Collagen is also found in bones

making the bones themselves slightly bendy and less brittle. Joining the bones are **ligaments**, which contain **elastin**. Elastin is a protein with branched fibres that can stretch to one-and-a-half times their original length and spring back again.

6 Refer back to the structure of proteins (AS book p 59)
a Why is it important that tendons do not stretch?
b How does the structure of the collagen molecule prevent stretching?

Fast twitch and slow twitch muscle fibres

Muscle physiologists use biopsies to study the make-up of muscles from athletes who compete in different types of events. A biopsy uses a special type of needle to remove about 50 mg of living muscle tissue from a muscle. Studying samples has shown that all muscles contain two types of fibres, fast twitch and slow twitch.

Fast twitch fibres can produce ATP very quickly via glycolysis. Their contraction speed is very rapid. Fast twitch fibres are used mainly for sprinting and jumping or escaping from danger. Slow twitch fibres contract at about half the speed of fast twitch fibres. These slow twitch fibres contain more mitochondria than fast twitch fibres, so they produce ATP mainly via aerobic respiration. They are used mainly during walking or jogging. Middle distance running, or sports like football and hockey use both types.

The table below shows some of the properties of fast twitch and slow twitch fibres. Most muscles contain a mixture of the two sorts of fibre, but people differ in their fast twitch / slow twitch ratios. The ratio is controlled by genes. Exercise increases the number of both types of fibre in muscles, but in the same ratio, so you are born either a sprinter or a long-distance runner.

You will need to revise Chapter 12 in the AS book before answering these questions

1 Apart from muscles, where is most of the body's glycogen stored?

2 Where are triglycerides stored in the body?

3 a What is the advantage to a sprinter of having creatine phosphate as the main energy source in muscles?
  b What is the main disadvantage?

4 What is the end product of anaerobic respiration?

5 Explain how lactic acid contributes to muscle fatigue.

6 What is the advantage to slow twitch fibres in having abundant mitochondria?

7 What is the advantage to slow twitch fibres in having myoglobin?

Type	Speed of contraction	ATP source	Respiration	Fatigue	Motor unit
Slow twitch	slow	glycogen and triglycerides	aerobic	slow	small
Fast twitch	fast	creatine phosphate	anaerobic	rapid	large

Drugs and muscles

Athletes are always looking for new and quicker ways to build muscle. While anabolic steroids may have been the thing in the 1980s, the 'hormonal manipulator' in the 21st century is Human Growth Hormone (HGH). Some athletes are using this to build bigger muscles without extra training, but at the price of side effects.

HGH is a polypeptide with a molecular mass of 21 000 (composed of 191 amino acids), and is produced by the pituitary gland. HGH affects many body tissues. In adolescents it stimulates growth and the maturation of the bones. The activity of messenger RNA is affected, causing increased protein synthesis in muscle cells. In addition, HGH stimulates the intracellular breakdown of body fat so that more fat is used for energy. The synthesis of collagen (the sticky substance that is the glue of the body) is stimulated, which is necessary for strengthening of cartilage, bones, tendons, and ligaments.

Some individuals naturally produce too much HGH. This may have two effects – *gigantism* and *acromegaly*. Gigantism results in an abnormally large physical stature; acromegaly leads to enlarged hands, toes, nose and face.

The hormone can now be produced synthetically by genetic manufacturing techniques. The synthetically produced hormone differs from the natural pituitary-derived hormone in that it contains an additional methionine at the end of the primary structure.

1 Suggest why the extra amino acid does *not* affect the function of HGH.

2 Explain how increasing RNA activity will increase the size of muscles.

3 How does HGH improve athletic performance?

6.3 Animals with exoskeletons

The group of animals called the **Arthropods** includes insects, spiders and crustaceans. These animals have jointed limbs, but they do not have bones. Their skeleton is the outer layer of the body, the **cuticle**, so it is called an **exoskeleton**. The muscles are attached to the internal surface of this as shown in Fig 6.9.

The exoskeleton plan does not work well for large animals. Hundreds of millions of years ago, some dragonfly-type insects evolved with wing spans of 1.5 metres, but these soon became extinct. The problem is that to be strong enough to support a large animal they have to be very heavy – putting the animal at a big disadvantage in the speed takes. Another problem is that animals with exoskeletons have to shed them in order to grow. A cockroach sheds its exoskeleton four times before it attains adult size. Animals are very vulnerable between shedding one skeleton and the next one hardening.

7
a Which of the muscles X and Y is:
b the flexor?
the extensor?

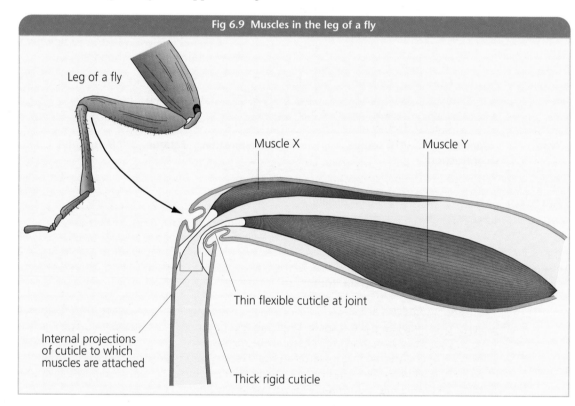

Fig 6.9 Muscles in the leg of a fly

Leg of a fly

Muscle X

Muscle Y

Thin flexible cuticle at joint

Internal projections of cuticle to which muscles are attached

Thick rigid cuticle

KEY FACTS

- Muscles do work by contracting.

- Many muscles are arranged in **antagonistic pairs**; contraction of one muscle pulls the bone in one direction, contraction of the other muscle pulls the bone in the opposite direction.

- The muscle that causes bending at a joint is called a **flexor**.

- The muscle that straightens at a joint is called an **extensor**.

- In arthropods, the skeleton is on the outside of the body; it is called an **exoskeleton**. The muscles that attach to the skeleton are internal.

1 The diagram below shows part of a myofibril as seen through an electron microscope.

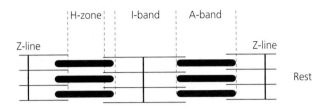

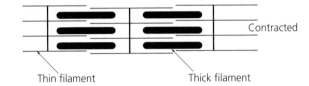

Fig 6.Q1

a Name the main protein present in
 i the thick filaments;
 ii the thin filaments. (2)

b Describe the mechanism that brings about the change in position of the filaments when the myofibril contracts. (4)

Total (6)

BY04 June 2000 Q4

2

a Describe how the sliding filament theory explains how a muscle contracts. (4)

b Skeletal muscle fibrils are made up of a large number of sarcomeres. The sarcomeres in a fibril are always the same length as each other, but that length changes depending upon the state of contraction of the muscle. The graph in Fig 6.Q2 shows the force produced by a skeletal muscle fibril in relation to the length of its sarcomeres. Use the information given to explain why:
 i no force is produced by the muscle fibril when the sarcomere length is 3.7 μm;
 ii maximum force is produced by the muscle fibril when the mean sarcomere length is 2.3 μm. (4)

c
 i Explain why a muscle in its contracted state cannot lengthen by itself.
 ii Describe how it is returned to its starting length. (4)

Total (12)

BY04 March 98 Q9

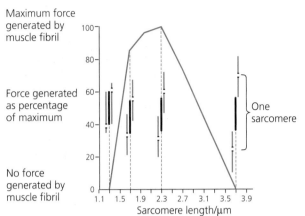

Fig 6.Q2

3 The diagram below shows a neuromuscular junction.

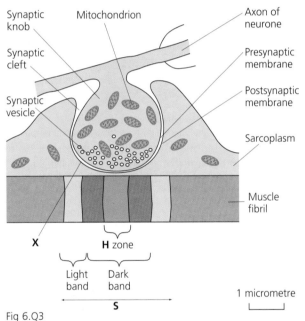

Fig 6.Q3

a
 i Name the neurotransmitter that is released from the synaptic knob. (1)
 ii By what process does this neurotransmitter cross the synaptic cleft? (1)
 iii Calculate the width of the synaptic cleft at X. Show your working. (2)

b Suggest two functions of the energy released by the mitochondria in the synaptic knob. (2)

c Describe how the appearance of the section of the muscle fibril labelled S would change when the fibril is stimulated by the neurotransmitter. (2)

Total (8)

BY04 March 99 Q3

7 Inheritance

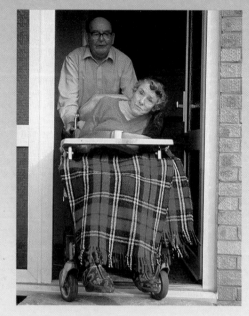

This woman has Huntington's disease, a genetic disorder that results in degeneration of the basal ganglia in the brain

In 1968, the young Nancy Wexler's mother, a geneticist, was diagnosed as having Huntington's disease. Nancy's three uncles, all brothers of her mother, had already died of the distressing condition, the symptoms of which only appear in middle age and include relentless loss of co-ordination and mental deterioration. Nancy realised that she had a 50:50 chance of developing the disease in later life. However, the Wexler family was not prone to giving in easily.

Nancy's father, Milton, resolved to set up a research foundation to find a cure, if possible in time to save his wife. Sadly, the search was to take much longer than their optimistic hopes. Nancy's mother died ten years later, but Nancy remained as a driving force in the hunt for the elusive gene that causes the disease.

The first breakthrough came when a Venezuelan doctor reported a family in a remote part of his country with large numbers of cases of the disease. Nancy Wexler immediately organised a research team to collect blood samples and eventually traced 11 000 descendants of one nineteenth century woman who had carried the fatal gene. Back in the USA, the team analysed the blood samples and discovered that the gene was situated somewhere on chromosome 4.

The gene was much more tricky to find than those of several other genetic disorders, but in 1993, after searching through some 5 million nucleotide bases on chromosome 4, its position was located. The mutant form of the gene responsible for the disease is nicknamed the 'stuttering gene' because one DNA triplet was found to be repeated up to 100 times in people suffering from the disease.

Identifying the gene makes it much easier to test, before any symptoms appear, whether individuals in affected families have actually inherited the disease, and to identify affected children before birth. The next stage is to understand how the mutant form of the gene actually affects the brain and wreaks its terrible havoc. Then treatment and a cure become a real possibility.

Source: adapted from an article by Susan Katz Miller, New Scientist, 24 April 1993.

7.1 Setting inheritance in context

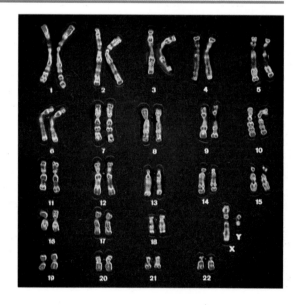

The full complement of human chromosomes (male) arranged in numbered homologous pairs. This full set of chromosomes is called the karyotype.

Inheritance defined

Inheritance is the way characteristics are passed on from one generation to the next. Today, we talk about inheritance in terms of the way genes are passed on; monohybrid inheritance refers to the way a single gene that codes for an obvious characteristic is passed from parent to offspring (see page 104 in this chapter). Genetics, though, is not always as straightforward as this. Later in the chapter we look at how two genes on different chromosomes are inherited independently and we investigate how genes can affect each other. The chapter concludes with sex determination and genes that are carried on the X chromosome and that are therefore sex-linked when they are passed on.

Term	Definition	Further notes
	Table 7.1 Basic terms and definitions	
Chromosome	One long, supercoiled DNA molecule, with genes dotted along its length.	Every cell's genetic material is packaged together in the nucleus as chromosomes. Each chromosome contains a very long DNA molecule, as well as some proteins. Human body cells have 46 chromosomes (see the photograph on page 96); the number in cells in other organisms varies.
Homologous chromosomes	'Matching pairs' of chomosomes.	In body cells, the chromosomes occur in pairs, called homologous chromosomes. The DNA molecules of homologous chromosomes have the same genes in the same order.
Gene	A length of DNA that codes for one polypeptide or protein.	The protein produced when a gene is expressed produces a characteristic in the organism. It is unusual for one gene to code for a singe characteristic on its own – many of the characteristics that we can see or detect are the results of the activity of several genes. Each gene occupies a particular position on a chromosome, called the locus.
Locus (plural loci)	The position of a gene on a chromosome.	A body cell has two copies each gene, one on each homologous chromosome (see Fig 7.1).
Allele	Different forms of the same gene, e.g. a flower colour gene can have a red allele or a white allele.	Genes at the same locus may have slightly different sequences of nucleotides in their DNA. There may be many different alleles of the same gene, each with a slightly different DNA structure (see Fig 7.1). Homologous chromosomes may have a copy each of the same allele or they may have one of copy of two different alleles.
Diploid and haploid	A diploid cell contains one homologous pair of each chromosome. A haploid cell contains only half the number of chromosomes – only one copy of each chromosome.	Diploid human cells have 46 chromosomes. Haploid human cells have 23 chromosomes.
Mitosis	Type of cell division that results in growth or repair of body tissues, or that occurs in asexual reproduction.	One cell divides to give two identical cells. In humans, one diploid cell divides by mitosis to give two identical diploid daughter cells.
Meiosis	Type of cell division that produces the **gametes** (sex cells) – the **eggs** and **sperm**.	One cell divides to produce 4 daughter cells that are genetically unique. During this more complex form of cell division, the genes are shuffled and the chromosome number of the daughter cells is halved. In humans, one diploid cell divides by meiosis to produce 4 haploid daughter cells.
Chromatids	Unseparated pairs of chromosomes that result from DNA replication, before cell division.	During the early stages of cell division (mitosis and meiosis), the DNA of a cell is replicated (copied). When the chromosomes condense during the next stage of division, the chromosomes appear as double structures. Each unseparated chromosome with such a double structure is called a chromatid.

Gregor Mendel (1822–1884). Mendel's discoveries were the result of meticulous breeding experiments carried out in pea plants.

Some basic principles

It is a good idea to make sure that you are clear about some of the basic terms that you learnt during the AS course. You may want to start by revising Chapters 6 and 8 in the AS book; Table 7.1 should then act as a memory aid.

A historical overview

An interesting illustration of the way scientific ideas can suddenly develop in prepared minds took place in 1900, when the work of the Austrian monk, Gregor Mendel, was rediscovered. In the 1850s Mendel had carried out a now famous series of experiments with garden peas and had actually worked out the basic laws of heredity. The results of his work were published in the journal of a local Natural History Society in Austria. Not surprisingly, this had a rather limited readership and so was unknown to most scientists of the time. Mendel knew nothing of the processes of cell division, which were not described until the 1880s.

By 1900, however, the process of meiosis (see AS Biology, Chapter 8) was understood and the three scientists who rediscovered Mendel's work saw the connection. They realised that the way in which paired chromosomes separate during meiosis and recombine in fertilisation could explain how Mendel's 'hereditary particles', which we now call genes, pass from one generation to the next. The rest of the 20th century saw a rapid expansion in understanding of the laws of heredity; the genetic code was cracked, scientists learned how to manipulate genes and the molecular basis of inheritance is now much better understood.

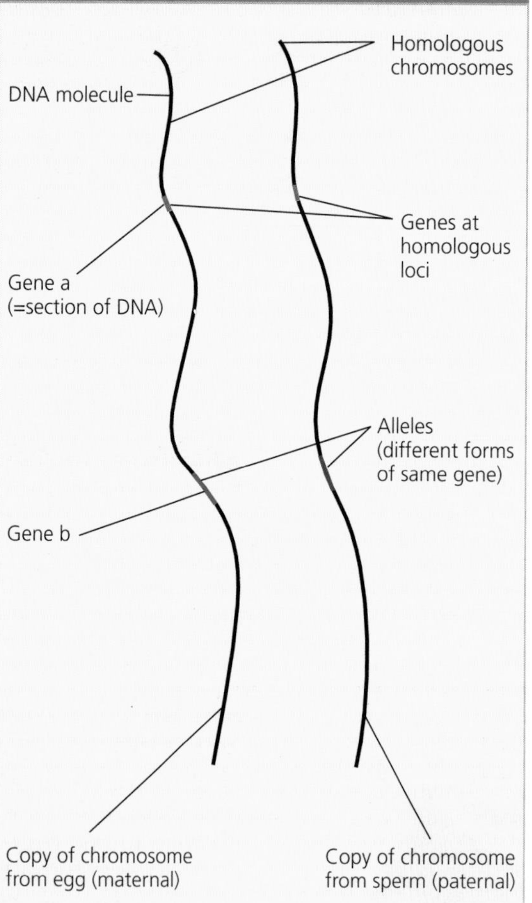

In this chapter we look in detail at what happens in monohybrid and dihybrid inheritance. However, before that, it is important to look at how meoisis – the process of cell division that produces sex cells – to see how we can go on to explain some of the observable laws of inheritance in terms of genes and chromosomes.

It's very easy to mix up mitosis and meiosis. Don't forget that mitosis occurs when your toes grows. Meiosis makes eggs in ovaries and sperms in semen.

1

a What is the diploid number of chromosomes in a human?

b What is the haploid number of chromosomes in a human?

c How many chromosomes does a nucleus of a human sperm contain?

2 During mitosis the chromosomes replicate during interphase, before the nucleus starts to divide. You may need to refer to Section 7.2 in the AS book to answer these questions.

a How many copies of a particular gene would the nucleus contain after replication?

b Complete the table to show the number of copies of this gene in each of the following.

Stage	Number of copies of gene
Nucleus during prophase	
Cell during metaphase	
Each nucleus in telophase	
Nucleus of a daughter cell	

Fig 7.1 The gene locus

Homologous chromosomes

DNA molecule

Genes at homologous loci

Gene a (=section of DNA)

Alleles (different forms of same gene)

Gene b

Copy of chromosome from egg (maternal)

Copy of chromosome from sperm (paternal)

7.2 Meiosis

Humans, like other sexually reproducing organisms, inherit their genes from their parent's sex cells. Haploid sex cells have only one of each pair of homologous chromosomes. When a sperm (a haploid cell) fertilises an egg (also a haploid cell) to form a **zygote** (a diploid cell), each contributes one set of chromosomes, and so one set of genes. It is important that one copy of each chromosome, and hence of each gene, is passed on from each parent, otherwise there would be an incomplete set of instructions in the zygote.

Gametes that do not have one copy, and one copy only, of each chromosome will not produce a viable zygote. If a chromosome or part of a chromosome is missing, there will be an incomplete set of instructions and some essential proteins will not be made. Extra chromosomes or fragments of chromosomes are usually harmful to the development of an embryo, which usually dies before birth. The survival of sexually reproducing species depends on accurate meiosis, and not surprisingly the process is quite complex.

The overall process of meiosis

Meiosis consists of two divisions, one followed by the other. Fig 7.2 gives a useful overview and Fig 7.3 describes the individual stages in detail. Before meiosis starts, each chromosome replicates to form two chromatids, as in mitosis.

- **The first division:** the homologous chromosomes separate. Each still consists of two **chromatids** and this part of the division allows crosssing over and swapping of bits of chromatids. As we shall see later, this leads to shuffling of genes so that the sex cells produced are genetically unique.

- **The second division:** the chromatids are pulled apart. This produces four haploid nuclei, each with one copy of each homologous chromosome.

In humans, a cell about to begin meiosis has 46 chromosomes, each consisting of 2 chromatids. At the end of the first division, one chromosome from each homologous pair has been separated into a new nucleus.

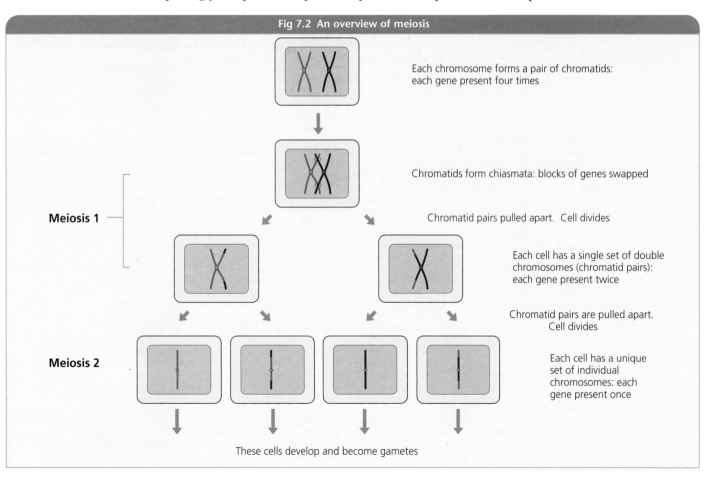

Fig 7.2 An overview of meiosis

Each chromosome forms a pair of chromatids: each gene present four times

Chromatids form chiasmata: blocks of genes swapped

Chromatid pairs pulled apart. Cell divides

Meiosis 1

Each cell has a single set of double chromosomes (chromatid pairs): each gene present twice

Chromatid pairs are pulled apart. Cell divides

Meiosis 2

Each cell has a unique set of individual chromosomes: each gene present once

These cells develop and become gametes

Fig 7.3 The stages of meiosis

Stage of meiosis	What is happening	What it looks like
First division Interphase	Just before meiosis, DNA replicates so cells which contained two copies of each chromosome, now have four. Chromosomes not yet visible	nucleolus
Early prophase I	Chromosomes become visible. Centromeres move to opposite sides of cell	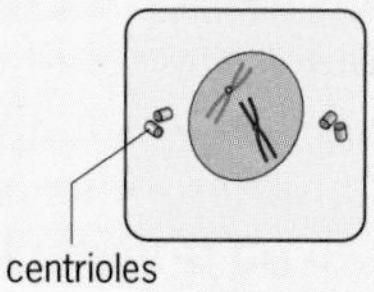 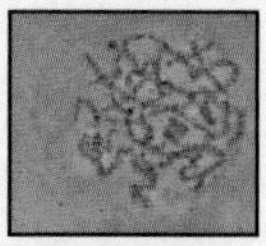 centrioles — Early prophase I
Mid prophase I	Each homologous pair of chromosomes comes together to form a bivalent	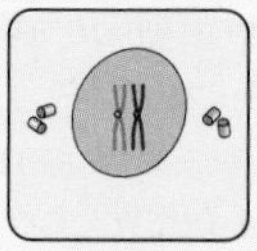 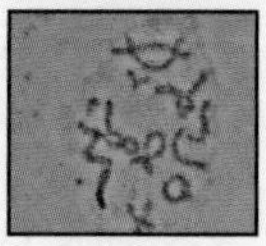 Mid prophase I
Late prophase I	Each chromosome in a bivalent forms two chromatids. Genetic mixing occurs: chiasmata, the points of cross-over, are visible	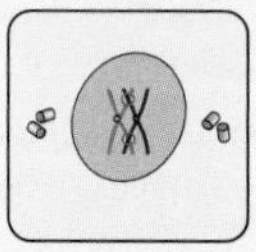
Metaphase I	The bivalents arrange themselves on the equator of the spindle	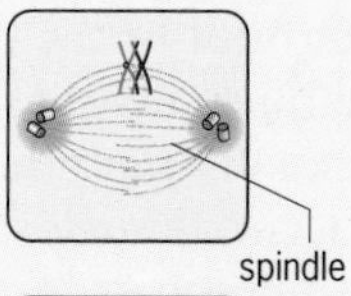 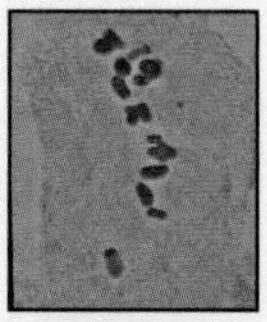 Metaphase I
Anaphase I	The chromatid pairs from each homologous chromosome split apart and move to opposite poles of the cell	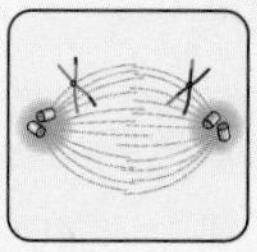 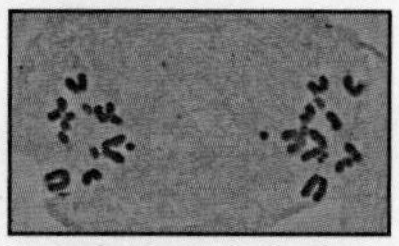 spindle — Anaphase I
Telophase I	Cytokinesis begins, two new cells form, each has two copies of each chromosome. These chromosomes are genetically different from those in the original cell	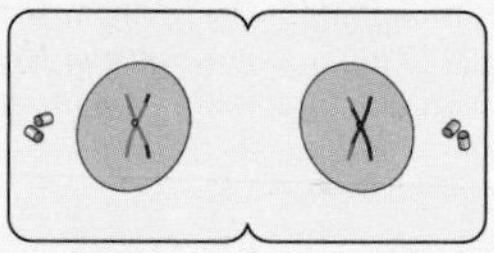 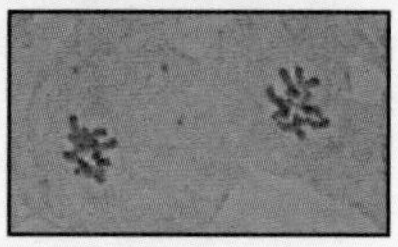 Telophase I
Interphase	A resting time (length varies between cell types)	
Second division Prophase II	A new spindle forms, at right angles to the first	
Metaphase II	Chromosomes, each of which is a pair of chromatids, align themselves on the equator of the spindle	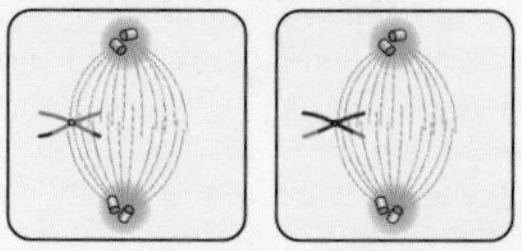 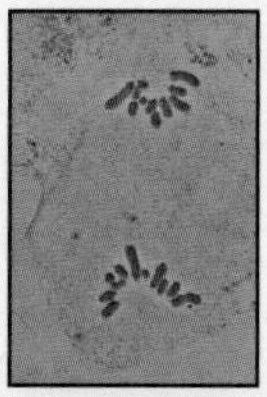 Metaphase II (1 cell only)
Anaphase II	Chromatids are pulled apart and move to opposite poles of the cell	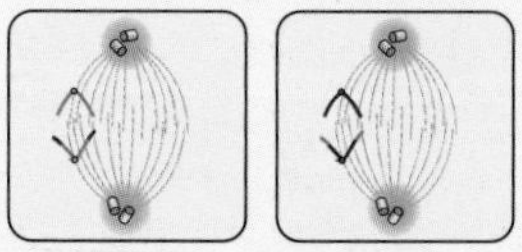  Anaphase II (1 cell only)
Telophase II	Cytokinesis begins. Four haploid cells, each with only a single chromosome, have been formed. Each chromosome is genetically different	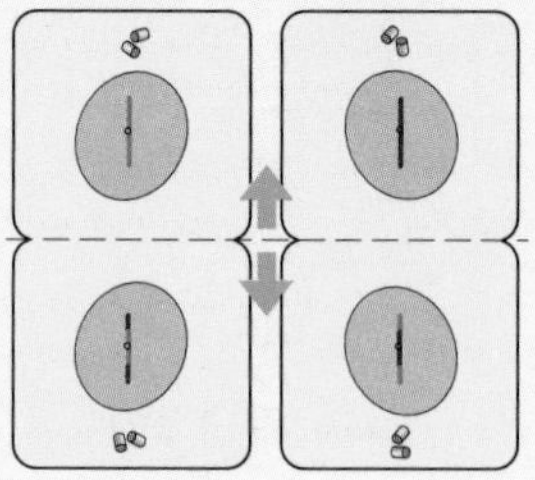 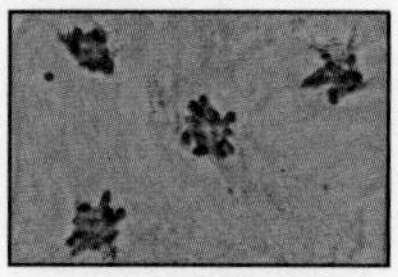 Telophase II

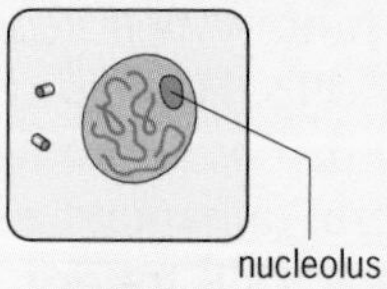

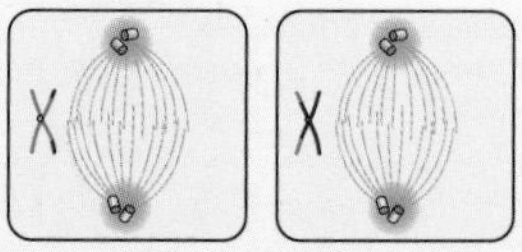

These two new nuclei have 23 chromosomes, but each chromosome still consists of a pair of chromatids. By the end of the second division, the chromatids have separated and are now independent chromosomes, so there are four nuclei with 23 chromosomes.

The stages of meiosis

Fig 7.3 on the opposite page summarises the main stages of meiosis and the individual stages are detailed below.

Interphase

The process of cell division in meiosis starts off in exactly the same way as it does in mitosis. Shortly before there is any visible signs of activity, the chromosomes replicate. Each chromosome forms two chromatids, which remain attached at a **centromere**. The DNA in the chromosomes is still stretched out, so the chromatids extend throughout the nucleus and cannot be distinguished with a light microscope.

The first division of meiosis

Prophase I The chromosomes contract and coil up. Since each consists of two attached chromatids, each chromosome appears to have two strands. Things then happen a little differently than in mitosis – the homologous pairs of chromosomes come close together. When lined up, the pair of homologous chromosomes is called a **bivalent**. Parts of the chromatids may be exchanged in a process called **crossing over** (see page 103).

Metaphase I As in mitosis, the nuclear membrane breaks down and a spindle of protein fibres forms across the cell. The bivalents move to the **equator** of the cell and the centromeres attach to the spindle.

Anaphase I The protein spindle pulls the two centromeres of each bivalent to opposite ends, or **poles**, of the cell. This ensures that only one chromosome from each homologous pair moves to each pole.

Telophase I The chromosomes, each of which still consists of two chromatids linked at a centromere, group together at the poles of the cell. The spindle disappears and the cell cytoplasm divides to form two cells.

The second division of meiosis

The first division of meiosis is followed by another division. In this second division, the two cells formed in telophase I split once more. Often, this second division starts almost immediately, maybe even before the two cells are fully formed. In sperm production, for example, meiosis is continuous and there is no prolonged interphase. Sometimes there is a lengthy interphase between the divisions. During the formation of ova in human ovaries the first division of meiosis is completed in the embryo. The process then stops and the second division starts only after a sperm penetrates the membrane of one of the cells after ovulation.

The second division of meiosis is very similar to mitosis. The two cells formed in telophase I contain chromosomes that already consist of two chromatids.

Prophase II A new spindle forms in each cell.

Metaphase II The centromeres of each chromosome attach to the spindle at the equator.

Anaphase II The chromatids are pulled to opposite poles.

Telophase II Four haploid cells are produced from the diploid cell that originally started meiosis.

3 Explain the advantage of the DNA of the chromosomes stretching out during interphase of meiosis.

4 How many chromatids are present in a human cell nucleus at the end of interphase, before the first division of meiosis begins?

5 Explain the advantage of the chromosomes contracting and coiling up in prophase I.

The ocean sunfish, *Mola mola* is a notoriously neglectful parent, but mass production of offspring ensures that some survive and keep the species going.

The advantages of meiosis

A female ocean sunfish can produce fifty million eggs. If every one was fertilised there could be fifty million baby sunfish, and every one would be different! Not surprisingly, since mother makes no effort to look after them, very few of these babies survive. But, because of the differences, some may be slightly better adapted for survival than others. That's the great advantage of sex. Meiosis followed by fertilisation greatly increases the amount of genetic variation. New combinations of alleles are produced, and these may give rise to individuals with new features that favour their survival. The survivors then pass on their successful gene combinations to their offspring.

Sources of variation

Combinations of alleles may be produced in three ways:

- independent assortment;
- random fertilisation;
- crossing over.

Independent assortment In each homologous pair, one chromosome is derived from the original female parent and one from the male. During meiosis these maternal and paternal chromosomes can be reshuffled in any combination – they are **independently assorted**. This process occurs at anaphase of the first division, because the maternal and paternal chromosomes move apart entirely randomly.

6 Use the pattern shown in Fig 7.4 to work out how many different combinations are possible if there are (a) 4 pairs of homologous chromosomes; (b) 23 pairs.

Random fertilisation Fertilisation of female sex cells is random – any female gamete can join with any male gamete. The gametes are usually from different individuals, each with chromosomes carrying different alleles of many of the genes. In humans there are about thirty thousand genes, many of which have several alleles, so the number of possible combinations is astronomical.

7 Look at Table 7.2 and describe three ways in which mitosis is similar to meiosis.

Fig 7.4 Independent assortment

A cell from an organism with two pairs of homologous chromosomes

The pink chromosomes are originally from the female parent

The purple chromosomes are originally from the male parent

There are four possible ways the chromosomes could be reshuffled in the gametes

A cell from an organism with three pairs of homologous chromosomes

There are eight ways the chromosomes could be reshuffled in the gametes

Table 7.2 Differences between mitosis and meiosis

Mitosis	Meiosis
One cell division only	Two stages of cell division
Two cells produced	Four cells produced
Daughter cells have the same number of chromosomes as parent cell	Daughter cells have half the number of chromosomes
Homologous chromosomes do not pair up	Homologous chromosomes pair in prophase I
No bivalents or crossing over	Crossing over occurs in bivalents

Crossing over Even more variation is introduced during prophase I by a process called crossing over, as Fig 7.5 shows. Once a homologous pair of chromosomes has formed a bivalent, two of the chromatids coil together like mating snakes. At the points where the chromatids cross over each other, they join together. These links are called **chiasmata** (singular – chiasma).

When the chromosomes separate again during anaphase, parts of the chromatids are swapped from one chromatid to another. As a result, the new chromatids have some sections that have been copied from the maternal chromosome and some sections that have been copied from the paternal chromosome. Fig 7.6 shows a close up of this process.

Fig 7.5 Meiosis and fertilisation in humans

A homologous pair of chromosomes has a gene for hair colour and a gene for hair structure. The maternal and paternal chromosomes carry different alleles for these genes.

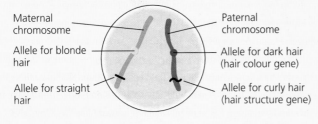

Maternal chromosome

Allele for blonde hair

Allele for straight hair

Paternal chromosome

Allele for dark hair (hair colour gene)

Allele for curly hair (hair structure gene)

The chromosomes replicate, forming two chromatids joined at the centromere

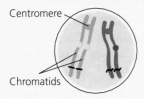

Centromere

Chromatids

The chromosomes come together as a pair, and two of the chromatids cross over

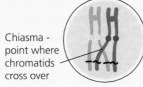

Chiasma - point where chromatids cross over

Four possible gametes can be produced by meiosis

This gamete has the same alleles as the maternal chromosome

These two gametes have new combinations of alleles – one for blonde and curly hair, the other for dark and straight hair

This gamete has the same alleles as the paternal chromosome

Fig 7.6 A possible crossing over

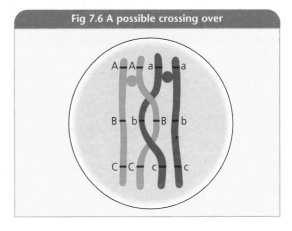

The great advantage of crossing over is that alleles of genes that occur on the same chromosome can be combined in new ways. If only whole chromosomes were passed on, much less genetic variation would be possible.

8 A chromosome has three genes on it. Each gene has two alleles, i.e. A and a, B and b, C and c. Crossing over occurs at two chiasmata, as shown in Fig 7.6. Use coloured pens to draw diagrams to show the chromosomes in the gametes that would be produced.

KEY FACTS

■ **Meiosis** is involved in the production of **gametes** (sex cells). This type of cell division halves the number of chromosomes in a cell. The gametes are **haploid**, having only one of each homologous pair of chromosomes.

■ In the first stage of meiosis the homologous pairs chromosomes of chromosomes pair up and form **bivalents**.

■ Meiosis continues in two stages. In the first the two chromosomes of each pair are separated, in the second, the **chromatids** are split apart.

■ New combinations of alleles result from **independent assortment** of the maternal and paternal chromosomes; from **crossing over** of sections of chromatids; and from **random fertilisation**.

7.3 Monohybrid inheritance

Monohybrid inheritance describes the situation when a characteristic controlled by a single gene is passed on from one generation to the next. Examples of monohybrid inheritance in humans are rare, but genetic diseases such as Huntington's disease and cystic fibrosis show how the effect of one gene can be **dominant** or **recessive**.

If both alleles of a single gene are identical, whether they are dominant or recessive in their effects on the individual they are said to be homozygous. If the alleles of a single gene are different, they are said to be heterozygous.

Huntington's disease; an example of dominance

Huntington's disease is due to a mutation in a single gene that occurs on chromosome 4. Every cell in the body has two copies of chromosome 4, and so every cell nucleus in the body has two copies of the gene that codes for a protein called Huntingtin. One copy is present on the chromosome derived from the ovum and one occurs at the same locus on the chromosome from the sperm. Most people have identical and normal alleles at this locus. However, people who develop

Huntington's disease, carry a mutation in one copy of their Huntingtin gene. We do not yet know exactly how it causes the disease, but Huntingtin is known to concentrate in areas of the brain that degenerate in Huntington's disease. This protein is necessary for normal brain development in the embryo, but when it is overproduced in the adult it causes damage. As the activity of the mutated protein is responsible for the symptoms, the disease develops even when only one copy of the Huntingtin gene is mutated, so this mutant allele is said to be **dominant**.

Cystic fibrosis

Huntington's disease is unusual. Most faulty alleles simply fail to code for a functional protein. When an individual has one healthy allele, they can still make the normal protein and so the effect of the mutation is masked. The effect of the mutated allele in this case is said to be **recessive**. Cystic fibrosis is an example of a disorder caused by a recessive allele. It appears only if both the copies of the gene on a homologous pair of chromosomes are mutated so that they cannot produce a functional protein.

APPLICATION

Huntington's disease

The diagram below shows a family tree where several members of the family developed Huntington's disease.

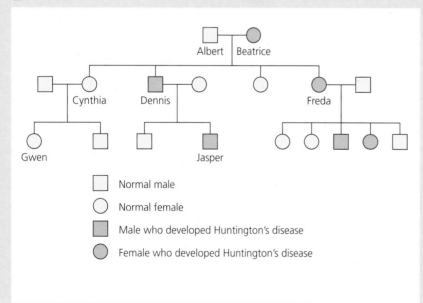

Normal male

Normal female

Male who developed Huntington's disease

Female who developed Huntington's disease

1

a How can you tell from the family tree that Beatrice was heterozygous for Huntington's disease?

b Gwen has three children. She is worried that they might develop Huntington's disease. What advice would you give her? Explain your answer with a genetic diagram.

c What are the chances that a child of Jasper will develop the disease?

d It would be possible to test Jasper's children when they are young, or even before birth, to find out whether they have the allele for Huntington's disease. Do you think that it would be right to do this? Give your reasons and explain what problems might result from such a test.

2 Huntington's disease, although deadly, only develops in middle age. Suggest how a dominant allele for such a disease has been able to survive in the human population.

In Chapter 10 of AS biology, we explained that the normal allele of the cystic fibrosis gene makes an important membrane protein, called CFTR. As long as one normal allele is present the cells are able to make CFTR and transport of chloride ions through the plasma membrane takes place normally. However, the mutated allele causes the production of a channel protein that does not transport chloride ions, so a person who is homozygous for this recessive allele suffers from cystic fibrosis. This results in sticky mucus that causes breathing and digestive problems. The genetic diagram in Fig 7.7 shows how cystic fibrosis can be inherited.

9

a What is the ratio of the phenotypes of the children in Fig 7.7?

b What percentage of the children in Fig 7.7 would suffer from cystic fibrosis?

c What percentage of the children would be carriers of the cystic fibrosis allele?

d About 1 in 25 people carry the cystic fibrosis allele. What are the chances of a carrier marrying another carrier?

e What are the chances of a child having cystic fibrosis if both parents are carriers?

f In the population as a whole, what proportion of children would you expect to be born with cystic fibrosis?

10 Explain why a person who is homozygous recessive for the cystic fibrosis gene produces channel proteins in the plasma membranes that do not transport chloride ions. You may need information from the AS book to answer this question.

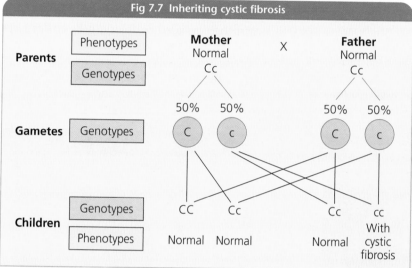

Fig 7.7 Inheriting cystic fibrosis

Genotype and phenotype

The full complement and combination of alleles that a person has is known as their **genotype**. Some alleles are recessive, some are dominant and some alleles affect how others impact on observable characteristics. The actual effect that the alleles have is called the **phenotype**. For example, the phenotype of a person that has one normal and one abnormal allele is that they will develop Huntington's disease. It is important to become familiar with these terms, and Fig 7.8 shows an example of their use. You can see from this genetic diagram how Nancy Wexler could predict that she had a 50:50 chance of developing the disease herself. Notice that, although we have used 'normal' to indicate the common allele that does not cause the disease, this is just to save writing 'without Huntington's disease' every time. This only refers to this gene, and the person with the faulty allele may be 'normal' in all other respects (if any of us can be said to be 'normal'!).

Codominance

Different alleles of a gene are not always either dominant or recessive. If two alleles both produce a protein that can function, the phenotype of the heterozygote may be different from that of either homozygote. The alleles are then said to be **codominant**.

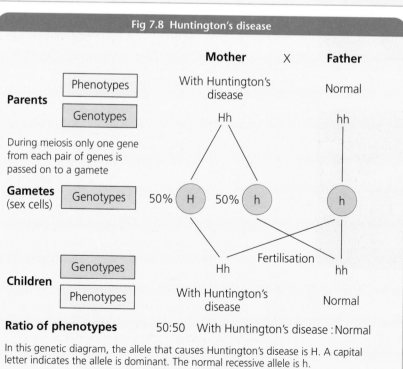

Fig 7.8 Huntington's disease

Ratio of phenotypes   50:50   With Huntington's disease : Normal

In this genetic diagram, the allele that causes Huntington's disease is H. A capital letter indicates the allele is dominant. The normal recessive allele is h.

Sickle cell anaemia as an example of codominance

Red blood cells depend on the presence of the complex protein, haemoglobin, to transport oxygen (Fig 7.9). A mutant allele of a normal haemoglobin gene causes one amino acid in the two beta (β) polypeptide chains to be different. The haemoglobin can still carry oxygen, but not as efficiently as the shape of the molecule is altered. Red blood cells that contain this altered haemoglobin tend to be crescent or 'sickle' shaped as Table 7.3 shows.

Sickle cells are easily damaged, and the reduced number of working red blood cells decreases the supply of oxygen to the tissues. The heart pumps harder in order to get more blood to the tissues and maintain the oxygen supply. However, the damaged cells tend to clump together, making the blood more sticky and harder to pump. This has many side-effects, including increased likelihood of kidney failure, strokes and heart attack. The

Fig 7.9 Haemoglobin

Four polypeptide chains make up the haemoglobin molecule. Each chain contains 574 amino acids.

Each chain is attached to a haem group that can combine with oxygen.

spleen is over-burdened by having to break down the damaged red blood cells and it loses its ability to remove bacteria from the blood, so the victim of sickle cell anaemia suffers from frequent infections.

Surprisingly, this condition, which can cause acute pain and distress, can also be

Table 7.3 Sickle cell anaemia

Hb^A Hb^A	Normal		Efficient oxygen transport. The malarial parasite can grow in the red blood cells, so there is no resistance to malaria.
	Red blood cells are normal	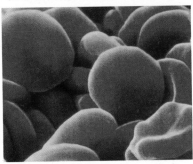 A coloured scanning electron micrograph of normal red blood cells.	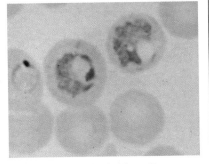 A light micrograph of malarial parasites growing in human red blood cells.
Hb^{S}Hb^S	Sickle cell anaemia		The red blood cells break up easily, resulting in severe shortage of red blood cells. The extra demand for oxygen supply to the tissues puts excessive strain on the heart. Most victims die in early childhood.
	Red blood cells are sickle shaped	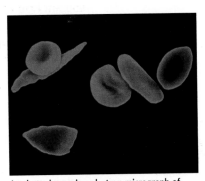 A coloured scanning electron micrograph of sickled and normal red blood cells.	
Hb^A Hb^S	Sickle cell trait		Sufficient oxygen transport. The malarial parasite cannot grow well in the red blood cells, so there is a high resistance to malaria.
	About one-third of the red blood cells are sickle shaped; the others are normal		

quite useful. This is because red blood cells that contain some sickle cell haemoglobin molecules are not so attractive to malarial parasites. People who have the sickle cell trait because they are heterozygous for the sickle cell gene have a survival advantage in parts of the world where malaria is common.

The two alleles of the sickle cell gene can be considered to be codominant because they produce different haemoglobin polypeptides and the phenotype of the heterozygote differs from that of either homozygote. However, some scientists disagree and consider the allele that codes for the normal haemoglobin polypeptide to be dominant over the allele that produces the abnormal form.

In some cases of codominance, alternative alleles may result in the production of distinctly different proteins, although neither can be said to be more 'normal' than the other. This is true in the case of the blood group antigens, A and B, as we see in the next section.

11

a What is the ratio of phenotypes in the children when the parents both have the sickle cell trait, that is they are heterozygous? Use the symbols shown in Table 7.3 and a genetic diagram to explain your answer.

b Use information from Table 7.3 to explain why the frequency of sickle cell anaemia is declining among the black population in the USA.

Blood groups and codominance

Accident victims often need a blood transfusion to replace the blood they have lost. When blood transfusion was first attempted in the nineteenth century, it was found to work sometimes, but on other occasions the blood coagulated and the patient died. Karl Landsteiner found an explanation for this in 1900, the same year that Mendel's work on genes was rediscovered. Landsteiner realised that different people could have different blood types, and he identified the A, B and O blood group system (Table 7.4).

The different blood groups arise because different people have different antigens on the surface of their red blood cells. Antigens are substances that, if foreign to the individual, stimulate the immune system to produce antibodies, just as foreign bacteria and viruses do. When antibodies attach to antigens the complex becomes 'sticky'. When antibodies attach to the antigens on red blood cells, they cause the cells to clump together – a process called agglutination. Antigens are often proteins, but the ABO blood group antigens are proteins with attached carbohydrate chains. Fig 7.10 shows the basic structure of the molecules found on red blood cells of the A, B and O groups.

You will see from Fig 7.10 that the three molecules are the same, except that antigens A and B have a different type of attached sugar monomer. The sugar monomers are attached by an enzyme coded for by a gene at a single locus. One allele, I^A, produces a variant of the enzyme that attaches N-acetylgalactosamine; another allele, I^B, produces a variant of the enzyme that attaches galactose. There is also a variant of the allele, I^O, which attaches neither monomer. This variant has a single base deletion in the DNA, and the enzyme produced is non-functional.

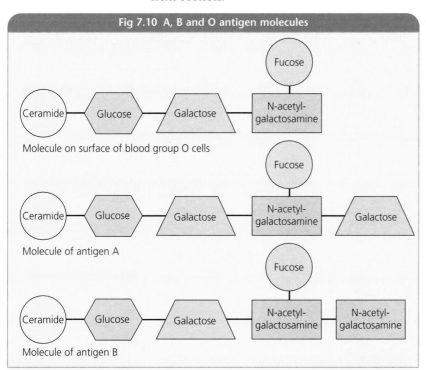

Fig 7.10 A, B and O antigen molecules

Molecule on surface of blood group O cells

Molecule of antigen A

Molecule of antigen B

Table 7.4 The A, B, AB and O blood group system			
Blood group phenotype	**Possible genotypes**	**Antigens on red cell membrane**	**Antibodies in blood plasma**
A	$I^A I^A$, $I^A I^O$	A only	anti-b
B	$I^B I^B$, $I^B I^O$	B only	anti-a
AB	$I^A I^B$	Both A and B	none
O	$I^O I^O$	none	anti-a and anti-b

APPLICATION

Good breeding

The study of genetics has helped us to understand human genetic disorders such as Huntington's disease and cystic fibrosis. It is also extremely useful when it comes to breeding domestic animals and improving the quality of crop plants. Most of the animals that we commonly use for food or have as pets are very different from their wild ancestors.

In cats a gene, C, is concerned with the colour of the coat. The normal allele, C^c, makes the cat's coat blackish and is dominant. Siamese and Burmese cats both have particular alleles of this gene. Siamese cats have a recessive allele, C^s, and they must be homozygous for this allele. This mutant allele codes for an enzyme that synthesises black pigment, but only when below body temperature. This is because the mutant allele codes for an enzyme with a tertiary structure that is slightly different from that of the normal enzyme; molecules of this enzyme happen to unfold (denature) at about 37 °C. The Siamese cat therefore is only black in the cooler parts of the body, such as the tail, ears and lower legs. The rest of the coat is pale cream coloured. This shows how the phenotype can be affected by both the genotype and the environment.

Burmese cats have a different allele of the gene, C^b, which makes the coat colour dark brown instead of pale cream. The extremities are black as in Siamese cats.

1 a What is the genotype of a Siamese cat and of a Burmese cat?

   b Most cats have the normal allele, C^c. What will the kittens be like if a Siamese cat mates with an ordinary homozygous black cat. Explain your answer with a genetic diagram.

2 When a cat breeder mated a Siamese with a Burmese cat, all the kittens had pale brown coats.

   a What is the genotype of this breeder's pale brown kittens?

   b Are the alleles in this genotype codominant? Explain your answer.

   c What results would you expect if two of these pale brown cats interbreed, producing large litters of kittens?

   d The breeder wants to sell kittens with the pale brown coat colour. How should she obtain litters of kittens which all have pale brown coats?

3 a You will have noticed that when two alleles of a gene are dominant and recessive respectively, crossing heterozygotes gives a 3:1 ratio of phenotypes in the offspring. What is the ratio of phenotypes when the two alleles are codominant?

   b Manx cats are tailless. When bred together they produce an apparently odd ratio of 2 tailless : 1 normal tailed. This is because embryos that are homozygous for the Manx allele fail to develop in the womb and are never born. The genetic diagram below shows how the ratio arises. What proportion of the kittens will have tails if a Manx cat mates with a tailed cat? Explain your answer.

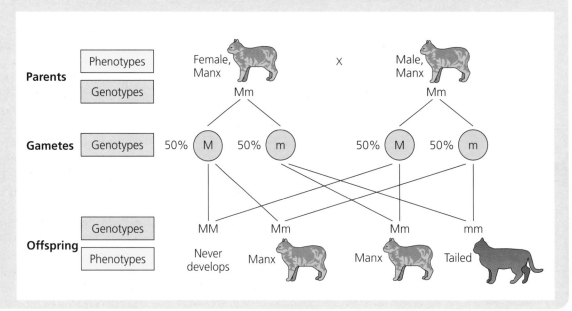

12 Table 7.4 shows the genotypes and effects in the blood of blood groups A, B, AB and O. You will see that alleles I^A and I^B are codominant, but allele I^o is recessive to both.

One of the particular problems with ABO blood groups is that the blood plasma normally contains antibodies for antigens that a person does not have, as shown in Table 7.4. This explains why early attempts at blood transfusion often had disastrous results.

Explain why it would be dangerous to transfuse group A blood into a person with blood group O.

13 The parents of a child have blood groups AB and O. Draw a genetic diagram to show the possible genotypes of their children.

14 Blood groups have been used in cases where there has been a dispute over who was the father of a child.
In one case the mother has blood group B. The child has blood group O. Two men who might be the father have groups AB and A.

a Could either of these men have been the father of the child? Explain your answer.

b Suggest why it is not possible to use the ABO blood groups alone to prove that a particular man is the father of a child.

■ **Monohybrid inheritance** describes the inheritance of a characteristic that is determined by one gene, situated at a particular locus on a pair of homologous chromosomes.

■ The gene may have more than one allele. One allele can be **dominant** over another, **recessive**, allele. Only the dominant allele is expressed in an individual with both alleles in the body cells, i.e. a **heterozygote**.

■ **Codominance** occurs when two different alleles are both expressed in the phenotype of a heterozygous individual.

■ The phenotype of an individual depends not only on the genotype, but also on the environment in which the individual develops.

7.4 Inheritance patterns for more than one gene

The inheritance of a single gene that controls a single characteristic is the simplest example. However, even the simplest organism contains hundreds of genes – humans have about thirty-five thousand. How they combine, interact and are passed on from one person to the next is enormously complicated. In this section we look at some specific examples – the inheritance of two independently inherited genes, how genes can be manipulated in breeding programmes in domestic animals, and the inheritance of genes on the sex chromosomes.

Dihybrid inheritance

Dihybrid inheritance is a term used to describe how two genes that code for single characteristics are passed from one generation to the next. When Gregor Mendel was experimenting with his ideas on inheritance, he used garden pea plants. He realised that, in order to prove that different characteristics were passed on independently of each other,

he needed to cross breed plants with two separate characteristics that differed. For example, Mendel had pea plants with tall and dwarf stems and pea plants with round and wrinkled seeds.

He knew that when he crossed a tall plant with a dwarf plant all the offspring were tall, provided the parents were pure-breeding, i.e. that their ancestors were also tall or dwarf. Similarly, when he crossed plants that produced seeds that were smooth and round when dried with plants that had seeds that became wrinkled as they dried, he obtained plants that all produced round seeds.

Fig 7.11 shows one of the crosses that Mendel carried out, with a modern interpretation in terms of genes. Notice the way the genotypes are set out in the second generation. This type of chart makes it easy to work out the all the possible crosses of the different gamete genotypes. It is called a **Punnett square**.

We now know that one gene determines

Fig 7.11 Pea crosses and the Punnett square

Pollen is transferred with a brush from the anthers of a tall plant grown from round seeds to the stigma of a dwarf plant, grown from wrinkled seeds.

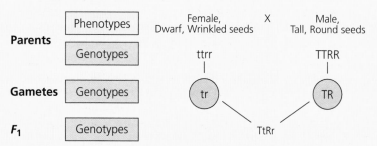

	Phenotypes	Female, Dwarf, Wrinkled seeds	X	Male, Tall, Round seeds

Parents

Genotypes — ttrr   TTRR

Gametes   Genotypes — (tr)   (TR)

F_1 Genotypes — TtRr

All the seeds of the first generation, called the F_1, will be round and will grow into tall plants. The flowers of the F_1 plants are allowed to self-fertilise, i.e. the pollen transfers to the stigma of the same flower. This generation is called the F_2.

F_2 genotypes and phenotypes

Pollen (male gametes)

Egg cells (female gametes)		TR	Tr	tR	tr
	TR	TTRR Tall Round seeds	TTRr Tall Round seeds	TtRR Tall Round seeds	TtRr Tall Round seeds
	Tr	TTRr Tall Round seeds	TTrr Tall Wrinkled seeds	TtRr Tall Round seeds	Ttrr Tall Wrinkled seeds
	tR	TtRR Tall Round seeds	TtRr Tall Round seeds	ttRR Dwarf Round seeds	ttRr Dwarf Round seeds
	tr	TtRr Tall Round seeds	Ttrr Tall Wrinkled seeds	ttRr Dwarf Round seeds	ttrr Dwarf Wrinkled seeds

Ratio of phenotypes   9 Tall, Round seeds : 3 Dwarf, Round seeds : 3 Tall, Wrinkled seeds : 1 Dwarf, Wrinkled seed

whether the stem of a pea plant is long or short. The allele for tallness, T, is dominant to the allele for dwarfness. Another gene, at a locus on another pair of homologous chromosomes, controls production of an enzyme involved in starch synthesis in the pea seeds. Normally peas have the allele, R, for this enzyme, and the seeds fill with starch as they mature, making them smooth and round. The mutant allele, r, has an extra section of DNA. The enzyme produced does not work, and as a result the seeds contain more sugar and less starch than normal, which makes them look wrinkled.

15

a What is the genotype of a pure-breeding tall plant?

b What is the genotype of a plant with wrinkled seeds?

c Explain why wrinkled seeds have more sugar and less starch than normal seeds.

16 Because the wrinkled seeds have more sugar they taste sweeter, and many people prefer them. A grower who has a dwarf variety of pea that produces wrinkled seeds wants a tall variety that has wrinkled seeds. He carries out the crosses shown in Fig 7.11

a What proportion of plants in the F_2 generation would be tall with wrinkled seeds?

b What proportion of tall plants with wrinkled seeds would be pure-breeding, and what would be the genotype of these plants?

c The grower could not tell which of the tall plants with wrinkled seeds were pure-breeding. He grew plants from the wrinkled seeds and allowed them to self-fertilise. Some plants in the next generation were dwarf. Draw a genetic diagram to show how these seeds could produce dwarf plants after self-fertilisation.

d How could the grower guarantee that he had a stock of plants that would only produce tall plants with wrinkled seeds?

Manipulating the inheritance of several genes

Plant and animal breeders often need to manipulate the alleles of several genes to get the desired characteristics into a particular variety of organism. For example, a new strain of rice produces 25% more grain by having seed heads on every shoot. Before this variety can be of commercial use it has to have other features bred into it. Resistance to fungal disease is one essential characteristic. Fortunately there are genes that provide this resistance, and the new variety will be cross-bred until the right combination of genes has been introduced and the plants are pure-breeding. Often genes for features such as resistance to disease occur in wild strains of cultivated plants – which is why geneticists stress that naturally occurring varieties should be conserved whenever possible.

17

a Cultivated varieties of crop plants tend to be homozygous for a large proportion of genes. Explain how artificial breeding causes this.

b A number of societies maintain stocks of old-fashioned breeds of animals, which often have poorer yields or qualities than more modern varieties. What are the possible benefits of keeping these breeds?

Using cats to explain epistasis

The inheritance of coat colour in cats is complex. Several different genes are involved. When a cat breeder wants to breed particular combinations of colour in her Siamese cats, she has to take more than one coat colour gene into account. To be a Siamese cat the coat colour gene, C, must be homozygous for the allele, C^s. (See Section 7.3, page 108). There are also two other genes that control the colour of the tail, face, legs and ears (the 'points' as cat breeders call them). One gene makes the hair on the points either black or brown. The other affects the spread of pigment in the points, making the hair either darker or lighter. Table 7.5 shows the effects of the alleles of these genes.

The two genes affect each other. For example, a cat with the allele for black hair, B, which also has the allele for evenly spread pigment, D, has dark black points that breeders call 'seal'. If instead the cat is homozygous for patchy pigment, d, the points will look paler and are called 'blue'. Similarly, brown hair may be either dark brown (chocolate) or pale brown (lilac). When a physical characteristic occurs because of an interaction between genes at different loci, we call this interaction **epistasis**.

18 Using Table 7.5, what colour are the points if the genotypes are BBDd, bbDd, BBdd and BbDd?

Table 7.5 Siamese cats				
Gene	**Allele**	**Genotype**	**Phenotype**	
Colour of hair in points	B	BB Bb	Black hair	
	b	bb	Brown hair	
Density of hair colour in points	D	DD Dd	Pigment in hair evenly spread and therefore dark	
	d	dd	Pigment in hair patchy and therefore lighter	

This seal-point cat could have the genotype BBDD.

This blue-point cat could have the genotype Bbdd.

This chocolate-point cat could have the genotype bbDD.

This lilac-point cat must have the genotype bbdd.

KEY FACTS

■ Dihybrid inheritance is the result of a cross between individuals that differ in two characteristics, such as stem length and seed shape in pea plants. Genes that are on different pairs of homologous chromosomes are separated independently, and all combinations of the alleles are possible.

■ Where one of the alleles of each gene is dominant, a 9:3:3:1 ratio of phenotypes results from a cross between the heterozygotes.

■ If two genes are linked together on the same pair of chromosomes, the alleles remain linked during meiosis, unless crossing over takes place between them.

7.5 Sex determination

Whether a baby develops as a girl or as a boy depends not on a single gene but on a pair of chromosomes. These are the X and Y chromosomes, which you can see in the karyotype in the photograph on page 96. The

karyotype has one X chromosome and a much smaller Y chromosome – this set of chromosomes was taken from a male. A female has two X chromosomes.

Fig 7.12 shows how the sex of a baby is determined. The proportion of males and females is kept more or less balanced in the population by this method.

The full details that explain how the chromosomes actually determine the sex of the child are not yet known. As the Y chromosome is much smaller than the X, many of the genes that are present on the X chromosome are missing from the Y. However, there is one gene, the SRY gene, which is thought to be the key to maleness. It is situated on the Y chromosome but is absent from the X chromosome. This gene causes the developing reproductive organs to become testes rather than ovaries. It is probable that the hormones that the testes produce then stimulate other male features to develop. However, there may well be other genes involved.

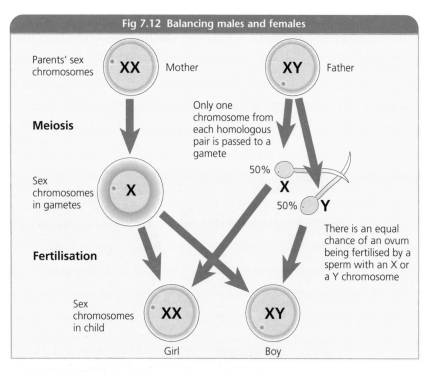

Fig 7.12 Balancing males and females

Parents' sex chromosomes: XX Mother, XY Father

Only one chromosome from each homologous pair is passed to a gamete

Meiosis

Sex chromosomes in gametes: X, 50% X, 50% Y

There is an equal chance of an ovum being fertilised by a sperm with an X or a Y chromosome

Fertilisation

Sex chromosomes in child: XX Girl, XY Boy

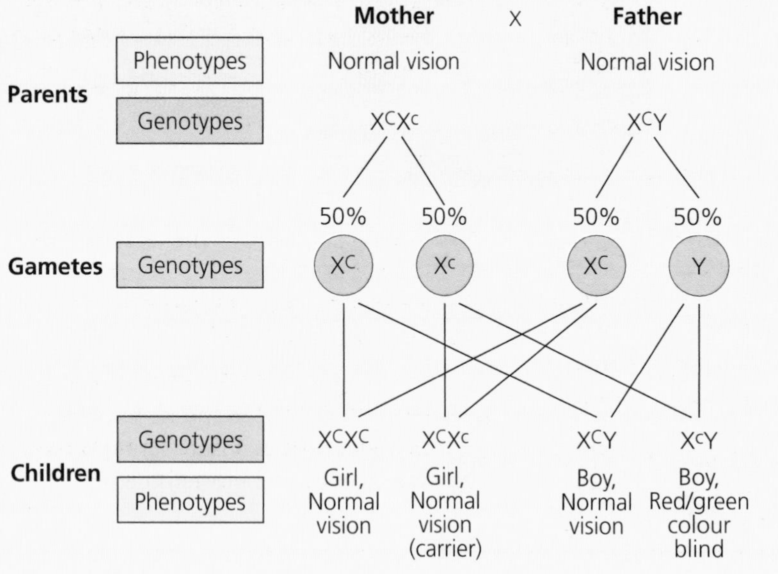

19

a Does the ovum or sperm determine whether a baby is a boy or a girl? Explain your answer.

b Dairy farmers may want all their calves to develop into cows for milk production. The cows in the herd are artificially inseminated, that is sperm is collected from a bull and injected into each cow's vagina. Suggest how, in principle, it would be possible to ensure that only cows are produced.

c What problems do you think would arise if parents could choose the sex of their child?

Sex linkage

The X and Y chromosomes are not just concerned with sex determination – they also have genes for other characteristics. As the X chromosome is much larger than the Y, many of these genes occur on the X chromosome but not on the Y. This means that the pattern of inheritance of affected genes is linked to the sex of the individual.

One gene that occurs only on the X chromosome affects a pigment in the retina

Fig 7.13 Colour blindness

In genetic diagrams, a sex-linked gene is shown alongside the sex chromosome. In red/green colour blindness, the allele for normal colour vision is C, and the mutant is c. A chromosome with the normal allele is written X^C, and with a mutant allele, X^c. The Y chromosome has no gene for this characteristic.

Mother x **Father**

Parents
- Phenotypes: Normal vision | Normal vision
- Genotypes: $X^C X^c$ | $X^C Y$

Gametes
- Genotypes: 50% X^C, 50% X^c | 50% X^C, 50% Y

Children
- Genotypes: $X^C X^C$ | $X^C X^c$ | $X^C Y$ | $X^c Y$
- Phenotypes: Girl, Normal vision | Girl, Normal vision (carrier) | Boy, Normal vision | Boy, Red/green colour blind

Sex can be confusing

Genetic abnormalities can confuse the difference between male and female. In the introduction to Chapter 8 in the AS book, we saw that examination of stained cells with a light microscope can usually identify that an individual is female. This is because one of the X chromosomes is inactivated early in development. It forms a distinctive dark blob, called the Barr body (See the photograph below). However this is not totally reliable as a sex test, and a more reliable technique uses the polymerase chain reaction to make copies of the SRY gene.

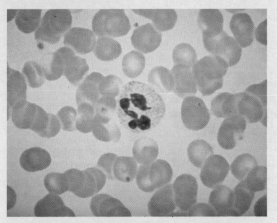

A light micrograph of a white blood cell, surrounded by red blood cells. The white blood cell has a large nucleus with five lobes. On the right of the top lobe, you can see a drumstick-shape sticking out. This is the condensed X chromosome, or Barr body.

A variety of chromosomal abnormalities can obscure the distinction between the sexes. For example about 1 girl in 3000 has only one X chromosome in each body cell. This is called Turner's syndrome. The condition often results in late or non-development of secondary sexual characteristics and infertility. It is also quite common for individuals to have extra sex chromosomes. In Klinefelter's syndrome, an individual has a chromosome complement of XXY. People with XXX, XXXY, XYY and various other combinations are also not unusual. It is possible to have females with XX chromosomes who have abnormally masculine bodies and muscle strength because their adrenal glands do not respond to female hormones in the usual way. It is also possible for people with female body shape and muscle strength to have XY chromosomes, because their cells do not respond to male hormones as normal.

1
a How many chromosomes would a person with Turner's syndrome have in their body cells? Explain your answer
b How many SRY genes are present in each cell of a normal adult male? Explain your answer.

2 For which of the following chromosome complements would you expect the person to show male characteristics and which would be female: XXY, XXX, XYY, XXXY. Explain your answer.

3
a Explain how the polymerase chain reaction would make copies of the SRY gene.
b Suggest why this is a more reliable method of sex testing than looking for the presence of a Barr body.

of the eye. A mutant allele of this gene causes red/green colour blindness. This means the sufferer cannot distinguish between red and green. Since males have only one X chromosome, they have only one copy of this gene. If this gene is the mutant allele they will be red/green colour blind. Females will only be red/green colour blind if they inherit the allele on both chromosomes. This explains why this type of colour blindness is much more common in men than women.

Males have a 1 in 2 chance of inheriting the condition if their mother carries the mutant allele, as shown in Fig 7.13.

20
a What percentage of the children from the cross shown in Fig 7.13 is colour blind? What percentage of girls and what percentage of boys?

b What parental genotypes could produce a red/green colour blind girl?

c Explain why a son never inherits red/green colour blindness from his father.

Haemophilia as an example of a sex-linked disorder

Haemophilia is an inherited disease in which the blood fails to clot easily. Haemophiliacs suffer from internal bleeding, especially in the joints, and the commonest reason is shortage of a blood clotting protein known as Factor VIII. The gene for Factor VIII synthesis occurs only on the X chromosome, so it is sex-linked. Males are much more likely to inherit haemophilia because they have only one copy of the X chromosome. Females can carry the alleles, and pass it on to their sons, but they themselves show no signs of haemophilia.

The normal allele that produces Factor VIII is written as X^H, and the recessive allele that results in failure to produce Factor VIII is X^h.

Genetic counselling can help people to decide whether or not to have children. Couples whose babies are at risk from a serious genetic disorder like haemophilia may choose to have tests during the early stages of pregnancy and perhaps opt for an abortion if the embryo is affected. When a haemophiliac man marries a woman who does not have haemophilia, the couple may opt for genetic testing to find out if the woman is carrying the allele for haemophilia. This would be very unlikely but if it were the case, all boy children born to the couple would be haemophiliacs and all girl children would be carriers. Under these circumstances, the couple may make an informed decision not to have children at all.

If the woman is not carrying the allele, none of their children will have the disorder, because sons will inherit an X chromosome with a normal allele from their mother. None of the boys will carry the gene for haemophilia so they cannot pass it on to

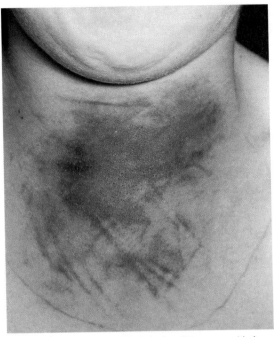

Haemophilia is a disorder of blood clotting. This woman with the disease shows extensive bleeding under the skin of her neck, caused by scratching.

their children. However, the girls will carry the haemophilia allele, because they inherit one of their X chromosomes from their father and this must carry the recessive allele. Later in life, they should be aware that they have a 50% chance of their sons having haemophilia, assuming that they do not themselves marry a haemophiliac.

21

a What is the genotype of a haemophiliac male?

b Haemophiliac females are very rare. What would be the most likely genotypes of the parents of a haemophiliac girl?

1 Fig 7.Q1 shows some stages in the formation of a mammalian egg cell.

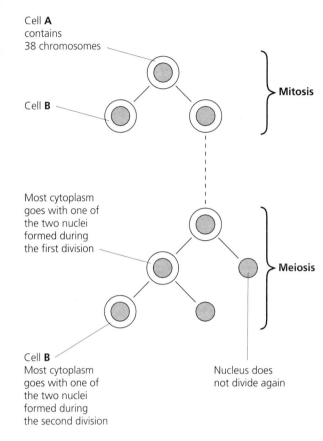

Cell **A**
contains
38 chromosomes

Cell **B**

Mitosis

Most cytoplasm
goes with one of
the two nuclei
formed during
the first division

Meiosis

Cell **B**
Most cytoplasm
goes with one of
the two nuclei
formed during
the second division

Nucleus does
not divide again

Fig 7.Q1

a How many chromosomes will there be in
  i cell B; (1)
  ii cell C? (1)

b Suggest **one** advantage in the way in which the cytoplasm divides during meiosis. (1)

c Describe and explain **two** ways in which the events of meiosis cause the egg cells to be genetically different from one another. (4)

Total (7)

BY02 June 1998 Q7

2 During meiosis the homologous chromosomes sometimes fail to separate, and the resulting gametes have two sets of chromosomes. When such a gamete takes part in fertilisation, the offspring that is produced also has an extra set of chromosomes. In plants such offspring, even though they have increased numbers of chromosomes, are often viable. Having one or more extra sets of chromosomes is called polyploidy.

Einkorn wheat was first cultivated about 12 000 years ago. Fig 7.Q2 shows how modern bread wheat has been produced by a combination of polyploidy and hybridisation. The figures in brackets show the number of chromosomes in the somatic (body) cells of each species.

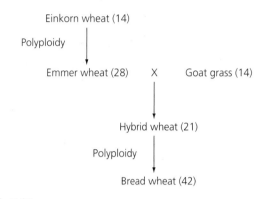

Einkorn wheat (14)

Polyploidy

Emmer wheat (28)   X   Goat grass (14)

Hybrid wheat (21)

Polyploidy

Bread wheat (42)

Fig 7.Q2

a How many chromosomes would there normally be in a gamete produced by:
  i goat grass;
  ii emmer wheat? (1)

b Suggest why the hybrid wheat produced by crossing emmer wheat and goat grass was sterile. (1)

c Describe two advantages of the hybridisation of emmer wheat with goat grass. (2)

Total (4)

BY07 February 1997 Q7

3 Fig 7.Q3 shows the pathway by which phenylalanine is normally metabolised.

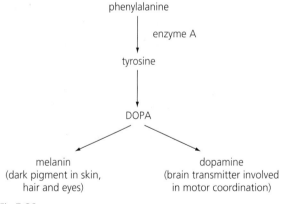

phenylalanine

enzyme A

tyrosine

DOPA

melanin
(dark pigment in skin,
hair and eyes)

dopamine
(brain transmitter involved
in motor coordination)

Fig 7.Q2

Phenylketonuria (PKU) is a condition which results from the absence of enzyme A. People with PKU are homozygous for a recessive allele which fails to produce this enzyme.

a Use the information shown in the diagram to give one symptom you might expect to be visible in a person who inherits PKU. (1)

b Explain how gene mutation may result in an allele which fails to produce a functional enzyme. (3)

c

i A child with PKU was born to two unaffected parents. Copy and complete the genetic diagram below to show how this is possible. (2)

Parental phenotypes

Parental genotypes

Genotypes of gametes

Genotypes of children

Phenotypes children

ii What is the probability that a second child born to these parents will have PKU? (1)

Total (7)

BY02 June 1999 Q4

4

a Use a genetic diagram to explain how equal numbers of male and female offspring are produced in humans. (2)

b Explain why the sperms produced by a man are genetically different from each other. (2)

c In honeybees the sex of the offspring is determined by the female parent, the queen. The queen honeybee mates early in her lifetime, and stores the sperm in her body for use during the rest of her life.

Cell	Haploid or diploid
Female honeybee body cell	Diploid
Male honeybee body cell	
Honeybee ovum	
Honeybee sperm	

Table 7.Q4

She produces a female by fertilising an ovum as it passes the store of sperms. She produces a male by allowing an ovum to pass the store without releasing sperms onto it.

i Using this information, copy and complete Table 7.Q4 to show which of the cells are haploid and which are diploid. (2)

ii Explain why the sperms produced by a male honeybee are genetically identical to each other. (1)

Total (7)

BY02 March 2000 Q1

5

a The gene for the shape of radish roots has two alleles, long (C^L) and round (C^R).

Heterozygous radishes (C^LC^R) have roots which are oval in shape.

A crop of radish plants with oval roots pollinate amongst themselves. Complete the genetic diagram to show the outcome.

Parental genotypes C^LC^R C^LC^R

Genotypes of gametes

Genotypes of offspring

Phenotypes of offspring

Ratio of phenotypes of offspring

(3)

b The appearance of the coat in rabbits is controlled by two genes which are on different chromosomes. The gene for colour has two alleles, black (B) and brown (b). The gene for colour distribution has two alleles, spotted (D) and plain (d).

A black, spotted rabbit (genotype BbDd) is crossed with a brown, spotted rabbit (genotype bbDd).

Complete the genetic diagram at the top of the page opposite to show the outcome.

Parental genotypes   **BbDd**   **bbDd**

Genotypes of gametes

Genotypes of offspring

Phenotypes of offspring

Ratio of phenotypes of offspring

(4)

Total (7)

BY02 February 1997 Q5

6 It has been suggested that a gene for fur colour in rabbits is sex-linked and is carried on the X chromosome. With this gene, the allele for black fur, b, is recessive to that for white fur, B.

a Copy and complete the genetic diagram below to show the expected result of a cross between a white male rabbit and a black female. (3)

Phenotypes of parents	Male white	Female black

Genotypes of parents

Genotypes of gametes

Genotypes of offspring

Phenotypes of offspring

b How would such results show that the gene was not carried on an autosome (a non-sex chromosome)? (1)

Total (4)

BY02 June 1998 Q5

7 The allele for Rhesus positive, R, is dominant to that for Rhesus negative, r. Haemophilia is a sex-linked condition. The allele for haemophilia, h, is recessive to the allele for normal blood clotting, H, and is carried on the X-chromosome. Fig 7.Q7 shows the Rhesus blood group phenotypes in a family tree where some individuals have haemophilia.

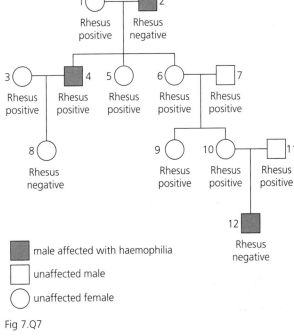

■ male affected with haemophilia

□ unaffected male

○ unaffected female

Fig 7.Q7

l

  i Use the information in the diagram to give one piece of evidence that the allele for the Rhesus negative condition is recessive. (1)

  ii Explain the evidence from the cross between individuals 3 and 4 that the gene controlling Rhesus blood group is not sex-linked. (2)

b Give the full genotype of
  i individual 6; (1)
  ii individual 12. (1)

c What is the probability that the next child of couple 10 and 11 will have the same genotype as the first child? Show your working. (3)

Total (8)

BY02 June 2000 Q5

People vary but we all take it for granted that we can recognise each other by our distinctive physical features. Some of the more obvious characteristics are used to group people into races, but closer analysis shows patterns of differences that do not match with generally accepted racial groups. Our genes suggest that we share many more similarities than differences.

Each human being has around thirty-five thousand functional genes. Of these, about two-thirds seem to be identical in all individuals. The other third are genes that have two or more alleles. These alleles combine in a vast number of different ways, so no two fertilised ova are exactly the same. It is rather like doing the pools with 30 thousand teams!

Two randomly chosen people of the same race have 85% to 88% of their genes in common. If the two people happen to be from different races, the proportion changes by less than 2%. Though small, this difference is finding an unexpected application – in archaeology. When a set of bones is unearthed, tests can be done to find out more about the person and their life. Analysis of their carbon and nitrogen isotopes can reveal how much meat and fish they ate, and DNA analysis can reveal their racial origins. Key sequences in the human genome are known to be a 'fingerprint' of people whose ancestors lived in, say, the middle East, or Roman Britain. These sophisticated techniques can supplement the more traditional techniques used in archaeology to build up an accurate picture of the past.

No two faces in a crowd are the same.

A reconstruction of a human face based on information provided by the shape of a skull found during an archaeological dig.

8.1 Introduction to our differences

In this chapter we look at how the differences arise between individuals of the same species. Both genetic and environmental factors contribute to variation. It is variation that has made evolution possible. We will see how variation results in some individuals being better equipped for survival than others and how the idea of 'survival of the fittest' is the basis of Darwin's theory of natural selection. We also study the evidence that evolution really has happened as a result of natural selection.

You will need to be familiar with meiosis and fertilisation from Chapter 7 of this book. You will also need to understand how new alleles of genes can be produced by mutation, as described in Chapter 6 of the AS book.

Discontinuous variation

Sometimes, variation in a characteristic may be very clear-cut, such as the distinction between being hairy or hairless. This is **discontinuous variation**. More often, especially in humans, there is a range of variation, e.g. from tall to short, and this is called **continuous variation**.

A good example of discontinuous variation is the human blood grouping system. We saw in Chapter 7 (page 107) that all human beings have one of four major blood groups, A, B, AB or O. Each of us must be one of these four possible phenotypes. You cannot be halfway between groups A and O, or just slightly blood group B. Such variation is called discontinuous because each of the phenotypes is quite distinct. Discontinuous variation is caused by differences in a single gene. As we saw on page 107, blood group is determined by a single gene, one that has three alleles, I^A, I^B and I^O. Alleles I^A and I^B code for the production of a cell surface protein – you either have it, or you don't. There are no states in between. Furthermore, your blood group depends entirely on which alleles you inherit from your parents. Your blood group is not affected by environmental factors, such as the amount or type of food you eat.

Knowledge of the ABO blood groups is vital for doctors performing blood transfusions. If the blood is not matched correctly between donor and recipient, the result can be fatal. Other cell surface proteins are also important when doing tissue typing for organ transplants. These antigens are found on the surface of white blood cells. Two of the most important are known to have at least 23 and 47 alleles respectively. Each produces a slightly different antigen molecule, which can be detected by a technique called human leucocyte antigen (HLA) typing.

If HLA antigens are not matched well between organ donor and recipient, the result is not as dramatic as transfusing ill-matched blood, but it is just as deadly. After a few days, a host-versus-graft reaction takes place and cells from the immune system of the person who has been given the new organ go to work. The transplant is treated as a foreign organism. The same processes that destroy disease-causing bacteria and viruses come into play. The cells of the new organ are damaged and it starts to die.

HLA genes also show discontinuous variation, even though they have such a large repertoire of alleles. Each antigen produced is still distinctly different – you either have one or you don't. Any characteristic that shows two or more clear-cut phenotypes is described as showing discontinuous variation. Eye colour in humans is another good example.

However, do not be misled into thinking that discontinuous variation is limited to humans. There are, in fact, rather few examples in mammals; discontinuous variation is much more common in plants and other less complex organisms. The features of Mendel's garden peas, such as round and wrinkled peas, are also quotable examples of discontinuous variation for exam answers.

Continuous variation

In humans, most characteristics show continuous variation. This type of variation is called continuous because it is difficult to sort out all the possible types into distinct groups. It is not only physical characteristics, such as mass, length of big toe, hair colour and nose shape that have a range of continuous variation, but also metabolic characteristics such as rate of heart beat, speed of reaction, muscle efficiency and the ability of the brain to process information (or 'intelligence', or whatever we choose to call it!).

Characteristics that vary continuously are usually the result of several different genes acting in such a complex way that it is not possible to distinguish separate phenotypes. A person's height depends on many different factors, including the growth rate of several different bones, hormone production and metabolic rate. Each factor may be controlled directly, or indirectly, by several genes. In most cases the interaction of different genes causes the majority of individuals to lie near the middle of the range, with many fewer at the extremes. For example, very tall and very small adults are rare – most people are clustered around the 'average' heights for men and women. This range and distribution

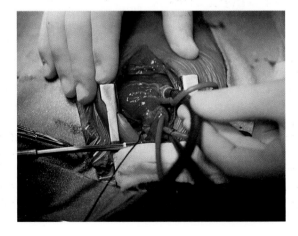

A heart transplant in progress. Donors for heart transplants must be matched carefully with the recipient to avoid the new heart being rejected. It is rare to find two people with similar HLA antigen patterns – which is why it can be so difficult to find an organ for someone who is desperately ill.

Ian Wright and Kate Sharman with Rhadouane Charbib, the World's tallest man; he is a shade under 7 feet 9 inches (236 cm).

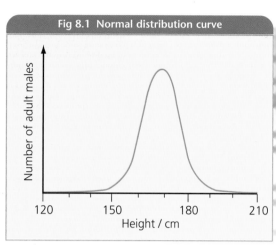

Fig 8.1 Normal distribution curve

can be illustrated in a graph called a **normal distribution curve** (Fig 8.1).

Continuous variation and the environment

Characteristics that vary continuously are also subject to interaction with the environment. A person's adult height may well be affected by diet or disease during childhood. Often it is very difficult to distinguish the contributions made by genes and by environmental factors. For instance, there is

much disagreement between scientists about intelligence. Is it determined by a person's genes? Or is it solely to do with their environment? Probably the true answer lies somewhere between the two.

1 Which of the graphs or bar charts in Fig 8.2 shows the number of individuals in a population for each of the following characteristics? In each case give a reason for your answer.

a Human ABO blood groups.

b Human earwax type, which is either wet or dry and is determined by a gene with two alleles. It is unaffected by environmental factors.

c Human mass, which is determined by several genes and is affected by environmental factors.

d Tall and dwarf peas, determined by a gene with two alleles and affected by environmental factors.

2 What environmental factors might affect how tall a plant grows?

The effect of temperature on the pigment gene in Siamese cats, as described in Chapter 7 on page 108, is another good example of how environmental factors can affect continuously variable characteristics. However, alligators provide one of the most interesting illustrations of the interaction between genes and the environment. In these ancient reptiles, temperature affects the genes that determine sex. Eggs incubated at 30 °C all develop into females; eggs incubated at 33 °C become males. The position and depth of a nest can therefore affect whether male or female young are produced. This means that alligators can produce more females than

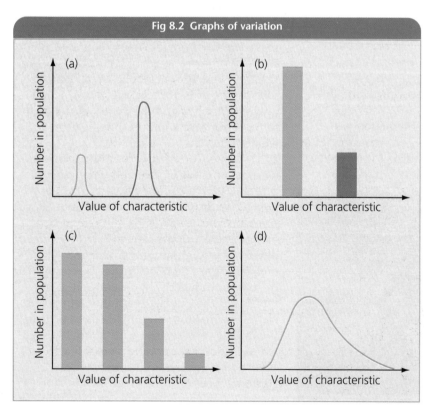

Fig 8.2 Graphs of variation

(a) Number in population / Value of characteristic

(b) Number in population / Value of characteristic

(c) Number in population / Value of characteristic

(d) Number in population / Value of characteristic

An alligator on its nest of eggs in Florida.

males, and in practice there may be as many as eight females for every male.

It is becoming clear that many people have alleles of genes that make them more likely to develop certain diseases, such as some forms of cancer. However, the disease may only occur if the genes are triggered by something, such as a chemical, in the environment. This may, for example, explain why many heavy smokers develop lung cancer in middle age, whereas others carry on well into old age without being affected.

3 Explain how the phenotype of Siamese cats is affected by the effect of temperature on the pigment gene.

4

a Suggest an advantage of alligators having a ratio of eight females to one male in a population.

b How might rising environmental temperatures affect the alligator population?

APPLICATION **Genetics and human history**

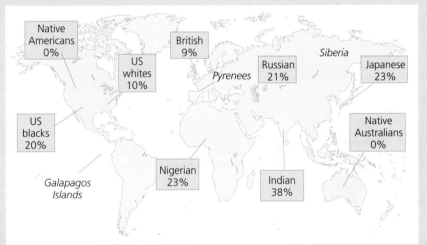

Native Americans 0%

US whites 10%

British 9%

Pyrenees

Russian 21%

Siberia

Japanese 23%

US blacks 20%

Galapagos Islands

Nigerian 23%

Indian 38%

Native Australians 0%

By studying the distribution of blood groups and HLA types it is possible to build up a picture of the complex patterns of migration that have taken place in human history. It seems that the first humans originated in Africa and then spread around the world. Study of the genes of the native (original) inhabitants of North and South America suggests that a small group of people, with a limited range of alleles of some genes, reached North America from Siberia and then gradually populated the continent.

The map above shows the different proportions of people with blood group B in some populations in different parts of the world.

1 It is suggested that none of the group of people that reached North America from Siberia carried the blood group allele, I^B.
  a What evidence from the map supports this suggestion?
  b Which two blood groups would you expect to be absent in these people, and which genotypes would you expect to be present?

2 a Is the occurrence of blood group B correlated with skin colour? Use evidence from the map to explain your answer.
  b How might the different proportions of group B in US blacks and US whites be explained?

3 Most West European populations have about 9 or 10% with blood group B. However, the Basque people, who live in the Pyrenees have a much lower percentage.
  a What does this suggest about the origins of the Basque people?
  b What additional information might now be available to help confirm relationships between peoples from different parts of the world?

KEY FACTS

- There are many differences between individuals of the same species. This is **variation**.

- Variation results from both genetic and environmental influences.

- Where only one or a small number of genes cause the variation in a characteristic, there are clear-cut differences. This is **discontinuous variation**.

- Where many genes and environmental factors are involved, there is a range of variation, without distinct types. This is **continuous variation**.

8.2 What causes variation?

Table 8.1 summarises the main causes of genetic variation. Most of these you will have already have come across in other parts of the course.

5 Which of the causes of variation in Table 8.1 could cause the offspring of an asexually reproducing organism to differ from the parent?

6 What could cause identical twins to differ from one another? Explain your answer.

7 Why do the two unfertilised ova which give rise to non-identical twins differ from each other?

These two girls are identical twins.

Arnold Schwarzenegger and Danny DeVito are non-identical twins!

Only their mother can tell them apart.

The advantages of variation

Despite the wide range of variation, people of all nationalities are quite clearly human beings. Human beings always give birth to human beings; cats always produce cats; earthworms produce earthworms; and so on. Why, then, do so many species reproduce sexually and thereby boost the amount of variation? What are the advantages of individuals of the same species being different? Why don't members of the same species become more and more alike until they have produced the perfect specimen? Alternatively, why do members of a species not become more and more varied until they are no longer remotely similar to each other?

Fig 8.3 shows a theoretical model of how a group of rodents on an isolated island might change as a result of variation over a period of time. This model is simple compared with what happens in a real ecosystem. However, you can see that even quite a small selective advantage or disadvantage can, over just a few generations, have a significant effect on a particular phenotype.

Despite the broad range of variation, you might predict that, in time, all the unfavourable alleles would disappear from the population and that the rodents would all be homozygous for the favourable alleles.

Table 8.1 .The main causes of genetic variation	
Cause of variation	**How the variation is produced**
Gene mutation	An error occurs during replication of the DNA of a gene. A change in the order of bases alters the amino acid sequence in the protein encoded by the gene. (AS Biology, Chapter 6, page 100).
Independent assortment	During meiosis the maternal and paternal chromosomes are reshuffled. The chromosomes of each parent, and so the alleles of the genes, can combine in new ways. (This book, Chapter 7, page 102.)
Crossing over	During the first stage of meiosis, sections of the chromatids in bivalents are exchanged. Blocks of genes are moved and linked alleles may separate and rejoin in new combinations. (This book, Chapter 7, page 103.)
Chromosome mutation	During cell division sections of chromosomes are sometimes displaced, for example, as the chromatids are pulled apart during anaphase. This can result in genes being deleted or duplicated, or in sequences of genes being inverted.
Random fertilisation	Each parent is genetically different and can produce huge numbers of gametes. The alleles on the chromosomes of these gametes will differ. Which pair of gametes fuses during fertilisation is a matter of chance, and totally random. (This book, Chapter 7, page 102.)
Environmental factors	The expression of genes may be affected by factors such as diet, disease or temperature during development. (Section 8.1 of this chapter, page 120). Mutagenic agents may cause gene mutations in tissues, which then grow abnormally. (AS Biology, Chapter 6, page 101.)

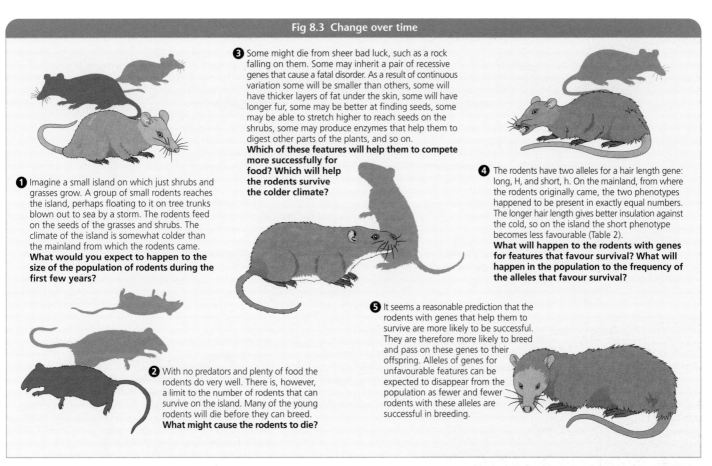

Fig 8.3 Change over time

1 Imagine a small island on which just shrubs and grasses grow. A group of small rodents reaches the island, perhaps floating to it on tree trunks blown out to sea by a storm. The rodents feed on the seeds of the grasses and shrubs. The climate of the island is somewhat colder than the mainland from which the rodents came. **What would you expect to happen to the size of the population of rodents during the first few years?**

2 With no predators and plenty of food the rodents do very well. There is, however, a limit to the number of rodents that can survive on the island. Many of the young rodents will die before they can breed. **What might cause the rodents to die?**

3 Some might die from sheer bad luck, such as a rock falling on them. Some may inherit a pair of recessive genes that cause a fatal disorder. As a result of continuous variation some will be smaller than others, some will have thicker layers of fat under the skin, some will have longer fur, some may be better at finding seeds, some may be able to stretch higher to reach seeds on the shrubs, some may produce enzymes that help them to digest other parts of the plants, and so on. **Which of these features will help them to compete more successfully for food? Which will help the rodents survive the colder climate?**

4 The rodents have two alleles for a hair length gene: long, H, and short, h. On the mainland, from where the rodents originally came, the two phenotypes happened to be present in exactly equal numbers. The longer hair length gives better insulation against the cold, so on the island the short phenotype becomes less favourable (Table 2). **What will happen to the rodents with genes for features that favour survival? What will happen in the population to the frequency of the alleles that favour survival?**

5 It seems a reasonable prediction that the rodents with genes that help them to survive are more likely to be successful. They are therefore more likely to breed and pass on these genes to their offspring. Alleles of genes for unfavourable features can be expected to disappear from the population as fewer and fewer rodents with these alleles are successful in breeding.

In practice, however, things change. In this example the climate of the island might become even colder or might warm up. Some new predators might reach the island. As a result of the rodents feeding on the plants, there might be a change in the plant populations; for example it might be that only very prickly shrubs or shrubs that produced fruits with a very hard shell, or poisonous flesh, were able to survive.

Table 8.2 Percentages of genotype hh

Generation	% of genotype hh failing to breed		
	2%	10%	50%
0	50	50	50
5	48	40	11
10	46	31	4
15	44	24	2
20	42	18	1

8 In the model in Fig 8.3, what factors could limit the size of the population that can live on the island?

9

a Suppose that each pair of rodents produces about 20 young in a year. What would happen to the population if all of these young survived and bred?

b If the adults live on average for only a year, how many of these young must survive if the size of the population is to stay roughly constant?

10

a Table 8.2 shows the percentage of short-haired rodents in the population on the island when different percentages fail to breed in each generation. Draw a graph to show the data in Table 8.2.

b Assuming that the population stayed constant at 10 000, how many individuals would show the phenotype of the recessive allele after 20 generations at each of the three selection pressures?

c What would happen to the frequency of the h allele in the population in each case?

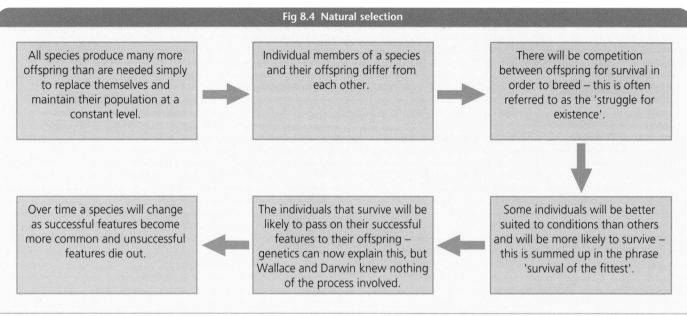

Fig 8.4 Natural selection

All species produce many more offspring than are needed simply to replace themselves and maintain their population at a constant level. → Individual members of a species and their offspring differ from each other. → There will be competition between offspring for survival in order to breed – this is often referred to as the 'struggle for existence'.

↓

Over time a species will change as successful features become more common and unsuccessful features die out. ← The individuals that survive will be likely to pass on their successful features to their offspring – genetics can now explain this, but Wallace and Darwin knew nothing of the process involved. ← Some individuals will be better suited to conditions than others and will be more likely to survive – this is summed up in the phrase 'survival of the fittest'.

11 Suggest why a dominant allele for an unfavourable condition is likely to disappear from a population by selection more rapidly than a recessive allele for an unfavourable condition.

The theory of natural selection

The ideas that you have just worked through form the basis of Charles Darwin's **theory of natural selection**. Alfred Russel Wallace independently came up with much the same hypothesis, and it was his pressure that persuaded Darwin to publish his ideas in 1858. The idea of evolution had been around for many years; the ancient Greeks had proposed it well over 2000 years before Darwin. Darwin's theory was put forward as an explanation of how evolution could have occurred.

Fig 8.4 shows the main steps in the theory of natural selection. Other ideas had been suggested before, but Darwin was the first

Darwin was ridiculed by many for the suggestion that humans had evolved by natural selection from ape-like ancestors, and the lack of direct evidence was often used to dismiss Darwin's ideas.

scientist to supply detailed supporting evidence for his theory. He pointed out that artificial selection of features when breeding animals can produce startling changes within a few generations. Today, the breeds of dog that have been produced in the last 100 years or so are a good example of this. At the time, however, Darwin could not provide direct evidence that natural selection had produced change in a particular species, and many people challenged his explanations.

Since Darwin's time evidence has been accumulated in support of his theory. One well-documented example of change involves the peppered moth, *Biston betularia*. The typical form of peppered moth has white wings speckled with black scales in an irregular pattern. Collections of moths from about 1850 show that at this time almost all peppered moths in Britain were this speckled form.

All of these varieties were produced by artificial selection from wild dogs. Without human intervention, most would not survive.

Peppered moth, *Biston betularia*, resting on a birch trunk.

The melanic form of peppered moth has wings that are almost entirely black. It appeared quite suddenly: a small number of specimens first appear in moth collections made after 1850, just after the industrial revolution had begun. By the end of the century nearly all the peppered moths in some areas, such as around Manchester, were melanic. Over the same period of time, sulphur dioxide killed most of the lichens (compound organisms consisting of an association of fungi and algae) living on tree trunks in industrial areas, and deposits of soot particles blackened the bark.

It is important to realise that the melanic form of the moth developed as a result of natural selection after a chance mutation. It was because the environment became black and sooty that black moths could not be seen by predators, and so survived more successfully than speckled moths. The mutation was entirely random; you must not say in an exam answer the black moths were coloured by soot (it has been known...).

Wing colour in the peppered moth is controlled by a single gene, the melanic allele being dominant to the speckled allele. Intermediate phenotypes also occur in which the blackness of the wings is modified by genes at other loci. Studies of the distribution of the typical and melanic forms showed that by the 1950s in the heavily polluted parts of Britain the melanic form was by far the more common, whereas in western areas with very little pollution almost 100% of the peppered moths were still the typical speckled form.

Table 8.3 Recaptured moths		
Site where moths released	Percentage recaptured	
	Speckled	Melanic
Dorset (unpolluted)	12.5	6.3
Birmingham	15.9	34.1

12 Suggest how the theory of natural selection could explain the change from speckled to melanic forms of peppered moth in industrial areas of Britain.

13 The melanic moths spread very rapidly in industrial areas. How would the genetics of wing colour explain this rapid spread?

Although the increase in the number of melanic moths correlated with the increase in pollution, this did not prove that natural selection had occurred. It was just possible that there was some other explanation, such as that a pollutant was causing black pigment to be produced in the moths. The first step was to check that the melanics really did have a selective advantage in polluted areas. A biologist called Henry Kettlewell released marked moths of each type in an unpolluted wood in Dorset and in a polluted wood near Birmingham. He then compared the proportions of each type recaptured after a few days. The results are shown in Table 8.3.

14 Describe how the results support the hypothesis that natural selection occurred.

Next, Kettlewell attempted to establish whether the difference in survival rates really was due to differences in predation. The fact that people can see the speckled form more easily on polluted tree trunks does not prove that birds find the moths more easily. So Kettlewell placed moths of each type on tree trunks and then filmed them. He found that birds did indeed catch more of the speckled form on blackened trunks, and vice versa. More recent researchers have criticised this experiment because the moths rarely rest on exposed trunks. Usually the moths select sites such as the underside of smaller branches. Increasingly detailed knowledge of the behaviour and habits of the moth have shown that the story is more complex than was first thought. Nevertheless, the evidence strongly suggests that the melanic form has been selected in industrial areas mainly because it survives predation more successfully than the speckled form.

15 As sulphur dioxide and soot pollution are reduced, in many areas the lichens are returning and tree trunks are becoming less black. What do you predict will be the effect of natural selection on the peppered moth populations in these areas?

Darwin's finches

One hallmark of a good scientific theory is that it allows us to make predictions. One prediction that follows from the theory of natural selection is that a species will adapt to changing conditions, within the limits of its range of variation. Is there any evidence to support this prediction?

The medium ground finch lives in the Galapagos Islands, an isolated group of volcanic islands in the Pacific Ocean, about 600 miles west of South America. Darwin visited these islands and was impressed by the fact that on each island the animals and plants were slightly different. Thirteen species of finch inhabit the islands, even though few other species of small birds live there. It was this that made Darwin question the idea of Creation and the literal truth of Genesis. Why should God create different finches on each island in such an isolated group? His observations on the islands were a major influence in the development of the idea of natural selection.

The finches of the Galapagos islands have been closely studied for many years. In 1983 a significant climate change occurred when a warm ocean current brought prolonged rainfall to the normally dry islands. Many of the cacti died in the wet conditions. This reduced the supply of large, hard seeds. On the other hand, plants that produced small, soft seeds flourished. So, the range of food available to the seed-eating finches changed considerably. There was a remarkably rapid response in the population. Whereas birds with large, heavy beaks had been particularly successful in dealing with cactus seeds, they could not pick up the smaller seeds of other plants very easily.

The medium ground finches with small beaks prospered; within a few generations the mean size of beak in the population had decreased appreciably. Mathematicians predicted the change in beak size on the basis of the estimated selective advantage. The actual results closely matched their predictions. Moreover, as the climate became drier again in the following years, the trend was reversed in precisely the expected way. This adaptation to changing conditions was only possible because there was continuous variation in beak size in the population, and this variation could be inherited.

16 Another species of ground finch on the islands has a much larger beak and specialises on cactus seeds. Numbers of this species fell sharply during the very wet years. There was no adaptation of beak size such as occurred in the medium ground finches. Suggest why this species was unable to adapt to the changing conditions.

Fig 8.5 Darwin's finches

Medium ground finches on Isla Santa Cruz, Galapagos.

Equator · Galapagos Islands · Ecuador · Pacific Ocean · 0 500 km · 0 500 miles

---

■ According to the theory of natural selection, changes take place in populations because individuals with the most favourable characteristics are most likely to survive and produce young.

■ Natural selection occurs because:
- Individuals in a population are not identical. Their characteristics show a range of variation.
- Some variations are better able survive than others.
- Many more young are produced than are needed to replace their parents. Many are killed.
- Individuals with less favourable variations are more likely to die.

- Alleles of genes for favourable characteristics are passed on to offspring.
- Alleles for unfavourable characteristics are not passed on, so these alleles are selected out of the population.
- There is a gradual change in the population resulting in better adaptation to the conditions.

APPLICATION Racial differences

The oxygen available for respiration in the atmosphere at high altitudes can be half that available at sea level. Quechua Indians in Ecuador have adapted to the high altitude environment.

Large numbers of observations and experiments have shown that species can change under natural conditions, and that the changes do result from the selection of genes that increase the chances of survival. Does the same happen in humans?

Skin pigment is produced by cells in the lower part of the epidermis – the outer protective layer of the skin. People with dark skin do not have any more pigment-producing cells than pale-skinned people. The cells simply produce more of the black pigment, melanin. The production of melanin depends on an enzyme, and several genes at different loci seem to be involved in determining the amount produced. This means that there is a wide range of possible skin colours. Environmental factors are also involved. Ultra-violet light can stimulate melanin production, and many pale-skinned people look forward to getting a suntan every summer.

Nobody can be sure how the skin colour of different peoples arose. It is likely that the dark pigment provided protection from intense sunlight in tropical areas. Ultra-violet is a mutagenic agent. In pale-skinned people exposure to high levels of ultra-violet light considerably increases the chances of developing skin cancer. On the other hand, ultra-violet light also stimulates vitamin D production in the skin below the pigmented layer. Vitamin D is essential for calcium ion absorption and the growth of healthy bones and teeth. It is possible that people migrating into the duller climates of the north would not synthesise enough vitamin D, and that having little pigment in the skin was a selective advantage because more vitamin could be made in the weaker sunlight.

Other hypotheses have been suggested, for example that skin colour might be related to temperature regulation or camouflage, or even to selection of a mate, rather like the peacock's tail. There is no simple answer, since the darkness of pigmentation does not correlate across the world in any straightforward way with ultra-violet levels, temperature or any other obvious factor. It is quite probable that a number of different factors have been involved at different times and at different places in the process of selection.

Some variations are easier to explain. In Chapter 7 we saw that the sickle cell allele is common in people who live in malarial regions. It is virtually unknown in, for instance, Northern Europe where malaria does not occur. People who are heterozygous for the sickle cell allele are at an advantage in the malarial regions because they are more resistant to the parasite. Therefore they are more likely to survive and have children.

Under certain conditions individuals with some variants of a phenotype have a selective advantage and are more successful at producing offspring and passing on the relevant alleles. As conditions differ in different parts of the world, people have developed different features. The more obvious ones, such as skin colour, have been used to separate people into races. However, only a very small number of genes are responsible for these visible differences, and people from different races all share the vast majority of genes, each with a similar range of different alleles. Modern genetics shows that, although the balance may differ between people of apparently different race, this results from a continuing process of selection that ensures that humans, like other species, are best adapted to their local environment. As circumstances change, so is this balance likely to change.

1 Explain why the sickle cell allele is at a selective disadvantage in non-malarial regions.

2 The Quechua Indians live at high altitudes in the Andes in South America. Here the amount of oxygen in the atmosphere may be only half that found at sea level.
  a Quechua Indians have over 20% more red blood cells than people living near sea level. Suggest how this is likely to be a selective advantage.
  b The Quechua Indians also have particularly large lungs. Suggest how this feature may have been selected.

1

a Ladybirds are small beetles. In one species of ladybird, individuals vary in the amount of yellow and black colouring on their wing-cases. They range in colour from all yellow to all black but most individuals are between 30% and 60% black.

   i Name the type of variation shown by this example. (1)

   ii Studies have shown that the variation in colour of the wing-cases of this ladybird is mainly genetic. What does the pattern of variation suggest about the genes controlling the colour of the wing-cases? (1)

b The colour of the wing-cases in the 2-spot ladybird is determined by a single gene. The allele for red wing-cases is dominant to that for black wing-cases. In a series of mating experiments, equal numbers of homozygous males and females of the two colour forms were put together and observed. The number of matings between the different colour forms is shown in the table below.

		Male	
		red	black
Female	red	47	26
	black	39	35

Table 8.Q1

   i Give two general conclusions that might be drawn from the results of this investigation about the pattern of mating of the male ladybirds. (2)

   ii Explain how this pattern of mating could affect the frequency of these alleles in the next generation of ladybirds. (2)

Total (6)

BY02 June 1998 Q4

Table 8.Q2

Cause of variation	Percentage of total variation in mass				
	birth	1 mnth	2 mnths	4 mnths	8 mnths
Genes inherited from father	16.7	3.5	7.9	9.6	21.9
Genes inherited from mother	17.5	5.6	7.9	11.2	21.7
Sex of lamb	4.4	1.2	1.4	2.1	2.6
Age of mother	11.3	3.6	7.1	4.4	0.0
Number of young in litter	7.1	38.6	31.7	30.7	6.9
Other environmental factors	43.1	47.5	44.2	41.9	46.9

2 Table 8.Q2 (bottom left) shows the percentage of the total variation in the mass of lambs due to some genetic and environmental factors.

a Give two reasons why you would expect the mass of lambs at birth to show continuous variation. (2)

b What is the percentage of the variation at birth that is due to environmental factors? (1)

c Describe and explain the changes in the percentage of variation in mass caused by differences in the number of young born in a litter. (3)

Total (6)

BY02 March 1998 Q6

3 Cob length in maize is controlled by many genes. Two varieties of maize, Tom Thumb and Black Mexican, both homozygous for these genes, have different lengths of cobs. They were crossed to produce an F_1 generation. These F_1 plants were then self-pollinated to produce an F_2 generation. The lengths of the cobs produced by the plants in the parental, F_1 and F_2 generations are shown in Fig 8.Q3, below.

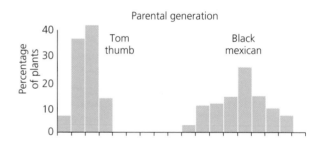

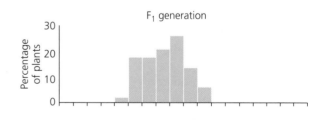

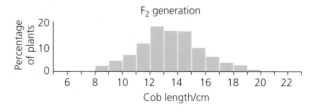

Fig 8.Q3 a, b and c

a What type of variation is shown in the F₁ generation? (1)

b Both genetic and environmental factors can cause variation.
  i Give two pieces of evidence from the graphs that genetic factors are involved in determining the length of maize cobs. (2)
  ii Describe the evidence that environmental factors are also involved in determining the length of maize cobs. (2)

c A cross was carried between a plant from the F₁ generation and a Tom Thumb plant. Sketch a graph using the axes similar to the ones below to show the expected cob lengths of the offspring. (1)

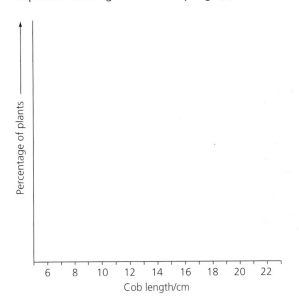

Fig 8.Q3d

Total (6)

BY02 March 2000 Q4

4 In wheat, the flag-leaf is the leaf on the stalk which carries the grain. The concentration of chlorophyll in the flag-leaf is determined by a single gene. The allele for high chlorophyll concentration, H, is dominant to the allele for low chlorophyll concentration, h.

A cross was carried out in which plants of the genotypes HH and hh were crossed to produce an F₁ generation. The plants in the F₁ generation were then allowed to interbreed to produce an F₂ generation. The graphs show the chlorophyll concentration in the flag-leaves of each of the parent plants, the F₁ generation and the F₂ generation.

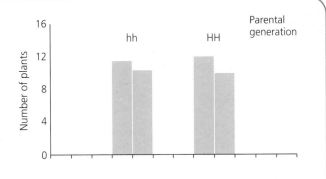

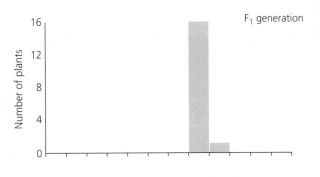

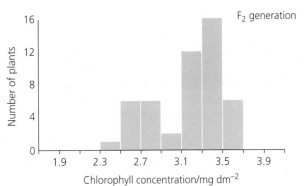

Fig 8.Q4

a What is the evidence from the graph that:
  i the allele for high chlorophyll concentration is dominant to that for low chlorophyll concentration; (1)
  ii the environment has an effect on the chlorophyll concentration of the flag-leaf? (1)

b Explain the results for the F₂ generation. (2)

c Describe the shape of the graph you would expect if you determined the concentration of chlorophyll in the flag-leaves of a group of plants obtained from a cross between an F₁ plant and a recessive homozygote, hh. (1)

Total (5)

BY02 June 1998 Q6

9 Evolution and species

Scientists have so far given a name to about two million species of living organism. Over half of these are insects. In Britain alone there are over 3500 different species of beetle. In the rainforests of the world there may well be millions of still unnamed species; one estimate says that there could be 28 million species still to find.

You may wonder how it is possible to estimate the number of unknown and unnamed species. One way is to collect, say, a hundred different species of insect from a sample area of rainforest,

The giant squid was thought to be a mythical creature until fisherman landed one in their nets, just off the coast of New Zealand in the 1980s.

or even from one species of rainforest tree. The insects are then checked against the databases of such organisations as the Natural History Museum in London to see whether they have been described and named previously. From the proportion of unnamed species in the sample it is possible to calculate the likely number of unknown species in rainforests. Although most of the new discoveries are small and apparently insignificant, there are still occasional discoveries of much larger organisms in remote situations. For example, two new species of mammal, the Giant Muntjac and the Vuquang Ox were found in the forests of south-east Asia in the 1990s.

Studies made in other habitats and of other invertebrates, plants and microorganisms such as bacteria, reveal our staggering ignorance about the vast majority of inhabitants of the planet. For example, we know little about the deep oceans, which may well conceal many species of fish and large invertebrates, such as types of squid, previously unknown to science. Huge numbers of species are destined to disappear without humans having any knowledge of them. Too often we have come to regret the havoc caused by moving a species into a new environment, such as rabbits to Australia. We know even less about the complex relationships between different species, and how the results of human activities, such as global warming, may disrupt these relationships.

9.1 Introducing biodiversity

In this chapter we will explain how vast numbers of species have evolved and also explain the system that biologists use to give them names and describe how they are related to one another. Classifying this biodiversity is a first step in understanding our environment and is important in enabling humans to live in harmony with the natural world, as we shall see in later chapters.

What is a species?

We can recognise a dog, a pig and a human as being different species because they look completely different. However, difference in appearance is not enough to distinguish one species from another. The two dogs in the photograph opposite are far from being look-alikes, yet they belong to the same species.

We describe them as different breeds, because their distinctive features are the result of **artificial selection**.

Artificial selection is a process very similar to natural selection. Dogs with specific features have been chosen as mating partners so that those features were retained in the resulting litter of puppies. For example, the Great Dane was bred for hunting large animals such as wild boar and deer stags, and mating pairs were chosen for their size and strength. The terrier was selected for its ability to follow small prey into underground burrows. Despite the great difference in size, the two dogs would mate happily with each other given half a chance. The puppies that would result from such a mating would be mongrels – dogs showing a mixture of the features of the two breeds.

A Great Dane and a Yorkshire terrier.

In some instances, different species can look very similar, e.g. the chiffchaff and willow warbler. These are difficult to tell apart, even for experienced birdwatchers. They do, however, have quite different songs, so the birds themselves are not confused. Although they may live together in the same wood, they do not interbreed.

A chiffchaff.   A willow warbler.

These two examples lead us to one of the most important features of a species; members of the same species can interbreed. There are examples however, where members of different species mate and produce offspring. A mule is the result of a mating between a

male donkey and a female horse. Donkeys and horses would not normally mate together in the wild, but do so when they are put in the same field. Genetically, donkeys and horses are quite distinct. Wild horses have 66 chromosomes but donkeys have only 62. While the mule offspring are generally healthy, they have one important deficiency; they are infertile, and so are unable to breed. They are an example of a hybrid, i.e. the offspring of closely related species or breeds.

 Use your understanding of meiosis to explain why mules are sterile.

Defining a species

From the examples we have just seen, we could say that members of a species interbreed and produce fertile offspring. But it is difficult to define a species with precision, particularly if their mating habits are not well known. Visible features are not reliable – many species of insects and roundworms, for example, can only be distinguished by careful microscopic examination, and some micro-organisms only by biochemical tests. As we saw in Chapter 8, species change due to natural selection. In practice we have to take all these aspects into account. A good working definition is therefore:

A species is a group of organisms that:
- have similar physical, biochemical and behavioural features;
- can interbreed to produce fertile offspring;
- do not normally interbreed with any other group of organisms.

How can new species develop?

Imagine that you can observe a species of animal over many thousands or even millions of years. Just as with the imaginary rodents in Chapter 8 (Fig. 8.3), you would almost certainly notice significant changes. The animals may increase in size, alter their diet, improve their camouflage and so on. As a result of random variation and natural selection, they will adapt to the conditions in which they live. The unsuitable, or unfit, individuals will be weeded out, and with them the less successful alleles. In effect, the species will move with the times.

It is important to realise that this process is random and not necessarily 'progress'. It is

A mule.   A donkey.

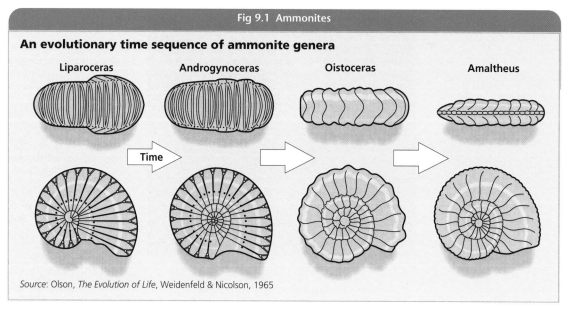

Fig 9.1 Ammonites

An evolutionary time sequence of ammonite genera

Liparoceras   Androgynoceras   Oistoceras   Amaltheus

Time

Source: Olson, *The Evolution of Life*, Weidenfeld & Nicolson, 1965

possible for changes to be reversed. A larger animal may have an advantage when food is plentiful, but it might not do so well after a drought when food is in short supply. In this situation, the smaller animals would become more successful again. There is no destination, no perfect form, towards which a species is moving.

If, instead of being able to observe the changes, what if you could obtain fossil remains from stages many years apart? Animals from different times might look so different that you would think they were different species. In fact, each fossil represents a stage in a continuous process. Often it is difficult to pin-point a specific time when a new species came into existence.

This fossil ammonite shows the appearance of the species at one point in time. Ammonites were very common in the oceans for well over a hundred million years. They were rather like modern squids, but with coiled shells that were about 2 metres in diameter in the largest specimens. Although we recognise many different species from their fossils, the fossil record also shows that some types changed very little over long periods of time.

 2 Suggest why some ammonite species may have changed very little over long periods.

In your imaginary journey back in time, you may find that the species you observe is spread over a large area. Part of the population might become separated from the rest by a river in flood, or by a volcanic eruption, or because part of the land dries out and turns to desert. Over the millions of years that you keep watch, major geological upheavals cause areas of land to split away and volcanic activity to produce new islands. The separated populations do not experience the same conditions – the climate, the food supply, the competition, the physical environment could all be significantly different. Some adaptations would be successful on one side of a mountain range, others would be favoured on the opposite side and so the separated populations would evolve in different ways.

The processes of selection that we looked at in Chapter 8 go in slightly different directions on opposite sides of the mountain. In the separated populations there will be a range of variation. Individuals will have different combinations of alleles, and gene mutation may produce new alleles. The animals with alleles that favour survival in their local environment will be more likely to pass on these alleles to their offspring. As the allele frequency changes, the phenotypes of the two populations will become more and more different. After a few million years the animals in the two locations might be quite

APPLICATION   Island isolation

One of Darwin's great achievements was the idea that the different types of finch on the Galapagos Islands could have evolved because populations of one species had been isolated on separate islands. He suggested that after the islands had formed from an erupting oceanic volcano, they had been colonised by a small selection of plants and animals that reached them by chance from the mainland of South America. Perhaps a small group of finches, all of the same species, had arrived. The finches were successful and gradually spread to all the islands. But on each island conditions were different. On each island the finches developed a specific way of feeding and living, as a result of natural selection. In each population the frequency of certain alleles changed. Birds from different islands rarely interbred, so alleles were not introduced from other populations. Gradually the finches on different islands became so different that they were, in effect, different species.

1 How would you decide whether finches from two different islands were separate species?

If Darwin was right, you would expect islands in other parts of the world to have species of plants and animals that are distinctly different from, yet recognisably similar to, species found on the nearest continental land masses. This is exactly what we do find, as in the example of the monitor lizards and Komodo dragons shown in the photographs.

2 Suggest what sort of conditions resulted in the Komodo dragons evolving to a much larger size than their ancestors on the mainland.

Monitor lizards are common in Southern Asia, and feed on carrion, insects and small mammals.

On the Indonesian island of Komodo lives a giant relative, the Komodo dragon, which is a fierce predator of deer, pigs, goats and even humans.

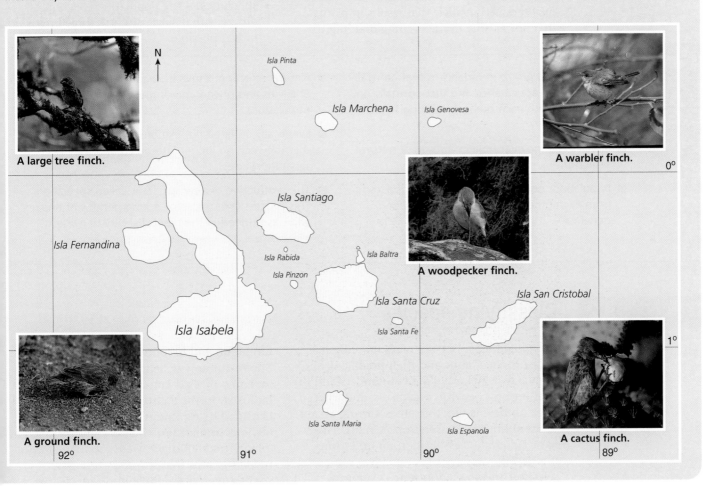

A large tree finch.

A warbler finch.

A woodpecker finch.

A ground finch.

A cactus finch.

Isla Pinta

Isla Marchena

Isla Genovesa

Isla Santiago

Isla Fernandina

Isla Rabida

Isla Baltra

Isla Pinzon

Isla Santa Cruz

Isla San Cristobal

Isla Isabela

Isla Santa Fe

Isla Santa Maria

Isla Espanola

N

0°

1°

92°   91°   90°   89°

dissimilar, both from each other and from their ancestors. They may be so different that they can no longer interbreed successfully, even if brought together again. They may have become new species.

For new species to develop, separated populations must be genetically isolated. If they live close together and can still interbreed regularly, the groups will continue to exchange alleles. They will then not separate into populations with distinct sets of alleles. Isolation is not always due to physical separation. If something happens to stop two groups of organisms from breeding, they can become genetically isolated. The natural selection process continues in both groups and may quite rapidly result in the two groups becoming genetically different. Eventually, the two groups become separate species.

To understand how this can happen, imagine a field with a species of plant that flowers all day. A mutant allele arises that causes some plants to flower only in the morning. These may attract a species of insect that flies to gather pollen only in the early part of the day. Another mutation in other plants may produce an allele that results in plants that flower only in the evening or at night.

These attract a different species of insect for pollination. Both alleles are successful, but the plants form separate populations that are pollinated by one species of insect only. They no longer exchange alleles. Further changes in phenotype can occur in both groups – slightly altered petals or stigmas could make pollination by the insect concerned even more efficient. There would then be selection for these alleles and, gradually, the two sets of plants could develop into two distinct species. The key to producing new species, called speciation, is **isolation**.

So, to summarise, new species arise as a result of:

- **isolation** – two populations are separated;

- **genetic variation** – each population contains a wide variety of alleles and therefore has a range of phenotypes among its members.

- **natural selection** – in each population the alleles which help particular phenotypes to survive in the local conditions are selected;

- **speciation** – the populations become so different that successful interbreeding is no longer possible.

KEY FACTS

- A **species** is a group of organisms that generally are similar in appearance and that normally only interbreed with each other, producing fertile offspring.

- Species change over time as a result of **natural selection**.

- Populations of a species may become isolated from each other, either geographically or genetically.

- Natural selection results in changes to the frequency of alleles and phenotypes in the separate populations.

- Eventually, isolated populations may be so different that they can no longer interbreed and they become separate species.

- The production of new species is called speciation. This process takes place over long periods of time and has resulted in the great diversity of living organisms.

9.2 Classifying species

Classifying organisms involves more than giving them a name and then producing a catalogue. It helps biologists to understand the relationships between organisms, and to keep track of the changes that are occurring as a result of human pressures on habitats. The basic system of classification, or **taxonomy** as it is called, was devised before ideas of natural selection and speciation were developed.

Linnaeus and taxonomy

The taxonomic system we use today was invented by Carl Linnaeus, a Swedish biologist, in the eighteenth century. He classified living things into groups based on obvious similarities. The large groups, such as 'plants' and 'animals', were subdivided into smaller groups that showed even closer similarities. For example birds are clearly

Taxon	Description	Example
Kingdom	The largest group. Living organisms are divided into five kingdoms (See page 137)	Animals
Phylum	Group of organisms that share a common body plan, such as having an external skeleton made of chitin and jointed limbs	Arthropods
Class	A major group within a phylum, e.g. all the arthropods with 3 pairs of jointed legs.	Insects
Order	A subset of a class, with similar features, such as all the beetle-like insects.	Beetles
Family	A group containing organisms with very similar features.	Ladybirds
Genus	A clearly closely related group within a family.	*Coccinella*
Species	A specific type of organism.	Seven-spot ladybird

Table 9.1 Overview of how organisms are classified

animals and not plants, but they are obviously similar in that they all have wings and feathers, features that distinguish them from other animals. Such a system in which large groups are split into smaller and smaller groups is called a **hierarchy**.

These are the basics of a taxonomic hierarchy:

- Organisms are classified in groups, which are further subdivided into yet more groups.

- Organisms are classified on the basis of similar or shared features. These features may be obvious, or they may be features determined by biochemical or genetic tests.

- There is no overlap between the groups; an organism must be either a bird or a reptile, for example; it cannot fall halfway between the two.

Table 9.1 shows the groups, each called a **taxon**, that we use to classify living organisms. In order to describe a species precisely, biologists use both the **genus** and **species** name, the so-called **binomial system** of Linnaeus. These names are international, understood by scientists in all countries in the world, and are often based on Latin or Greek. The binomial name for the seven-spot ladybird, for example, is *Coccinella septem-punctata* (from the Latin meaning 'bright red with seven spots').

Notice that a binomial name is always printed in italics, and that the genus name starts with a capital letter but the second word has a small letter.

The process of classification

Originally organisms were classified according to similarities in their appearance. We now know we cannot always rely on this. Species have arisen through natural selection operating over millions of years. Organisms have developed with many different adaptations. Some species will have arisen quite recently from a common ancestor, and they will share many features and genes. They can therefore be considered as close relatives. The common ancestor will itself have originated by a similar process. You can represent this process as a branching tree, with its main boughs and trunk going far back into geological time (Fig 9.2).

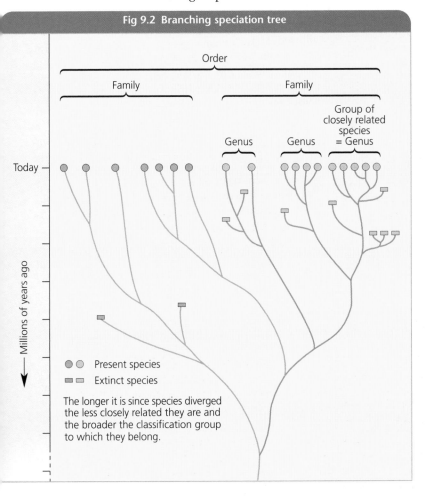

Fig 9.2 Branching speciation tree

Order

Family Family

Genus Genus Group of closely related species = Genus

Today

Millions of years ago

● ● Present species
▭ ▭ Extinct species

The longer it is since species diverged the less closely related they are and the broader the classification group to which they belong.

Modern biologists aim to reflect the ancestry of species when they classify organisms. This system of classification is said to be **phylogenetic** – it takes account of evolutionary history. To obtain evidence about evolutionary relationships, taxonomists study not only the anatomy of organisms and the fossil record, but also the structure of their proteins and DNA. New research means that detailed classification of some species is being revised as new information about how those species have evolved comes to light. However, it is never possible to be certain about the actual pathway of evolution, and scientists often disagree about how a particular species should be classified.

3 The structure of haemoglobin and of the genes responsible for haemoglobin production can provide evidence for evolutionary relationships. Suggest how these structures can provide evidence.

4 Draw a simple 'tree diagram' to show the following information:

Members of a species of bird reached three isolated islands from the mainland a million years ago. A distinct species evolved on each island. The species living near the coast on the mainland did not change. This species had evolved 5 million years ago when a mountain range was formed, separating the coastal population from another in lowland forest. The lowland forest species died out 2 million years ago when the climate became much drier and the forest disappeared.

5 Which kingdoms include organisms that:
a are single cells?
b have cell walls made of cellulose?
c can photosynthesise?
d have mitochondria?

APPLICATION   **The naked ape**

Humans differ from other primates in that most parts of the body are hairless and they walk entirely on two legs, as well as having a much larger brain. Biologists have speculated for many years about how these features evolved, and several hypotheses have been put forward. The article describes one suggestion.

1 If Professor Wheeler's hypothesis is correct, how might natural selection have resulted in hominids losing most of their body hair and becoming 'naked'?

2 Suggest why a larger brain would require a more efficient cooling system.

3 Another hypothesis is that early hominids evolved around shores, lagoons or lakes, where they moved around in shallow water. It would be an advantage to be able to stand upright and keep the head above water. Support for this idea derives from pollen analysis of deposits from 2 to 3 millions years ago, which indicates that most of Africa was forested at the time and that grassland plains were uncommon.
Suggest how each of the following hominid features might support this 'aquatic origin' hypothesis.
a There is a much thicker layer of fat under the skin than in other primates.
b Their teeth are smaller and less suited to chewing tough vegetation.
c New-born babies can float and swim.
d Humans produce large quantities of dilute urine.
e Humans can deliberately stop breathing for short periods, whereas in other primates breathing is not under voluntary control.

4 Can you think of counter-arguments to the hypothesis suggested in Question 3?

Men and women walk tall to stay cool. Researchers have shown that a two-legged gait allowed early humans to screen out most of the searing heat of our equatorial African homeland.

Instead of beating down on our backs, the sun's rays would have fallen vertically on our heads – a far smaller area. We would have kept cooler and have needed less precious water, giving us a kickstart to biological supremacy.

In addition, cool humans would no longer have needed the thick pelts that shield other animals on the grassland plains from the sun. So we became naked apes. Also, 'by walking on two feet, humans developed the animal world's most powerful cooling system, and that allowed us to acquire large brains', said Professor Peter Wheeler of John Moores University in Liverpool.

To demonstrate this theory, Professor Wheeler made a model of *Australopithecus*, which he named Boris. This model could be bent to either an upright or four-legged position while the movements of the sun overhead were simulated. A camera recorded the area exposed to the rays of the sun. 'We discovered that there was a 60% reduction in the heat received by Boris in his two-legged position compared with his quadruped posture', reported the Professor. He also calculated that far more of the body is raised away from the heat radiating from the hot ground, and that only just over half as much water would be lost in sweat.

Source: adapted from article by Robin McKie, *The Observer*, 14 November 1993

Kingdom Animalia

- Includes all the invertebrates such as jellyfish, roundworms, arthropods and molluscs, as well as vertebrates such as fish and mammals.
- Eukaryotic and multicellular. Cells do not have walls, and are specialised for a wide variety of functions.
- Animals can't photosynthesise; they depend on other organisms for organic nutrients.
- Most can move from place to place and have a nervous system for co-ordination.
- Growth is not confined to a limited number of cells as in plants, so most have a compact body form.

Kingdom Plantae

- Includes mosses, liverworts, ferns and conifers as well as flowering plants.
- Eukaryotic and multicellular. Cell walls contain cellulose. In mature cells there is usually a large vacuole.
- The plant body consists of specialised organs, including roots, stems and leaves. Most have a branching structure and have only small groups of cells that grow, e.g. at the ends of roots and stems.
- The great majority of plants contain

The Kingdoms

All living organisms belong to one of the five kingdoms. Four of these are eukaryotic; animals, plants, fungi and the obscure one, Protoctista, which seems to contain all the organisms that don't fit easily into the other three. The fifth kingdom is Prokaryotae; the bacteria. This section summarises the distinguishing features of each kingdom.

chlorophyll and make organic compounds by photosynthesis. A few have become adapted as parasites.

Kingdom Fungi

- Includes moulds, yeasts and mushrooms.
- Eukaryotic, but most do not have separate cells.
- In most fungi the main body consists of thread-like hyphae, which contain many nuclei. The yeasts are unicellular.
- Hyphal walls do not contain cellulose; most are made from chitin.
- Fungi cannot photosynthesise; most are saprophytic, absorbing nutrients from decaying matter after extracellular digestion. Some are parasites.

Animalia: Southern giant anteater: *Myrmecophaga tridactyla*
Plantae: Liverwort: *Marchantia polymorpha*
Fungi: Bread mould: *Mucor mucedo*
Protoctista: Diatom: *Gyrosignia sp*
Prokaryotae: Bacteria: coloured scanning electron micrograph of bacteria on the surface of a decomposing leaf.

Kingdom Protoctista

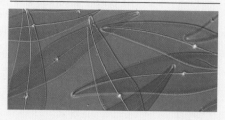

- Includes single-celled protozoans, such as *Amoeba*, and a broad range of algae, such as the seaweeds.
- The cells are eukaryotic, i.e. they have a nucleus and organelles with membranes, such as mitochondria and sometimes chloroplasts. Algae have cell walls containing cellulose.
- The basic body structure is relatively simple, being either unicellular or fairly unspecialised as in the leaf-like fronds of seaweeds. They may either photosynthesise or feed on organic matter from other sources.
- This kingdom is not a very satisfactory taxon, since it contains a hotchpotch of organisms that do not seem to fit into any other kingdom.

Kingdom Prokaryotae

- Includes the bacteria and blue-green bacteria (Cyanobacteria).
- Prokaryotic cells are very small, typically less than 10 micrometres across.
- Cells have no distinct nucleus. The nucleic acid is contained in a single chromosome that has no protein.
- Cells do not have organelles such as mitochondria or chloroplasts that are surrounded by plasma membranes.

KEY FACTS

- Evolutionary change over millions of years has resulted in huge numbers of different species.
- The classification of organisms is based on their presumed evolutionary history. This is called **phylogenetic classification**.
- Closely related species, which diverged relatively recently in evolution, are grouped together in one **genus**.
- Genera are grouped together into larger groups (**taxa**) called families. Increasingly large groupings comprise a **hierarchy**, with the largest being a kingdom.
- The order of the taxa from largest to smallest is: kingdom, phylum, class, order, family, genus, species.
- There are five kingdoms: Animalia, Plantae, Fungi, Protoctista, Prokaryotae.

1 The purple saxifrage is a flowering plant found in the Arctic. It has two distinct forms, one growing on dry ridges, the other in the valleys.

● On dry ridges, where the temperature is higher and the growing season longer, the plants grow in upright tufts. These plants are drought tolerant and store carbohydrate which they use in times of stress.

● In the valleys, where it is colder and the growing season is shorter, the plants grow very close to the ground. These plants have a higher rate of photosynthesis and grow more rapidly.

Both forms usually complete their life cycle in the short Arctic summer. In unfavourable years, plants in the valleys may produce pollen but are unable to form seeds. Some pollen from the valley plants fertilises plants on the ridges. The seeds may then be washed down to the valleys. Those that develop and complete their life cycles are all low-growing plants. When plants from the ridges and the valleys are grown under identical conditions in the laboratory, they have the same growth form as they did when in their original environment.

(Reproduced from *The Biologist*, R. M. M. Crawford by permission of Institute of Biology)

a What is the evidence in the passage that the two forms of the purple saxifrage
  i are genetically different; (1)
  ii belong to the same species? (1)

b When cross pollination between the low-growing and upright forms occurs, both forms of plant develop when the seeds produced are grown in the laboratory. Explain why only low-growing plants develop from the seeds which are washed from the ridges into the valleys. (2)

c Under the conditions described, the two forms of the purple saxifrage are unlikely to evolve into separate species. Explain why. (2)

d The effect of global warming on the environment of the Arctic is uncertain. Suggest why species such as the purple saxifrage are likely to survive even if changes in climate do occur. (2)

Total (8)

BY02 June 2000 Q4

2 Copy and complete the following passage:

The classification system of living organisms consists of a hierarchy in which groups are contained within larger groups with no overlap. These groupings are phylogenetic because they are based on the .... relationship between organisms.

The lion, *Panthera leo*, is classified as belonging to the genus .... It is recognised as a different .... from the tiger, *Panthera tigris*, because lions and tigers cannot breed together to produce .... offspring. All the different genera of the cats are grouped into the .... Felidae. Further groupings occur until the largest unit of classification is formed, the .... (6)

BY02 March 2000 Q5

3 The diagram shows the way in which four species of monkey are classified.

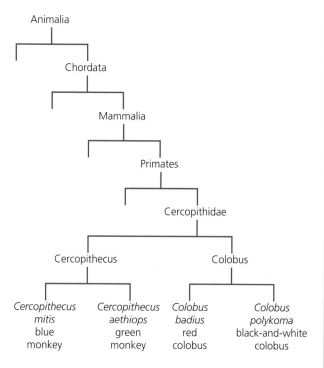

Fig 9.Q3

a This system of classification is described as hierarchical. Explain what is meant by a hierarchical classification. (1)

b
  i To which genus does the green monkey belong? (1)
  ii To which family does the red colobus belong? (1)

c What does the information in the diagram suggest about the similarities and differences in the genes of these four species of monkey? (2)

Total (5)

BY02 March 1998 Q3

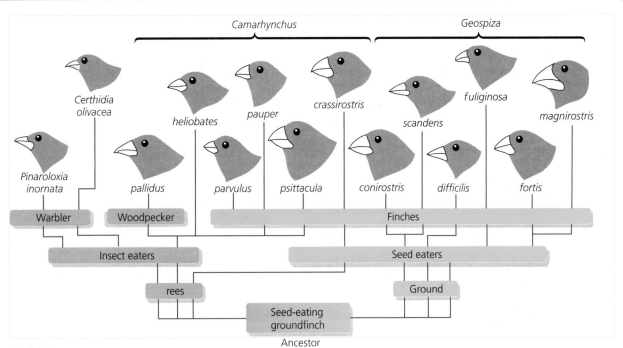

Fig 9.Q4

4 Fourteen different species of finch live on the isolated Galapagos Islands. The finches are all believed to have evolved from a single common ancestor. The diagram shows the suggested evolutionary relationships amongst the species.

a Suggest why these fourteen types of finch are considered to be different species. (1)

b Use the information in the diagram to identify
 i the species of ground finch which eats the largest seeds;
 ii the number of genera which are present on the islands. (2)

c Suggest how two distinct species, one insect-eating and the other seed-eating, may have evolved from a common ancestor. (4)

Total (7)

Paper 1 (end of course) June 1999 Q14

5 The coyote, jackal and dingo are closely related species of the dog family. Fig 9.Q5 shows their distribution.

Suggest and explain how these three distinct species evolved from a common ancestor. (4)

BY02 February 1997 Q6

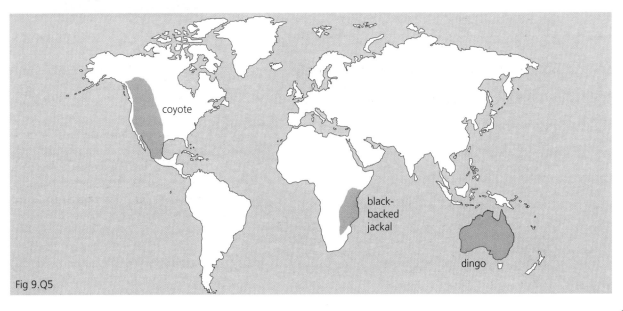

Fig 9.Q5

10 Energy flow and cycles

Most people are now aware of global warming and associate it with turbulent weather, floods and the threat of sea defences being overwhelmed in low-lying coastal areas. Many scientists have been forewarning of the dangers of global warming for several decades, yet so far relatively few measures have been taken to counteract its effects. Why? Predictions are notoriously unreliable. The weather has always been very variable. Experts disagree, allowing politicians and the public to dismiss the issue. Without public backing it is very difficult for politicians and other decision-makers to adopt measures that are likely to affect people's current quality of life in order to prevent possible, but uncertain, problems in the future.

Flooding in Cambridge, October 2000. Perhaps scenes like this have begun to convince many people that the dangers of global warming are real.

10.1 Why ecology is important

So, how certain can scientists be that global warming is a reality? There is no doubt that the concentration of carbon dioxide in the atmosphere has increased. Fig 10.1 shows measurements taken at a research station on the island of Hawaii in the mid-Pacific. Gases in the Earth's atmosphere mix freely, so the concentration measured is the mean global concentration. There is also evidence that

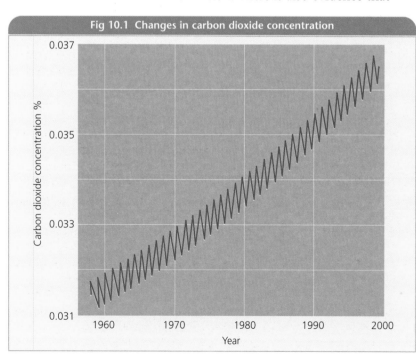

Fig 10.1 Changes in carbon dioxide concentration

mean temperatures around the world are rising, although the natural variability makes interpretation difficult. Experiments show that carbon dioxide absorbs heat energy much more readily than do oxygen and nitrogen. Increased carbon dioxide concentration, therefore, reduces the rate of radiation of heat energy from Earth into space and causes the greenhouse effect.

Scientists can use experimental data to create a computer model to find out how increasing temperatures are likely to change the climate. However, this is when uncertainty enters the equation. The Earth's climates are extremely complex. Computer models have to make simplifications. The models predict that, by the end of this century, mean temperatures might rise by anything from 1.5 °C to 6 °C, or

Could we see more barren landscapes like this if pollution and carbon dioxide emissions are not reduced?

even more. It is difficult to be sure that all factors have been taken into account:

- To what extent might rising temperatures increase the cloud cover and perhaps reduce the amount of solar radiation reaching the Earth's surface?

- Will loss of snow and ice cover reduce the amount of radiation reflected into space?

- Might changes to sea temperatures completely alter the patterns of ocean currents such as the Gulf stream, and thus have dramatic local effects on climate?

Politicians have to balance decisions on the basis of probabilities. The human population is increasing. People in developing countries have rising expectations and want their share of the world's resources and technological advances. Voters are not likely to welcome restrictions on their use of cars and labour-saving machinery. Some people perceive possible benefits arising from warmer temperatures, such as more sunbathing time and perhaps being able to grow vines on the slopes of the Pennines. There is a grave danger that some politicians will use the lack of unanimity among scientists as an excuse to reject all the evidence and do nothing. With elections looming, it is always tempting to consider only the short term. The problem is

that delay may set in motion catastrophic changes that are almost impossible to reverse. Measures to reduce emissions of greenhouse gases need to be based on sound understanding of the basic science, and the public needs to be convinced that the measures are essential. Biologists have an important role to play in the debate, particularly those with a special interest in ecology.

In this chapter we consider some of the basic science that forms the discipline of ecology. We look at the relationships between organisms and how interdependent they are. Rapid changes in climate could quickly disrupt this delicate balance. We then look at how carbon, the element at the centre of the global warming debate, is cycled and how the natural equilibrium can be preserved. Finally we study how supplies of nitrogen, equally important to living organisms, are maintained in natural habitats.

Ecology: some basic principles

Ecology is the study of organisms in the environment where they live. It is a relatively new science; it only became a major branch of biology in the last half of the twentieth century. Ecologists recognise that plants and animals cannot be studied in isolation without getting only half of the story. They interact both with each other and with their physical environment and this cannot be ignored.

The term **ecosystem** was coined, which includes both the living things in a particular area and the nature of the physical environment. Ponds, woods and rainforest – even a garden pond – can be considered as ecosystems. The living things in an ecosystem form a **community**, and the actual place in which they live is their **habitat**.

In practice every community is unique – no two ponds or woods have exactly the same things living in them in the same proportions. Within an ecosystem there may be several different habitats and therefore several communities. A wood may have areas with tall trees, areas with shrubs and parts that are open grassy glades. The organisms living in the tree tops may form a completely separate community from those living in the dead leaves on the ground. The job of the ecologist, just like any other scientist, is to establish the general rules that determine the interactions within ecosystems and to develop techniques for studying them.

10.2 Food chains and food webs

Most communities contain both plants and animals and probably members of the other three kingdoms as well (see Chapter 9 for more information about the kingdoms). All living organisms depend on a source of energy to sustain life, as we saw in Chapter 1. For the great majority this source is the Sun, and the route by which this energy enters a community is photosynthesis. A few prokaryotes can carry out chemosynthesis to use energy stored in chemical compounds. This process is similar to photosynthesis but is much rarer and does not really make a significant contribution to the energy supply in most communities. Some chemosynthetic bacteria are important in recycling elements such as nitrogen and sulphur.

Food chains
You should remember that species that photosynthesise are called **producers**, for the obvious reason that they produce organic compounds from inorganic ones. Things that feed on the producers get ready-made organic compounds; these are the **primary consumers**. Primary consumers are usually **herbivores**. Animals such as **carnivores**, which obtain their food by eating primary consumers, are **secondary consumers**. Above them are the **tertiary consumers** and so on. This sequence of feeding forms a **food chain**,

in which each of the stages represents a **trophic level**, as shown in Fig 10.2.

In addition, there are **decomposers** that feed on the dead bodies of organisms from all the trophic levels, as well as on animal waste. Organisms that feed on corpses and excreta don't have a very good public image, but they play a vital role in recycling the materials that they were made from, as we shall see later.

1 Some South American rainforest organisms are shown in the photographs on the opposite page. One food chain that can be taken from them is:

tree fruits → squirrel monkey → margay.

Use the information in the photographs to draw two other food chains.

Food webs
Food chains are a great simplification of the actual feeding relationships in an ecosystem. In the rainforest example shown in Question 1, the margay feeds on both the squirrel monkeys and the humming birds, and in practice would take a wide range of birds and small mammals. Many animals feed on both plants and other animals, so they may feed at two or more different trophic levels. In most communities it would be almost impossible to work out all the feeding relationships that

Fig 10.2 Food chains showing trophic levels

Terrestrial food chain

rose plant ⟶ aphids ⟶ ladybird larvae ⟶ blue tit ⟶ hawk

Producers ⟶ Primary consumers ⟶ Secondary Consumers ⟶ Tertiary consumers ⟶ Quaternary consumers

Freshwater food chain

phytoplankton ⟶ zooplankton ⟶ water fleas (daphnia) ⟶ stickleback ⟶ pike

A tamandua anteater feeds on termites.

A black-headed squirrel monkey feeds on tree fruits.

A margay hunts for prey such as monkeys and birds.

A great fruit-eating bat feeds on large fruit from trees.

A violet-eared humming bird visits a hibiscus flower for its nectar.

exist, but food web diagrams represent some of the complexity. Fig 10.3 shows some of the interrelationships in a British wood, which at least is a little less complex than a tropical rainforest.

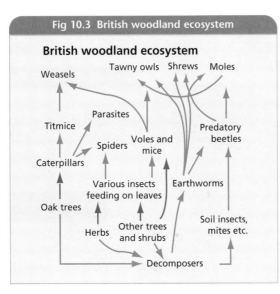

Fig 10.3 British woodland ecosystem

British woodland ecosystem

Weasels

Tawny owls   Shrews   Moles

Parasites

Titmice

Spiders   Voles and mice

Predatory beetles

Caterpillars

Various insects feeding on leaves

Earthworms

Oak trees

Herbs   Other trees and shrubs

Soil insects, mites etc.

Decomposers

2 Use information in Fig 10.3 to draw complete food chains containing:

a four organisms;

b five organisms;

c six organisms.

3 List all the secondary consumers in the British woodland food web.

4 To which trophic levels do humans belong? Explain your answer.

Ecological pyramids

In a food chain, organic compounds and the energy stored in them pass from one trophic level to the next. The arrows represent the direction of this flow of energy. No new energy can enter the chain, so all the consumers depend on the amount of energy that is incorporated by the producers.

143

Pyramids of numbers

Not all the energy available at a particular trophic level is transferred to the next, because some is lost to the environment at each level. Therefore, as a general rule, there are more producers than primary consumers, more primary consumers than secondary consumers, and so on. This can be shown in diagrammatic form as a **pyramid of numbers**.

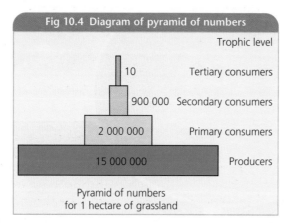

Fig 10.4 Diagram of pyramid of numbers

	Trophic level
10	Tertiary consumers
900 000	Secondary consumers
2 000 000	Primary consumers
15 000 000	Producers

Pyramid of numbers
for 1 hectare of grassland

In real ecosystems the situation is often more complex. Where the producers are small in size, as in the example shown in Fig 10.4, the rule may be true. However, where the producers are large – trees, for example – and can support many small primary consumers such as insects, the first trophic level is small, but the second is much larger. The diagram then looks more like a Christmas tree (Fig 10.5).

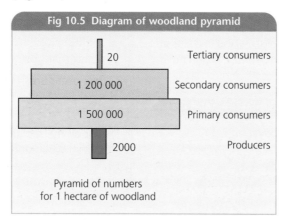

Fig 10.5 Diagram of woodland pyramid

20	Tertiary consumers
1 200 000	Secondary consumers
1 500 000	Primary consumers
2000	Producers

Pyramid of numbers
for 1 hectare of woodland

Other exceptions to these patterns in trophic levels may occur with parasites. For example, a few *Buddleia* plants may support a large number of caterpillars. Ichneumon wasps lay several eggs in each caterpillar and these eggs hatch into larvae that feed as parasites inside the caterpillars. The ichneumon larvae are often infested with large numbers of still smaller wasp larvae.

Larva of an ichneumon wasp emerging from the caterpillar of a peacock butterfly.

5 Draw a pyramid of numbers for the food chain:
Buddleia → caterpillars → Ichneumon larvae → wasp larvae

6 Draw a pyramid of numbers from the following information. A copse of sycamore trees is infested with aphids feeding on sap from the leaves. Blue tits are small birds that feed on the aphids. The blue tits have mites living among their feathers and feeding on dead skin.

Pyramids of biomass

Pyramids of numbers have their limitations when used to compare different ecosystems. It is not very useful to equate the number of grass plants in a meadow with the number of oak trees in a wood, or the number of sticklebacks in a pond with the number of whales in the Atlantic! One way of overcoming this is to measure the biomass of all the living organisms in each trophic level (Fig 10.6). The biomass of the grass plants would be the total mass of the grass plants in a given area. Because the mass of water in living organisms is highly variable, it is usually taken as the dry

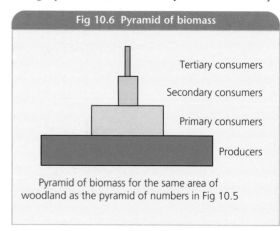

Fig 10.6 Pyramid of biomass

Tertiary consumers

Secondary consumers

Primary consumers

Producers

Pyramid of biomass for the same area of woodland as the pyramid of numbers in Fig 10.5

biomass, which is the mass after all the water has been removed by gentle heating.

The pyramid of biomass in Fig 10.6 is based on the same woodland ecosystem that was used as a basis for the pyramid of numbers in Fig 10.5.

7 It would be very difficult to measure the mass of all the grass in a meadow. Suggest how you could find the dry biomass of grass in a one hectare meadow (that's 100 metres by 100 metres).

In practice it is not easy to measure the biomass in a habitat. It is often not practical or desirable to find the dry biomass of the consumers. Just how you measure the dry mass of whales in the Atlantic is one of the enduring mysteries of ecology! Nevertheless, estimates of biomass can give a much more realistic comparison of trophic levels.

You might expect that all pyramids of biomass would have a clear pyramid shape, since the producer biomass must be greater than that of primary consumers in order that they have enough to feed on. Although this is true in most cases, there are some ecosystems that give misleading results. For example, in open sea, most of the producers are unicellular protoctists, the phytoplankton. Samples often show a lower biomass of photosynthesising organisms than of consumers. This is because the phytoplankton are eaten almost as quickly as they are produced and have a very short life, often less than 24 hours, whereas the animals that feed on them survive for much longer. If you measured the total biomass of the phytoplankton produced in, say, a month and compared this with the increase in mass of consumers, the mass of producers would be found to be much greater than the mass of primary consumers.

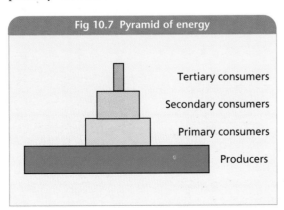

Fig 10.7 Pyramid of energy

Tertiary consumers
Secondary consumers
Primary consumers
Producers

Pyramids of energy

You can run into strange-shaped pyramids with both pyramids of numbers and pyramids of biomass, but if you calculate the total amount of energy that flows through each trophic level, you always get an upright pyramid, even in communities with phytoplankton. The largest box is always at the base, as shown in Fig 10.7.

When drawn to scale, pyramids of energy enable us to compare the amount of energy that enters the producers in an ecosystem, as well as the amount that flows through to each trophic level.

Energy flow in ecosystems

Ecosystems differ in the amount of energy that enters and is stored in the producers. Tropical rainforests are among the most productive ecosystems on Earth. The rate at which energy is stored in the producers in a community is called the **primary productivity**. The primary productivity of different ecosystems depends on:

- the amount of sunlight energy;
- the ability of different types of producer to use the energy to synthesise organic compounds;
- the availability of other factors needed for the growth of the producers, such as mineral ions.

Only a very small proportion of the solar energy that reaches the Earth's surface is actually stored in producers and is therefore available to other trophic levels in food materials. Much of it is not even used in photosynthesis because only a small percentage of the Earth's surface is covered with producers, so a lot of the energy is absorbed by rock or water. Of the solar energy that does fall on plant leaves:

- some is reflected;
- some passes straight through the leaves;
- some is the wrong wavelength; only visible light in the wavelength range 380 to 720 nm excites electrons in the chlorophyll and starts the light-dependent reaction.
- some is converted to heat during the reactions of photosynthesis.

At best, under 10% of the solar energy is incorporated into carbon compounds by photosynthesis.

Moreover, the producers do not use all of these carbon compounds to make new materials for growth. They use some of them to provide energy for other processes. This energy is released from the carbon compounds in respiration. It is rare for more than 3 or 4% of the solar energy that falls on a plant to be incorporated into its growth. Often it is much less. The amount of energy that is fixed by photosynthesis is called the **gross primary productivity** (GPP). The amount that actually goes into growth is the **net primary productivity** (NPP). (This is just like the gross takings of a shopkeeper, which are the total amount received from customers whereas the net profit is what is left after all the expenses of buying stock, paying assistants and so on).

We can express the relationship as an equation:

$$\text{Net primary productivity} = \text{Gross primary productivity} - \text{energy lost by plant respiration}$$

$$\text{NPP} = \text{GPP} - \text{R}$$

The net primary productivity of an ecosystem is the amount of energy that is available to be passed to the next trophic level. It is usually measured in units of energy per unit area per time, e.g. kilojoules per square metre per year ($kJ\ m^{-2}\ y^{-1}$). For a crop we might refer to megajoules per hectare per year ($MJ\ ha^{-1}\ y^{-1}$). Only the small proportion of solar energy that is incorporated into the structure of the producers can be passed on to primary consumers.

Like the producers, the primary consumers use some of this energy for growth, but, also like the producers, they too require energy for other processes. Being animals, they have even higher energy requirements, for example for moving around and, in the case of birds and mammals, to maintain body temperature. Therefore, an even lower proportion of the energy is incorporated into growth. The rest is lost to the environment as heat. The percentage that is passed from one trophic level to the next represents the efficiency of energy transfer. Similar losses happen at each succeeding trophic level. Therefore, only a limited number of trophic levels are possible before the energy 'runs out'.

Because most communities are so complex, it is very difficult to obtain accurate data about the efficiency of energy transfer. One set of data, shown in Fig 10.9, was obtained by research on an aquatic ecosystem in Florida, USA. The same data can be shown in a simplified form as a pyramid of energy (Fig 10.10).

From these data you can see that only a tiny proportion of the energy assimilated by producers during photosynthesis passed right through the food web to the tertiary consumers. At each trophic level a large amount passed to the environment in the form of heat energy as a result of respiration.

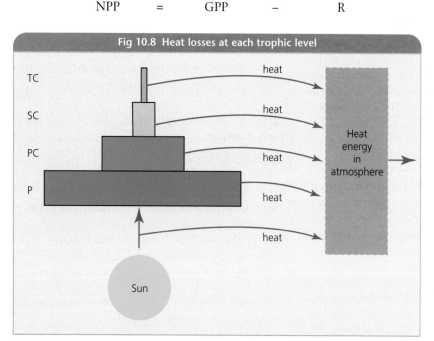

Fig 10.8 Heat losses at each trophic level

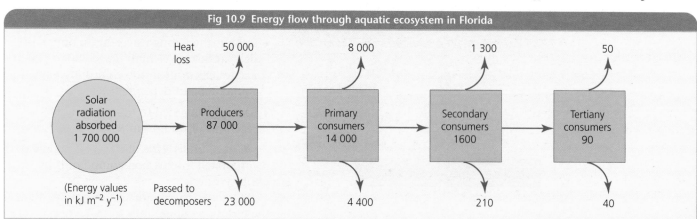

Fig 10.9 Energy flow through aquatic ecosystem in Florida

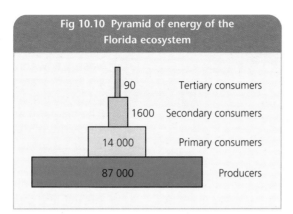

Fig 10.10 Pyramid of energy of the Florida ecosystem

90	Tertiary consumers
1600	Secondary consumers
14 000	Primary consumers
87 000	Producers

Not all the biomass of the producers was consumed by animals. Some parts would be inedible, but a considerable quantity remained when the producers died. This dead material was then broken down and absorbed by decomposers, which in turn released a large percentage of the energy by respiration. Dead animals would also be decomposed, as would materials that the animals passed out in faeces.

8 Calculate the percentage of energy passed to the next trophic level at each stage.

9 Suggest why the transfer of energy to the higher trophic levels is less efficient.

APPLICATION Photosynthetic efficiency

The mean energy value of solar radiation during daytime is approximately 1 kJ m^{-2} s^{-1}. The diagram shows what happens to each 1000 J of solar radiation that falls on the leaves of actively growing plants.

1 What is the overall percentage efficiency of the use of the solar radiation to produce materials for growth?

2 What percentage of the energy absorbed by chloroplasts is actually used to synthesise carbohydrate?

3 What percentage of the energy in the carbohydrate produced by photosynthesis is incorporated into growth compounds?

4 Use your knowledge of leaves and chloroplasts to explain the features that:
  a keep the amount of light transmitted to a minimum;
  b enable the chlorophyll to make use of the green wavelengths of light;
  c maximise the efficiency with which chlorophyll molecules absorb light.

5 The efficiency of net primary productivity given in the diagram on the right is close to the maximum ever found in nature and much higher than the average in most ecosystems. The mean percentage efficiency is rarely more than about one fifth of this value. Suggest reasons for the efficiency being much lower than the maximum possible.

6 It makes better use of the solar energy falling on an area of land for people to feed on crops rather than on animals, such as cattle.
  a Use your understanding of efficiency and energy flow to explain why.
  b Suggest why it may sometimes be an economical use of land and energy to use animals as a source of food.

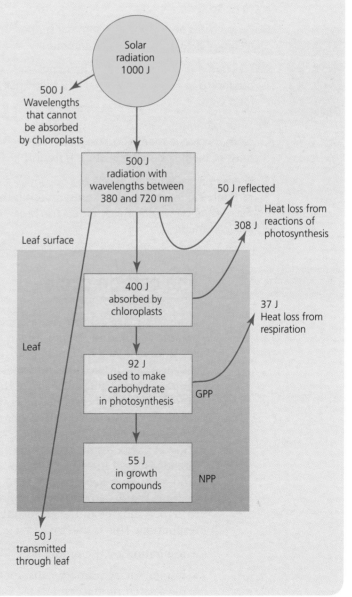

Fig 10.11 Energy flow in animals

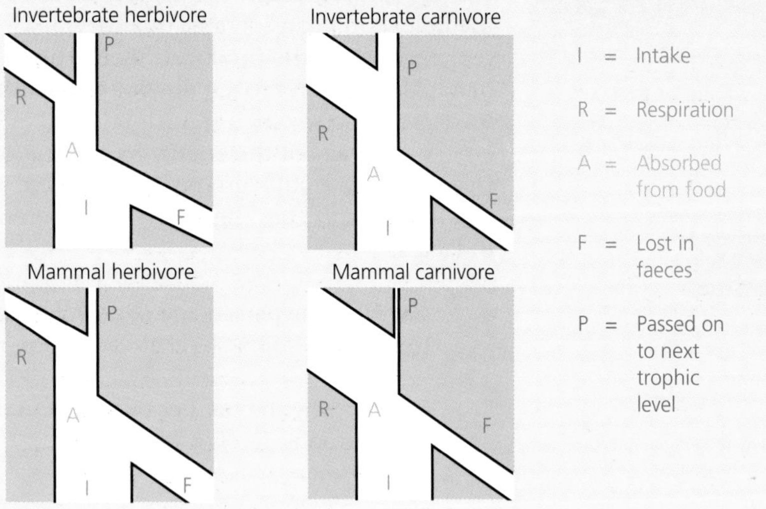

Invertebrate herbivore

Invertebrate carnivore

Mammal herbivore

Mammal carnivore

I = Intake

R = Respiration

A = Absorbed from food

F = Lost in faeces

P = Passed on to next trophic level

10 Flow diagrams can also be constructed for individual animals. Fig 10.11 shows energy flow through four types of animal: an invertebrate herbivore and carnivore, and a mammal herbivore and carnivore. The diagrams are drawn to scale, so that the width of the sections enables comparisons to be made.

a Suggest why the proportion of the energy passed on to the next trophic level (P) is greater in invertebrates than in mammals, and greater in mammalian herbivores than in mammalian carnivores.

b Suggest explanations for the variation in the proportions of energy lost in faeces (F) in the four organisms.

KEY FACTS

■ Food chains and food webs summarise the feeding relationships within a community.

■ A pyramid of numbers shows the number of organisms at each trophic level in a food chain or food web.

■ Since organisms vary in size, a pyramid of biomass gives a more accurate picture of the total mass of biological material at each trophic level.

■ Energy passes from producers to consumers through the trophic levels. Photosynthesis is the main route by which energy enters the organisms in a community.

■ Only a small proportion of the solar radiation that falls on the producers in a community is assimilated into biomass. This energy represents the net primary productivity.

■ Net primary productivity equals gross primary productivity minus energy lost by respiration.

■ The efficiency of energy transfer to successive trophic levels is low, with a high proportion being lost from food chains through respiration.

■ Energy flow through a community can be represented by pyramids of energy and energy flow diagrams.

10.3 The carbon cycle

Producers make carbohydrates and other organic compounds from inorganic constituents. When plants photosynthesise, they use carbon dioxide and water to build simple sugars. These sugars may then be used to make structural carbohydrates such as cellulose, or combined with other elements to produce proteins, phospholipids, nucleic acids, etc. As a result, the carbon from carbon dioxide is fixed into the structure as the producers grow (see Chapter 1).

Most of the carbon is eventually restored to carbon dioxide in the atmosphere by respiration. This is due to:

● respiration by the producers;

● respiration by primary consumers, which have eaten producers;

● respiration by secondary and tertiary consumers, which have eaten carbon compounds passed along food chains;

● respiration by decomposers, which have absorbed carbon compounds from dead organisms or from excretory products.

These processes can be summarised as the 'carbon cycle' (Fig 10.12).

Decomposers and detritivores

Decomposers play an important part in the carbon cycle, and in recycling other elements. When an organism dies, or when a consumer excretes organic compounds, other organisms soon get to work on breaking down the organic constituents. The corpses of dead animals are usually attacked first by a range of

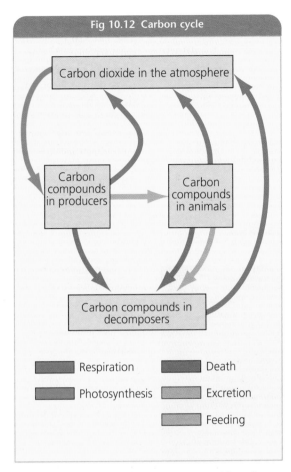

Fig 10.12 Carbon cycle

Carbon dioxide in the atmosphere

Carbon compounds in producers

Carbon compounds in animals

Carbon compounds in decomposers

Respiration
Photosynthesis
Death
Excretion
Feeding

contains a large percentage of cellulose, and few organisms can make cellulase, the enzyme needed to digest it. Most detritivores simply eliminate the cellulose in their faeces. Only a few, such as termites, can make use of the cellulose, and they do it by acting as hosts to microorganisms in their gut that do produce cellulase and so can break down cellulose into sugar monomers.

Most of the cellulose has to await the attention of fungi and bacteria that live in the soil. These are the true decomposers that complete the process of breakdown. Decomposers differ from detritivores in that they secrete enzymes and then absorb the products of digestion. The detritivores help by breaking dead matter into much smaller pieces. This makes decomposition more efficient because there is a much larger surface area for enzymes to work on. Soil with lots of earthworms is much more fertile because decomposition is much more rapid.

Fungi on a decaying tree trunk.

scavengers, such as foxes, crows and beetles, which is why the countryside is not littered with corpses.

Invertebrate animals that feed on partly broken down dead matter (detritus) are called **detritivores**, and these play an important role in disposing of dead plants. Earthworms and woodlice are detritivores. They eat the dead plant material and take it into their gut where digestive enzymes break down the organic compounds. One problem is that plant tissue

Decomposers use a method of feeding called **saprophytic nutrition**. We looked at this method in the AS course (see AS Biology, pages 84 to 85). After the carbohydrates, lipids and proteins have been digested, the products are absorbed by the decomposers, which use them as energy sources and for their own growth. As the decomposers respire they produce carbon dioxide and water. The carbon dioxide is released into the atmosphere and is then available again for photosynthesis. This is essential to keep the carbon cycle to going. Organic carbon

Eucalyptus wood infested by the Giant Darwin Termite, *Mastotermes darwiniensis*.

Vultures on a zebra carcass. Vultures have perfected the art of scavenging.

compounds such as sugars and cellulose must be broken down to carbon dioxide, because green plants are completely unable to absorb such compounds from the soil or water.

11 Which monomer is the product of cellulose digestion?

12 Decomposition is much more rapid in tropical rainforest than in British woods. Explain why.

Carbon sources and carbon sinks

The carbon cycle should, in theory, keep the carbon dioxide concentration in the atmosphere constant, since all living organisms eventually die. However, some dead organisms do not fully decompose, for example because they fall into deep water or marshes where there is very little oxygen for the decomposers. Over many millions of years their remains have accumulated and produced oil, coal and natural gas. Carbon

APPLICATION

Reducing the greenhouse effect

Even if scientists and politicians were to agree that there really is a greenhouse effect and that global warming is a threat, it would not be so easy to decide how to reduce it. The most obvious way to reduce the build-up of carbon dioxide is to burn less fossil fuel. Using biofuels as an alternative is one possibility (see Chapter 1), as well as greater dependence on renewable energy sources such as wind, wave and solar power. However, to reverse the rise of carbon dioxide it will be necessary to find ways of removing the gas from the atmosphere faster than it is being added. One possible way to do this is to make use of photosynthesis.

To achieve a reduction, the carbon fixed by photosynthesis must remain in organic compounds, such as the wood of trees. Restoring forests is, therefore, one of the best ways of taking carbon dioxide out of circulation. Even this, however, has its limitations. Trees do not go on growing indefinitely, especially the faster growing species. There comes a time, perhaps after 50 years or so, when the rate of absorption of carbon dioxide is in balance with the rate of loss, due to death and decomposition. It has

also been suggested that forests growing in more northerly regions bordering on the Arctic could decrease the amount of snow and ice and thus lower the amount of solar radiation reflected into space causing a rise in temperature. Nevertheless. it is almost certain that the best ways of reducing the more extreme effects of global warming are to grow more forests and to take measures to reduce carbon dioxide emissions. At the same time, we need to prepare for the consequences of some unavoidable rise in temperature, such as rising sea levels and more frequent extreme weather events.

1 Explain why coniferous forests like the one in the photograph above might reduce radiation from the Earth into space.

2 One proposal to cut carbon dioxide emissions from power stations was to bubble the waste gases through water, where some of the gas would dissolve. Green algae would be grown in this carbon dioxide enriched water. It was suggested that the algae could be harvested and used as compost for growing crops. Explain why this would not be effective in reducing the carbon dioxide concentration in the atmosphere.

3 An average driver may use about 1500 litres of petrol in a year. It is estimated that 180 square metres of actively growing forest are required to absorb the carbon dioxide produced by combustion of 100 litres of petrol. Calculate how many square kilometres of forest would be needed to absorb the carbon dioxide produced annually by the approximately 20 million cars on Britain's roads.

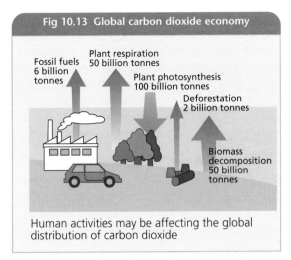

Fig 10.13 Global carbon dioxide economy

Fossil fuels
6 billion
tonnes

Plant respiration
50 billion tonnes

Plant photosynthesis
100 billion tonnes

Deforestation
2 billion tonnes

Biomass
decomposition
50 billion
tonnes

Human activities may be affecting the global distribution of carbon dioxide

exist in the ecosystems where they live. They may be able to tolerate warmer temperatures that are beyond the normal range for a time. But, constantly higher temperatures are liable to alter conditions too drastically, for example by causing prolonged droughts. Once the dominant producers, such as the trees, are affected, the whole network of relationships that constitute an ecosystem may be destroyed.

13
a Which kingdoms other than the plant kingdom include producers?
b Explain why producers need ATP from respiration.

14
a What are the products of combustion of fossil fuels?
b Explain how deforestation increases the carbon dioxide concentration in the atmosphere.

15 Fig 10.1 on page 140, shows measurements of the atmospheric carbon dioxide concentration. You will see that, as well as the overall increase, the concentration rises and falls each year. This happens because there is much more land and more vegetation and crops in the northern hemisphere than in the southern hemisphere. Use your knowledge of the carbon cycle to explain the annual rise and fall.

was locked away in these deposits, and this resulted in a gradual reduction in the amount of carbon dioxide in the atmosphere. Such deposits are sometimes called carbon sinks.

Humans are now plundering the fossil fuels as sources of energy, with the result that an extra 6 billion tonnes of carbon dioxide is being released into the atmosphere each year from their combustion. Rapid deforestation may also be adding another 2 billion tonnes, especially where land is being cleared by burning. Fig 10.13 shows the global carbon dioxide economy.

The most disruptive effects of global warming are likely to result from the sheer speed at which carbon dioxide concentration in the atmosphere is increasing. Organisms are adapted for survival in the conditions that

KEY FACTS

- Carbon in carbon dioxide enters communities via photosynthesis.

- Most of this carbon is eventually returned to the atmosphere through the respiration of plants, animals and decomposers. This is the carbon cycle.

- Decomposers break down dead organic matter by secreting enzymes and absorbing the products of digestion. This is saprophytic nutrition.

- Combustion of fossil fuels and deforestation are causing an increase in the concentration of carbon dioxide in the atmosphere. Carbon dioxide is a greenhouse gas, and this increase is almost certainly contributing to global warming.

10.4 The nitrogen cycle

Decomposition is not only important for maintaining the supply of carbon dioxide in the atmosphere. All the other components of living organisms have to be recycled. Mineral ions are released from cells as tissues break down. Vital mineral nutrients are also released by the digestion of certain substances, such as magnesium ions from

chlorophyll and phosphate ions from phospholipids and nucleic acids. Particularly important is the recycling of nitrogen compounds, since nitrogen is an essential element in all proteins and nucleic acids. Nitrates are often in short supply in soil and water, so it is vital to keep the cycle going.

The cycling of nitrogen is rather more

complex than that of most ions because digestion of proteins does not release the nitrate ions that producers require to synthesise their own proteins. There are three main stages in the production of nitrate ions from proteins. These are:

- Digestion of proteins to amino acids by decomposers – **saprophytic digestion**;

- Formation of ammonium compounds from amino acids – **ammonification**;

- Conversion of ammonium compounds to nitrates – **nitrification**.

Saprophytic digestion

We have already seen how saprophytes break down dead remains and digest proteins to amino acids. Partly decomposed organic matter in the soil is called **humus**. Humus plays an important part in maintaining the texture of soil, so that it is well aerated and drains easily.

Ammonification

Some ammonifying bacteria can continue the process of decomposition by removing the nitrogen-containing amino groups ($-NH_2$)

APPLICATION   **Nitrogen fixation**

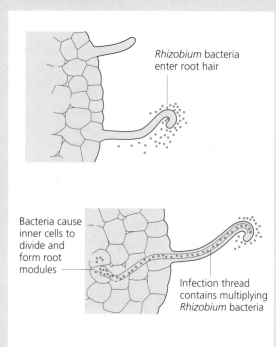

Rhizobium bacteria enter root hair

Bacteria cause inner cells to divide and form root modules

Infection thread contains multiplying *Rhizobium* bacteria

Source: adapted from Salisbury & Ross, *Plant Physiology*, Wadsworth, 1992

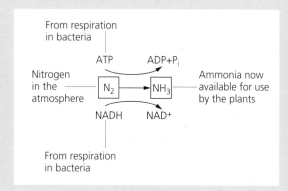

Nitrogen is a very unreactive gas, which is why it forms such a large percentage of the atmosphere. To get nitrogen to combine with hydrogen in a laboratory requires a high temperature and high pressure. Industrially, this is carried out on a large scale by the Haber process, which is used to manufacture fertilisers. Nitrogen-fixing bacteria, however, are able to carry out this process at low temperatures, using nitrogenase enzymes. Since nitrogen compounds are so important to all living organisms, it is perhaps surprising that nitrogenase enzymes have not evolved in other groups of organism.

Leguminous plants are adapted by the mutualistic association shown in the diagram. Infection by the *Rhizobium* bacteria stimulates the development of the nodules, which contain both the bacteria and plant tissues. For example, xylem and phloem tissues form within the nodules, and the outer layer of cells becomes largely waterproof with only a few pores for gaseous exchange. Nitrogen fixation requires considerable amounts of energy. This is supplied from ATP that is generated by respiration of glucose obtained from the plants. Since the ammonia produced is toxic, it has to be rapidly converted to less harmful amino acids, and both the bacteria and the plant tissues carry this out, again using energy from ATP. The biochemistry of the processes involved is complex and not yet fully understood. ATP production needs oxygen. However, nitrogenase activity is inhibited by the presence of high concentrations of oxygen. This problem is solved by having a reddish pigment very similar to haemoglobin in the tissues of the nodules, which often makes the nodules look pink. This pigment, called leghaemoglobin, keeps the concentration of oxygen low, but allows rapid release of oxygen to maintain respiration.

1 Use your knowledge of enzyme activity to explain how nitrogenase allows nitrogen and hydrogen to be combined at low temperatures.

2 Suggest how nitrogen reaches the bacteria in the nodules.

3 What are the advantages of developing xylem and phloem in the nodules?

4 Explain how leghaemoglobin can keep the oxygen concentration low, but allow rapid oxygen release to maintain respiration.

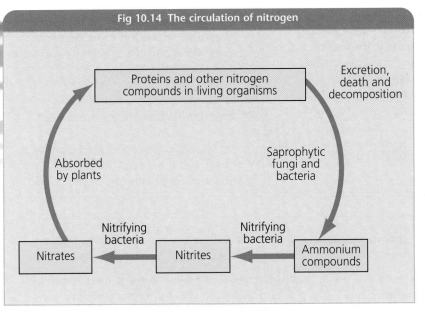

Fig 10.14 The circulation of nitrogen

from the amino acids. These are then combined to form ammonium ions (NH_4^+). This is very similar to the process of deamination that takes place in the liver of mammals and which produces urea (see Chapter 3). In fact, the urea excreted by mammals is also decomposed to ammonium compounds by some bacteria.

Nitrification

The ammonium compounds are oxidised by nitrifying bacteria to nitrates. This takes place in two stages, and different species of bacteria are involved at each stage.

$$NH_4^+ \text{ ions} \rightarrow NO_2^- \text{ ions} \rightarrow NO_3^- \text{ ions}$$
Ammonium   Nitrite   Nitrate

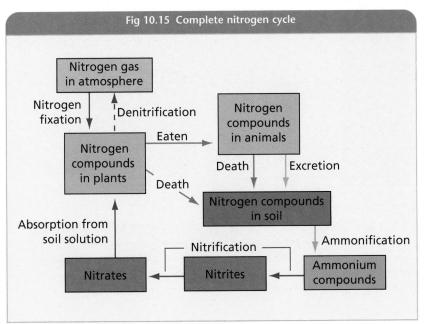

Fig 10.15 Complete nitrogen cycle

These reactions are oxidations because hydrogen is removed from the nitrogen and oxygen is added. The bacteria do not carry out the reactions out of the kindness of their hearts. As in the oxidations that occur during combustion, energy is released in the reactions. The bacteria use this energy to carry out chemosynthesis, in the same way as green plants use light energy in photosynthesis.

An overview of the nitrogen cycle

The core of the nitrogen cycle is summarised in Fig 10.14.

In theory this cycle could maintain the supplies of nitrates for plants indefinitely. However, there are a couple of complications in the real world. Where soils are waterlogged and there is little or no oxygen available for respiration, denitrifying bacteria use nitrate ions as electron acceptors for respiration instead of oxygen. This reaction produces nitrogen gas, which is released into the atmosphere, thus reducing the amount of nitrates in the soil.

Nitrogen fixation

The loss of nitrates is counterbalanced by bacteria that use nitrogen gas to synthesise nitrogen compounds. These bacteria can reduce nitrogen (N_2) to ammonia (NH_3) in a process called **nitrogen fixation**. In this process, nitrogen gas is combined with hydrogen ions obtained from water. Some of these nitrogen-fixing bacteria live freely in the soil or water, but others live inside green plants.

For example, *Rhizobium* bacteria live inside small lumps (nodules) on the roots of leguminous plants such as clover, peas and beans. The bacteria have nitrogenase enzymes that fix nitrogen and produce ammonia. This is immediately converted to amino groups that are used to synthesise amino acids inside the cells of the nodules.

This is an example of mutualism, because both the bacteria and the plants benefit from the relationship. The leguminous plants obtain amino acids without having to absorb nitrates, which are often in short supply in soil. The bacteria get sugars from the plants that they use as a source of energy in order to synthesise the ammonia.

The full nitrogen cycle

Once these additional processes are added to the diagram, the nitrogen cycle looks rather more complex (Fig 10.15). You can see how vital microorganisms are and why it is important to maintain healthy populations of them in the soil.

Macrophotograph of root nodules on the roots of white clover, caused by the nitrogen-fixing *Rhizobium trifolii*.

16 Use your knowledge of the biochemistry of aerobic respiration to suggest how denitrifying bacteria use nitrate and nitrite ions as electron acceptors.

17 Explain why good soil drainage is important in gardens and crop fields.

18 Traditionally, farmers rotated crops with clover and grass every fourth year. Suggest how this could improve the crop yield.

KEY FACTS

■ Microorganisms play a vital role in recycling nitrogen, as well as other mineral ions, within ecosystems.

■ In the nitrogen cycle, saprophytic bacteria decompose nitrogen compounds to ammonium compounds.

■ Nitrifying bacteria convert the ammonium ions to nitrates. The nitrates are absorbed by green plants and used to synthesise amino acids and proteins.

■ In anaerobic conditions, denitrifying bacteria may convert nitrates to nitrogen gas.

■ Nitrogen-fixing bacteria combine nitrogen gas and hydrogen ions to make ammonium ions, which are then used directly to make amino acids.

■ Leguminous plants have a mutualistic association with nitrogen-fixing bacteria that live in root nodules.

EXAMINATION QUESTIONS

1 The diagram shows a simplified food web for an oakwood.

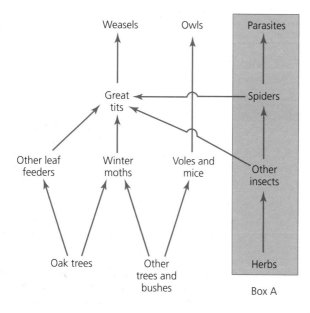

Fig 10.Q1

a Using the diagram, name an organism which is both a secondary and a tertiary consumer. (1)

b Sketch and label the pyramid of numbers and the pyramid of biomass you would expect for the part of the food web in Box A. (2)

c Explain why food webs rarely have more than five trophic levels. (2)

Total (5)

BY01 June 1998 Q6

2

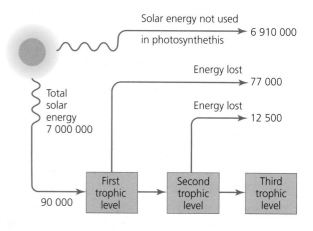

Fig 10.Q2

EXAMINATION QUESTIONS

a Suggest two reasons why not all of the solar energy can be used in photosynthesis. (2)

b

  i Calculate the amount of energy available to the third trophic level. (1)

  ii Describe one way in which energy is lost from the first trophic level. (1)

  iii Suggest one reason why the energy loss from the first trophic level is greater than that from the second trophic level. (1)

Total (5)

BY01 March 1999 Q6

3 The diagram shows what happens to the light energy falling on a leaf.

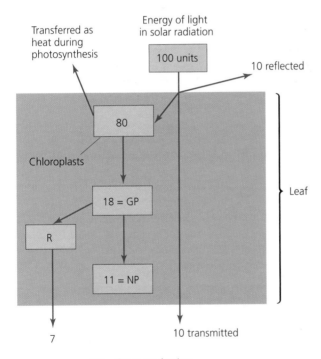

Fig 10.Q3

a Give one way in which the structure of a leaf minimises the amount of light that is transmitted through it. (1)

b Calculate the percentage efficiency of photosynthesis in using the light absorbed by the chloroplasts for carbohydrate production. (1)

c Write an equation to show the relationship between gross production (GP), net production (NP) and respiration (R). (1)

Total (3)

BY07 Feb 1997 Q2

4 The flow chart in Fig 10.Q4 summarises what happens to the energy in food eaten by a cow. The figures on the right-hand side of the diagram refer to the percentage of the total amount of energy in the food.

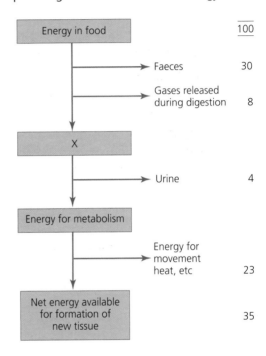

Fig 10. Q4

a

  i What is represented by Box X? (1)

  ii Write a simple equation summarising the relationship between energy for metabolism (M), net energy (N) and energy from respiration (R). (1)

b Higher yields can be produced from cows if they are kept in heated sheds rather than allowed to live outside. Use the information in the flow chart to suggest one explanation for this. (2)

c The amount of beef that can be produced from a given area of land is less than the amount of a plant crop such as wheat. Use your knowledge of food chains to explain why. (1)

Total (5)

BY01 March 2000 Q6

11 Ecological techniques

Until relatively recently, Britain was covered with deciduous forest with great swathes of oak, ash, beech and birch trees. Wolves and bears were free to roam and maintained quite large populations – quite a lot different to the Britain of today with its predominantly agricultural 'countryside'. In fact, it is reasonable to ask the questions, 'Does anywhere in Britain remain 'natural'? Is there anywhere that people's influence has not reached?' There are probably not many areas left.

So where did all this human influence begin? One of the first areas of Britain to be colonised was the chalk hills of southern England, some 5000 years ago. Large areas were cleared of woodland, and the exposed uplands (often, confusingly, called 'Downs') became huge pastures for grazing animals. The soil is shallow and water drains easily through the porous chalk. Nevertheless, chalk grassland supports a remarkably rich variety of species of flowering plants.

Chalk grassland flowers at Noar Hill, Hampshire. Ox-eye daisies, pyramidal orchids, Lady's bedstraw, knapweed and hawkbit all flourish.

11.1 Experiments in ecology

One of the earliest experiments in ecology was done on chalk grassland by Tansley and Adamson, who published their results in 1925. They studied the effect of grazing rabbits, recording the plant species they found in sample areas. When this preliminary study was complete, they fenced off these areas for six years to keep the rabbits out. After this time they counted the species again in the same areas. You might expect that grazing would destroy plants and reduce the number of species, but, as you can see from their results in Fig 11.1, the opposite happened. One type of grass grew so tall that it became dominant and excluded the many smaller species of flowering plants that had been able to flourish when the rabbits were about.

Fig 11.1 Tansley and Adamson's results

Before fencing

This shows the results of recording the species in one sample area of chalk grassland before rabbits were excluded. Each symbol represents a species of flowering plant. The leaves show the position of dandelions.

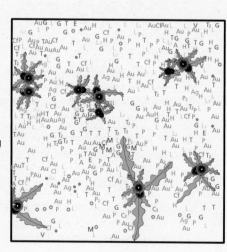

Six years after fencing

The area between the plants was entirely populated by Upright Brome grass.

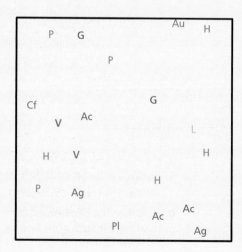

The interactions between plants and animals in an ecosystem are complex. To understand what is happening, ecologists have to make careful measurements of both the organisms that live there and the physical conditions in the habitat. Although rabbits may damage or kill plants they do not behave like lawn-mowers, cutting everything down to the same size. They may prevent any particular type of plant becoming too large, but they also create slightly different conditions in some parts of a habitat, for example depositing faeces and urine in uneven patches, producing areas with different amounts of nutrient and different pH.

In this chapter we look at some of the techniques that ecologists use to find out which organisms live in a particular habitat. We also see how they measure the physical conditions that may affect different species' ability to survive. Hardly any ecosystem in the world is unaffected by human activities. If some habitats are to be conserved for future generations, it is vital for biologists to record the plants and animals that live in places that are more or less natural, and to see how changing conditions affect these natural communities. Only by understanding these changes might it be possible to reverse some of the more damaging effects.

Sampling techniques

It is impossibly time-consuming for an ecologist to examine and count every plant in a meadow, every tree in a rainforest, or every barnacle on a shore. It is also unnecessary, since taking samples in a carefully controlled way will provide information about the distribution of species in a habitat that is just as valuable. The purpose of surveying the organisms in a habitat is not just to record what lives there. There are several reasons why ecologists might need accurate data. For example they might want to:

- find out what conditions a particular species needs for its survival;

- determine the effects of different treatments, such as adding fertilisers or spraying with herbicides or pesticides;

- see how the range of species changes over time, perhaps as a result of pollution;

- keep track of seasonal variations.

Carrying out detailed studies enables ecologists to see how human activities are affecting our environment and to take note of early warning signs. Industries are now employing ecologists to keep a check on the effects of waste products on their surrounding environment. Even minute traces of a pollutant or the most apparently innocuous effluent can sometimes have totally unexpected consequences. Substances are often much more toxic to other animals than they are to humans; for example, very low concentrations of drugs in the effluent from a factory making, say, contraceptive pills, could have disastrous results.

Ecologists use two main techniques when sampling – quadrats and transects.

Quadrats

A quadrat is a sample area in a habitat that is marked off so that the organisms within it can be studied. Ecologists often use a square frame. This may be made from thick wire or wood that can easily be moved in order to study several sample areas of the same shape and size.

Quadrats are particularly useful when ecologists need to compare the species in one area with those in another. For example, they could be used to compare the vegetation in fields that have been fertilised with that in unfertilised fields. Quadrats are best used in

Can pollution make fish change sex?

In the early 1990s, researchers at Brunel University noticed that male trout living in streams close to a sewage treatment plant near London had testes laden with eggs. The male fish had developed the sexual characteristics of both males and females.

Further investigation showed that caged trout placed downstream from sewage treatment plants in several British rivers showed the same effects. British researchers John Sumpter and Susan Jobling showed that the male fish had elevated levels of a protein called vitellogenin in their blood. Vitellogenin is responsible for making egg yolks in female fish. Usually, male fish do not make vitellogenin but they have the gene that codes for it; when male fish are exposed to oestrogen, the gene is expressed, and the male fish start to produce vitellogenin, and to make eggs.

So why did the male fish have vitellogenin. How were they being exposed to oestrogen? The story caught the interest of the press and there was plenty of wild speculation about female hormones in sewage as a result of women using contraceptive pills. However, the true reason for the apparent sex change in the fish turned out to be even more sinister.

Sumpter and Joblin found that several common industrial chemicals could induce vitellogenin production in the fish in a dose-dependent manner: Chemicals found to induce vitellogenin expression included octylphenol and nonylphenol (both alkyl phenol commonly used in detergents, toiletries, lubricants and spermicides); bisphenol-A (the building block of polycarbonate plastics); DDT (the banned pesticide; and Arachlor 1221 (one of the 209 varieties of polychlorinated biphenyls (PCBs)

Mixtures of the different chemicals were more powerful at producing vitellogenin than any of the individual chemicals alone. The studies also showed that the chemicals tended to accumulate in the flesh of the fish: as time passed so that even low concentration of a weakly oestrogenic chemical could eventually build up to a level that induced vitellogenin production in male fish.

But were the oestrogenic effects of common pollutants limited to one species. Could they affect humans? Could they be responsible in the falling sperm counts that have been observed in human males in Europe over the last 50 years of so? This remains an open question, and further research will be needed to find out but more recent studies have shown the same effect in other fish species.

In late 1996, US researchers published studies confirming that up-to-date sewage treatment plants in the US can cause the same effects in carp. Scientists examined male carp from five locations in the Mississippi River downstream from the Minneapolis sewage treatment plant, and from a tributary, the Minnesota River, which receives heavy agricultural run-off. They found that carp living near the Minneapolis sewage treatment plant produce high levels of vitellogenin and reduced levels of testosterone, the male sex hormone. Carp from the pesticide-contaminated Minnesota River had sharply reduced testosterone levels but no vitellogenin while Carp from the largely unpolluted St Croix River were normal.

1 a What is the usual function of vitellogenin in female fish?
  b What is its effect when produced in male fish as a result of exposure to environmental pollutants?

2 It has been suggested that because the oestrogen and testosterone molecules found in fish are very similar to those found in humans that this research could be extrapolated to humans - i.e. it could be taken as evidence that the expression of human sex hormones can be affected by pollutants. Do you think this is a reasonable assumption? Give reasons for your answer.

3 a What long-term effects do you think the pollution levels in streams near to sewage plants could have on the trout population in British rivers?
  b What do you think should be done to avoid these effects in the future?

ecosystems that do not have tall vegetation, such as grassland, meadows and shores. It is not easy to use frame quadrats where the ground is rough and bumpy. However, in areas like this, or where there are trees, bushes or other tall plants, string and pegs can be used to mark out quadrats.

Quadrats do not have to be square. For example, some fields have a pattern of ridges and furrows, often the remains of mediaeval farming practices. Different species may inhabit the drier ridges and the damp furrows. In this case it would be useful to use rectangular quadrats that fit into the furrows, and along the top of the ridges.

The best size of quadrat to use depends on the organisms being studied. For example, a small quadrat would be suitable if species were quite small and fairly evenly spread in the habitat. Quadrats with each side between 25 cm and 1 m long might be used. However, these would obviously be useless for studying the distribution of trees and shrubs in a wood; much larger quadrats are used for this.

It is important to record results from several quadrats in each sample area. The quadrats must be placed randomly in the study area. To avoid bias, the ecologist must not choose or influence where the quadrats are put down, even unconsciously. Throwing the quadrat over the shoulder does not give truly random positions, because the thrower chooses where to stand and how hard to throw. It's also not very sociable when working with other ecologists!

There are two ways of placing quadrats randomly in a study area. Both require making a grid map of the area and using co-ordinates, as shown in Fig 11.2. In the first method, the area is sampled in a regular pattern, for example at every fifth metre square. In the second, each square is assigned

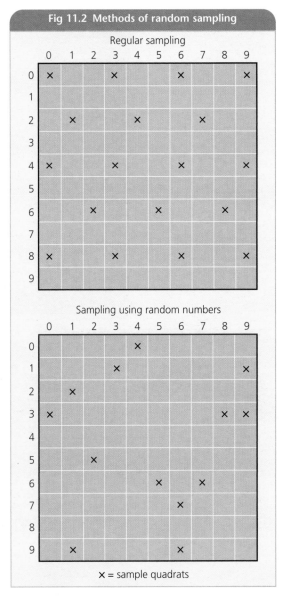

Fig 11.2 Methods of random sampling

Regular sampling

Sampling using random numbers

x = sample quadrats

a number based on the coordinates, and then a table of random numbers is used to select the positions for the quadrats.

Results may be recorded in various ways:

- Counting the number of specimens of every species in each quadrat. This can be useful when recording changes over a period of time, but is very time-consuming for large areas;

- Recording the quadrats in which a particular species occurs. This is useful to show up the pattern of distribution of a species within a habitat;

- Estimating the percentage of the area of ground in a quadrat that is covered by a particular species (Fig 11.3). This is better than simple counts for finding out how dominant a species is in a habitat.

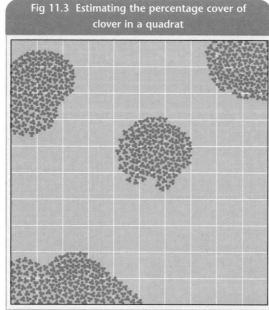

Fig 11.3 Estimating the percentage cover of clover in a quadrat

1

a A quadrat is 25 x 25 cm. Calculate its area in m^2.

b A student uses this quadrat to survey the plants in 20 positions in a habitat. What is the total area surveyed?

c The total area of the habitat being studied is 220 m^2. What percentage of the habitat has the student surveyed?

2 A student is studying the distribution of clover in a field, using a 50 x 50 cm quadrat. Fig 11.3 shows the parts where clover is growing in one quadrat.

a Estimate the percentage cover of clover in this quadrat to the nearest 5%.

b The student notices that the grass growing close to the patches of clover is greener and rather taller than the grass further away. Clover is a leguminous plant. Use your knowledge of leguminous plants to explain the student's observation.

Transects

A transect is a line through a habitat along which the organisms are sampled. Transects are particularly useful when studying an area where there is a gradual change from one set of conditions to another, such as across a roadside verge to a hedge, or up a sea shore from the low to the high tide lines (Fig 11.4).

The transect can be marked out either with a tape or string. Ecologists may record every plant that touches the line, or the plants touching at regular intervals, such as every 10 cm. In some cases it is useful to place quadrats along the transect at fixed intervals and then make records of the organisms in the quadrats. This gives a more complete picture of the variety of species present, especially where the conditions change over quite a short distance.

One advantage of transects is that they can be used on very uneven ground, such as across a series of sand dunes. Like quadrats, they can

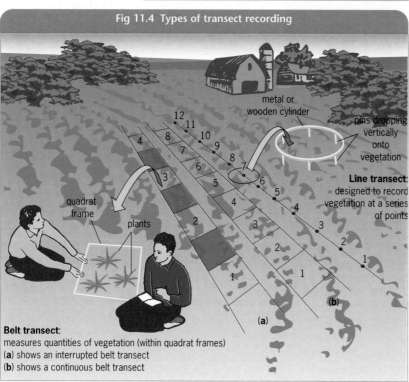

Fig 11.4 Types of transect recording

metal or wooden cylinder

pins dropping vertically onto vegetation

Line transect: designed to record vegetation at a series of points

quadrat frame

plants

Belt transect:
measures quantities of vegetation (within quadrat frames)
(a) shows an interrupted belt transect
(b) shows a continuous belt transect

(a)

(b)

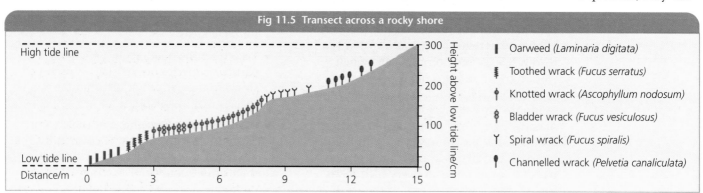

Fig 11.5 Transect across a rocky shore

High tide line

Low tide line

Distance/m

Height above low tide line/cm

Oarweed (*Laminaria digitata*)

Toothed wrack (*Fucus serratus*)

Knotted wrack (*Ascophyllum nodosum*)

Bladder wrack (*Fucus vesiculosus*)

Spiral wrack (*Fucus spiralis*)

Channelled wrack (*Pelvetia canaliculata*)

only be used to record species of plant, or of animals that remain stationary, such as molluscs on a rocky shore. To avoid bias it is best to record results from several transects across the same area, placed at regular intervals, such as every 10 m. It is also useful to record the main features of the environment along the transect, such as the change in height across a rocky shore (Fig 11.5).

3 Different species of seaweed live at different heights above the low tide line. Use Fig 11.5 to find the range of heights in which the different seaweeds lived.

Table 11.1 Transect results															
Species	**Rough grass**					**Trampled path**					**Rough grass**				
	Quadrat														
	1	2	3	4	5	6	7	8	9	10	11	12	13	14	15
Daisy					X	X		X	X	X		X			
Hoary Plantain						X	X	X	X	X	X				
Ribwort Plantain	X	X	X	X	X							X		X	X
Rock Rose		X	X	X										X	X
Salad Burnet	X	X	X	X	X			X		X	X	X		X	X
Meadow grass						X	X	X	X	X	X				
Sheep's fescue grass		X	X	X	X	X	X	X	X	X	X	X	X	X	X
Tor grass	X	X	X	X	X							X	X	X	X

4 A transect was placed across a path on chalk grassland. Quadrats with an area of 400 cm² were placed at regular intervals along the transect. The presence or absence of eight plant species in each quadrat was recorded. The results are shown in Table 11.1.

a The quadrats were square, with an area of 400 cm². What were the dimensions of each quadrat?

b Which species were seriously affected by people walking along the path?

c Suggest why some species are better able to grow on the trampled path than in the area on either side.

Different species of seaweed live in different parts of a rocky shore.

Judging the results of quadrat studies

Interpreting means

After using quadrats to survey an area, you may want to find the mean numbers of different species. For example, if investigating the earthworm populations in two different areas of grassland, you might extract the worms from 10 quadrats in each area, and then calculate the mean number of worms per quadrat. Suppose that the number of worms in the 10 quadrats in one area were: 12, 14, 11, 15, 13, 12, 16, 11, 14 and 12. The mean number is 13, and you could be reasonably sure that if you count a lot more quadrats in the same area the mean would be roughly similar.

Suppose that in the other area the results were: 2, 1, 0, 112, 5, 2, 3, 0, 4 and 1. The mean is again 13. If you count another 10 quadrats it is quite unlikely that you would get the same again, and to suggest that the populations in the two areas were similar would obviously be silly. It is much more likely that there happened to be something odd about the quadrat with 112 worms – maybe it was the site of a recently deposited large cowpat.

You therefore need to be careful when comparing means, but the differences will not always be so obvious. More commonly, the individual pieces of data that are collected will be fairly evenly distributed about the mean, as shown in the graphs in Fig 11.6.

In these two graphs, the mean values are the same, but one has a much greater range than the other. As well as calculating a mean,

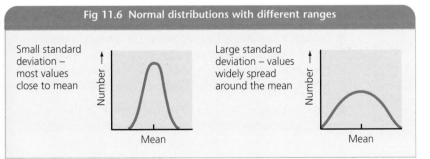

Fig 11.6 Normal distributions with different ranges

Small standard deviation – most values close to mean

Number ↑

Mean

Large standard deviation – values widely spread around the mean

Number ↑

Mean

statisticians use a formula to work out how big a range the data has. This formula gives the **standard deviation**. The larger the standard deviation, the larger the spread of the data. If the standard deviations of two sets of data are large, comparing them is likely to be unreliable because the values may overlap. Chapter 15 explains in more detail how standard deviations are calculated and used.

The chi-squared test

Scientific investigations proceed by a process of formulating and testing ideas (hypotheses). You can never prove anything in science, but you can gather support for your ideas. This is where the chi-squared test comes in – it helps scientists to decide how much weight to give to experimental results. (Chi is the Greek letter X, pronounced 'ky', as in Kylie, and is the mathematical symbol in the formula.)

Suppose that you are trying to find whether using fertiliser makes any difference to the species that grow in a field. You count the number of each of four species in 20

Table 11.2 Species distribution in fertilised and unfertilised areas		
Species	**Total number in 20 quadrats**	
	Fertilised area	**Unfertilised area**
A	0	182
B	2	51
C	88	124
D	91	102

quadrats from fertilised and unfertilised areas and obtain the results shown in Table 11.2 for the four species.

From the results shown in Table 11.2, you would feel pretty certain that fertilising the field affected species A and B. But the results

are much less clear for species C and D. You need to know whether there really is a significant difference between the numbers in the two areas, or whether the apparent difference might be due purely to chance. One way of deciding might be to keep on counting, but a quicker method is to use a statistical test, the chi-squared test.

The chi-squared test can be used when you are counting things, rather than measuring features such as height or mass. It is based on working out how likely it is that the results might have occurred by chance. If you toss a coin 20 times, you could expect that it would fall as 'heads' 10 times and as 'tails' 10 times. However, sometimes you might get, say, 12 heads and 8 tails, or even 15 and 5. The further the result is from the expected 10 heads and 10 tails, the rarer it will be. The test formula calculates how likely the actual results are compared with the expected results. In the example above, if the species were randomly distributed between the two areas, you would expect the numbers in each area to be the same.

For the purposes of the test, we assume that any difference between the actual results and the expected results is just due to chance. This is called the **null hypothesis**. The results of the calculation will tell us how rare it would be for the actual results to be due to chance. If the test results show that such results would occur by chance only 5 times out of 100 or less, we would consider it unlikely that the results were just chance and we would reject the null hypothesis. This means that we are suggesting that we think that our research has probably found a significant difference. Details of how the test is done and how to interpret the results are explained in Chapter 15.

KEY FACTS

■ Frame quadrats are used to measure the numbers and distribution of species in a habitat. They are particularly useful for comparing the vegetation in different areas. Either the frequency or the percentage cover of species within a quadrat may be measured.

■ To avoid bias, quadrats must be placed randomly. A grid of the area being studied should be produced. The quadrats should be positioned either at regular intervals using co-ordinates, or with a table of random numbers.

■ Transects are lines across a habitat, along which plants or sedentary animals are sampled. They are particularly useful for recording sequences of change from one area to another, such as across a shore.

■ Standard deviation is a measure of the spread of results about a mean. Comparisons between sets of results with low standard deviations are generally more reliable than between ones with large standard deviations.

■ The chi-squared test is used to assess whether there is a significant difference between sets of results or whether any differences are more likely to be due to chance.

11.2 Measuring abiotic factors

On a rocky shore, the different species of seaweed grow in very clear zones. Oarweed only grows close to the low tide line, whereas spiral wrack grows only near the high tide line. This is not just chance. Different species are adapted to different conditions. For example, oarweed is covered by water most of the time and is exposed to violent waves. Spiral wrack is exposed to the air between high tides for long periods, but gets more light since it is never covered by deep water, and wave action is less severe.

In every habitat the physical conditions vary from place to place. These non-living components of an ecosystem are called **abiotic factors**. They include such factors as temperature, light, pH, rainfall, humidity, wind and water currents. They contrast with **biotic factors**, such as predation and competition, which result from the activities of other organisms.

To understand how the distribution of organisms is controlled by abiotic factors, ecologists must measure them in the ecosystem. It is important to remember that conditions may vary considerably at different times and in different places. The survival of organisms may be dependent on the worst conditions that occur, and not just on the conditions that occur when ecologists happen to be around. Factors may have to be measured over long periods of time and at different times of day and in different seasons. For example, on a summer's day, when teachers and students prefer to do fieldwork, the temperature on opposite sides of a narrow valley may be very similar. But, in winter, when the sun is low, the south-facing slope may be several degrees warmer than the other side. Frost and snow may linger much longer on the colder slopes, and the vegetation can be quite different because only the hardiest plants survive.

Measuring instruments

Measuring instruments need to be suitable for use in the field. Mercury thermometers such as are used in the laboratory are not really suitable. They are easily broken and difficult to read in many situations, for instance when measuring soil temperature. Battery operated electronic instruments are much more appropriate. By using a probe attached to the main instrument by a long and flexible wire, it is much easier to record measurements in places where it is difficult to see a scale. The scale may be adjusted to cover only the range of values likely to be met in the field and can therefore be more sensitive.

For temperature...

Temperature can be measured with a probe that contains a thermistor or a silicon diode. A thermistor is very sensitive, but the temperature readings are not linear. This is because the thermistor measures change in electrical resistance, and this does not alter evenly as the temperature changes. It is therefore necessary to calibrate the instrument. This can be done by placing the probe in water baths at different temperatures, measured with an accurate conventional thermometer. A silicon diode does not need to be calibrated because the scale is linear, but it is slower to respond to changes in temperature than a thermistor.

For light intensity...

Light intensity is best measured with battery-powered light meters, called photometers or light sensors. Most light sensors need to be calibrated because they do not respond linearly to changes in light intensity. It is difficult to obtain an accurate measure of light energy, for example in kilojoules per square metre. Often the scale on the meter just gives the amount of light energy in arbitrary units. This enables light intensity at different times or in different places to be compared. In practice, light is difficult to measure accurately in the field, because it often varies from minute to minute. The measurement can also depend on the direction from which the light is coming. What matters to a plant is the total amount of light energy it receives in a given time, rather the intensity at a particular time. To record variations in light intensity over a long period, a data-logger is very useful.

For pH...

pH is another abiotic factor that is normally best measured electriconically, using a pH meter and a probe containing a pH electrode. The pH scale is a measure of hydrogen ion concentration, and can only be measured in aqueous solution. In natural ecosystems it is rare for the pH to be outside the range 4 to 8. A value of pH 7 is neutral on the pH scale. A value of pH 4 or below is quite strongly acidic, whereas above pH 8 it is increasingly alkaline. The scale is not linear. A lower number represents a higher concentration of hydrogen ions, but, for example, a reduction from pH 6 to pH 3 does not just double the acidity. It increases it a thousand times, i.e. the concentration of hydrogen ions is a thousand times as great.

Indicator solutions and indicator papers can be used, but they must be suitable for measuring accurately a narrow range of pH. To measure the pH of soil with indicator solution, a sample must first be shaken with neutral water. Since soil only settles very slowly, barium sulphate is used to make the particles clump together and fall quickly. Universal indicator, specially designed to give a range of colours over the pH 4–8 range, can then be used in the clear water.

Many organisms are very sensitive to the pH of their environment. Not many species of plant can survive the acid soils found on peat moorlands like these. Cotton grass and sphagnum moss are typical of the few that are adapted to a pH below 5. High rainfall causes basic ions, such as calcium, to be washed out of the soil. Water-logging reduces the rate of decay, and organic acids are released from partially decayed peat. These factors both contribute an excess of hydrogen ions to the soil.

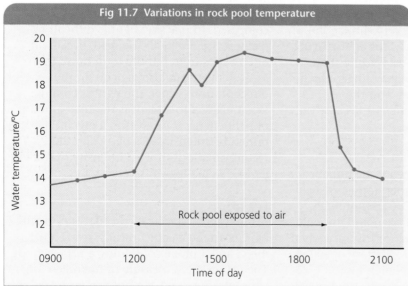

Fig 11.7 Variations in rock pool temperature

5 A student measures the pH of the water in a stream at several different times. Explain why it would not be valid to calculate the mean pH from the results.

6 Low pH can affect the activities of cells in two ways. The hydrogen ions may affect enzymes directly, and they may cause an increase in the concentration of heavy metal ions. Use your knowledge of enzymes to explain why each of these factors affects cell activity.

Rock pools at Kimmeridge Bay, Dorset.

7 The photograph above shows a rock pool on a rocky shore. Abiotic factors in the rock pool vary considerably at different times. For part of the day it is covered by sea water. When the tide goes out it is exposed to air, and some of the water evaporates. Fig 11.7 shows variations in the temperature of the water in the pool on a summer's day.

a Describe and explain the changes in temperature in the rock pool.

b Explain how a rise in temperature could affect the oxygen concentration in the water of the rock pool. How would this affect the animal life?

c Explain how the presence of seaweeds in a pool can affect the oxygen concentration while the tide is out.

d The concentration of salt in the water (salinity) is an abiotic factor that may vary considerably in a rock pool. Suggest what might cause the salt concentration in the pool to rise above the normal salinity of sea water, and what might cause it to fall below. How could changes in concentration affect living organisms in the pool?

Blue butterflies run out of thyme

The large blue butterfly became extinct in Britain in 1979. It once lived on the chalk grasslands in places like the one shown in the photo at the start of this chapter. The caterpillars depended for their survival on a remarkable relationship with a species of ant. The young caterpillars fed on the flowers of wild thyme, on which they were well camouflaged. As they grew larger, the caterpillars migrated from the thyme into the grass. From here the ants would transport them to their nest. When the ants stroked them with their antennae, the caterpillars were stimulated to secrete a sugary liquid, which was a ready-made source of food for the ants to feed to their larvae in the nest. The butterfly caterpillars, however, tucked into some of the ant larvae while they were guests in the nest. Having obtained enough protein from their hosts for a bit more growth, the caterpillars would turn into pupae inside the ant's nest, where they would remain through the winter. The following summer, the pupae would hatch into adult butterflies that crawled out of the nest, and set their life cycle in motion once again.

Wild thyme has short stems and grows as mat-like clumps in short grass. The chalk downs used to be heavily grazed by sheep and rabbits, but the numbers of sheep were reduced as a result of changes in farming practices. Then the viral disease, myxomatosis spread through the rabbit population and killed a very high proportion of it. The grass was no longer cropped short. As the grasses grew taller, many of the typical chalkland flower species died out.

Large blue butterfly (top) and wild thyme (bottom).

1 a An ecologist wants to compare the species of plant that grow on chalk grassland that is grazed by rabbits with an area that has no grazing. List the steps that would be necessary to carry out this research.

b Explain why the large blue butterfly became extinct on chalk grassland.

- Abiotic factors are those that result from the physical conditions in a habitat, such as temperature and pH.

- Measurements of temperature, light and pH in the field are usually carried out with battery-operated meters.

- The effects of abiotic factors on organisms are complex, and often cannot be readily judged from measurements taken on only a small number of occasions.

1 The number of earthworms in a field may be estimated by using frame quadrats. The quadrats are placed at random on the surface of the area being sampled. The ground is then watered with a very dilute solution of formalin. The earthworms which come to the surface are collected and washed.

a
   i Explain why the quadrats should be placed at random. (1)
   ii Throwing a quadrat does not ensure a random distribution. Describe a method by which you could ensure that the quadrats would be placed at random. (2)

b Give one advantage of describing the size of the population in terms of biomass rather than as the number of earthworms collected. (1)

c Similar sized populations of earthworms were kept in soils at different temperatures. The earthworms were fed on discs cut from leaves. The table shows the number of leaf discs eaten at each temperature.

Temperature/°C	Number of leaf discs eaten
0	0
5	178
10	204
15	174
20	124

Using information in the table, explain how mean soil temperature and feeding activity might affect the size of the earthworm population. (3)

Total (7)

BY05 March 1999 Q2

2 Many hill-top areas in The Peak District National Park have lost their vegetation cover, leaving areas of bare soil and peat. Experiments have been carried to investigate the re-colonisation of these bare areas. Several experimental plots, each measuring 12 m x 12 m, were seeded with heather (a moorland shrub) and then either fenced or left unfenced. The fencing was to keep out sheep. After three years the percentage cover of heather and two other common moorland plants was recorded.

Cover	Percentage cover fenced	unfenced
Heather	26.9	6.2
Bent grass	1.9	0.6
Wavy-hair grass	1.4	0.2
Bare soil	69.8	93.0

a Briefly describe one method that might have been used to obtain the data on percentage plant cover. (3)

b
   i From the data given, calculate the difference in total percentage cover of plants between the two types of plot. (1)
   ii Describe the effects that sheep have on re-colonization of the plots. (2)

c Name the process in which a community alters its environment and is replaced by a new community over a period of time. (1)

Total (7)

BY05 June 1997 Q6

3 A field is crossed by small ridges and furrows. The distribution in this field of two species of buttercup (*Ranunculus bulbosus* and *Ranunculus repens*) was investigated, using a transect across the ridges and furrows. The number of buttercup plants in each of a series of long narrow strips (15 cm x 200 cm) at right angles to the transect was counted. The results are shown in the graph below.

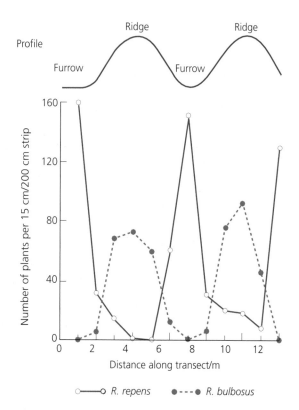

a
i Explain what is meant by a transect. (1)
ii Suggest why the counting was done in long narrow strips instead of in square quadrats. (1)

b Describe how the distribution of the two species of buttercup differed. (1)

c In a follow-up experiment, 50 seeds of each species were sown in pots. In half of the pots the soil was able to drain freely. The other pots had no drainage, so the soil was waterlogged. The results are shown in the table below.

Pot	Mean number of seedlings per pot	
	Ranunculus bulbosus	*Ranunculus repens*
Free-draining soil	32	12
Waterlogged soil	2	12

i Using these results, suggest an explanation for the different distributions of *R. bulbosus* and *R. repens* in the field. (2)
ii Explain how waterlogging of the soil might affect the rate of growth of a seedling. (2)

Total (7)

BY05 March 2000 Q5

4
a Describe the techniques that could be used to compare the vegetation in two areas of woodland. (6)

b In an investigation into the leaf length of bluebells in two areas of woodland, the standard deviations of the two populations were calculated. The results showed that there was a statistically significant difference between the two populations. Explain what is meant by

i standard deviation,
ii a significant difference. (2)

c As part of this investigation measurements of the abiotic factors were carried out in the two areas of woodland. Describe how two named abiotic factors could be measured and explain how each could affect the occurrence of vegetation in different areas. (4)

Total (12)

BY05 March 1998 Q8

5 Intercropping involves growing two or more different species of plants together. Maize and beans are intercropped in many tropical regions.

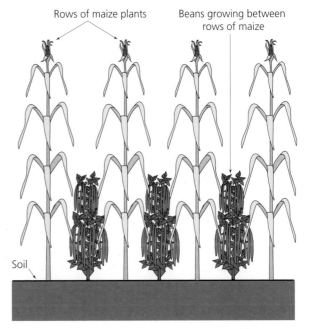

Rows of maize plants   Beans growing between rows of maize

Soil

Fig 11.Q5 Diagrammatic cross-section through a mixed crop of maize and beans

a Identify one abiotic factor which would affect the growth of maize plants. Describe how you could measure variation in this factor over a 24-hour period. (2)

b Describe two ways in which maize plants affect the abiotic environment of the bean plants. (2)

c The maximum yield that could be gained from a plot in which maize and beans are intercropped would be higher than that which could be gained if either maize or beans were grown alone. Explain why. (2)

Total (6)

BY05 June 1999 Q4

12 Populations and communities

A female rabbit can produce up to 10 young in a litter, and within 24 hours she may be pregnant again. A month later another litter is born. At this rate a rabbit population can quickly rise to a phenomenally high level. Within 3 years, one couple could have about 13 million descendants. So, why aren't we surrounded by swarms of rabbits? Obviously, only a small proportion of young rabbits actually survive and breed. All sorts of disasters can befall them, such as predation, disease, starvation or cold. In most circumstances the size of the population is kept in check.

In some circumstances, however, there can be dramatic increases. In the 19th century, European settlers introduced rabbits into Australia, partly for food, partly for sport, and perhaps partly to have something reassuringly familiar in an alien land. In Australia there were few predators equipped to take advantage of this new food source. The native grazing animals, marsupials, such as kangaroos and wallabies, carry their young in an external pouch, and their reproductive rate is much slower than that of a rabbit. Also, they do not graze as close to the ground as the rabbit. The rabbits therefore had little competition for food or space. With such limited restrictions on the survival of their young, the rabbit population soared, and not surprisingly rabbits soon became a serious pest and a major threat to sheep farming.

12.1 Population oscillations

A rabbit population can also suffer an equally dramatic decline. Early in the 20th century, a disease was found in rabbits from South America. Myxomatosis, later identified as a viral disease, was deadly to the European rabbit. Infected animals developed grotesque swellings around the face, often causing blindness, and they died within a couple of weeks. In 1950, infected rabbits were released in south-east Australia in a deliberate attempt to control the population. Within a couple of years 80 per cent of the rabbits had perished.

The control measure was so successful that the same strategy was repeated in France two years later. The virus is spread by mosquitoes, and by chance favourable warm winds carried mosquitoes laden with the parasite across the Channel to Britain. Myxomatosis spread rapidly, and it is estimated that about 99 per cent of the 60 million rabbits in Britain died. The effects of this sensational plunge were not confined to rabbits. Not surprisingly there were massive effects throughout the food web. We have already seen in Chapter 11 how

A wild rabbit suffering from myxomatosis.

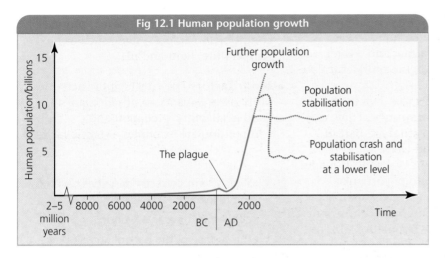

Fig 12.1 Human population growth

removal of grazing rabbits can affect grassland. In Britain, there was also a major decline in the populations of the predators that depended on the rabbits. Numbers of birds of prey such as buzzards and of weasels and stoats fell sharply.

It is rare in natural conditions for populations to vary so much but smaller oscillations occur in all populations. Usually, limiting factors come into play and any rise or fall is quickly curbed.

An exception to this general rule is the human population, which has grown exponentially for the last 1000 years (Fig 12.1) and which continues to rise relentlessly, at about 1.5% per year. This can't go on for ever, and, even though human ingenuity may delay the consequences, eventually, natural factors will impose limits on growth.

This leads to some difficult dilemmas:

- Should population growth be allowed to continue until competition, starvation and disease bring about a natural decline?
- Should urgent measures be taken to control population growth?
- Might continued expansion cause so much environmental damage that the planet becomes unable to sustain human life?
- How can we ensure that the plants and animals survive to maintain the natural cycles that are vital for our survival?

Understanding the factors that control the stability of ecosystems is a vital first step. In this chapter we shall look at how different populations interact in an ecosystem. We shall see how each species is adapted for survival in a limited set of conditions, and how small changes in these conditions can put its survival in peril. We also investigate how newly created habitats can undergo a gradual sequence of changes, allowing a succession of different species to survive there.

An introduction to abiotic and biotic factors

As we saw in Chapter 10, an ecosystem includes all the living things in a particular habitat and the physical conditions of the environment. If we think of a simple ecosystem such as a small pond (Fig 12.2), the physical conditions, or abiotic factors (see Chapter 11), include the depth, temperature, acidity, clarity and nutrient content of the water.

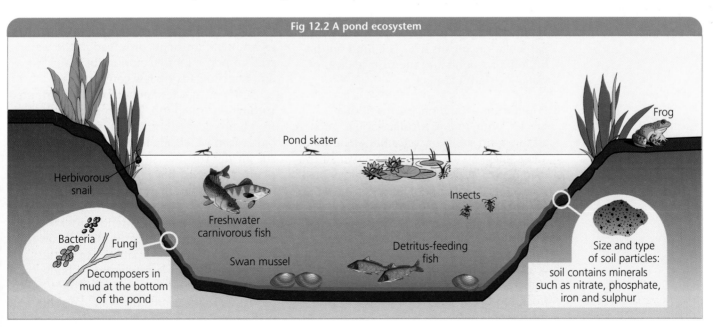

Fig 12.2 A pond ecosystem

169

The abiotic factors may vary in different parts of the pond. The water, for example, might be less deep and warmer and clearer near to the edge but colder and murkier in the middle.

The plants and animals that live in the water form the **pond community**. They form feeding relationships that are part of one or more complex food webs. A population of organisms in the pond is made up of all the organisms of one particular type. Different species in the ecosystem interact with other, so the population size of one species can affect the population size of another. For example, the more water plants in the pond, the more food there is for pond snails, and also the more shade and shelter for insects.

When the activities of living organisms influence other organisms, we call their effects **biotic factors**. Biotic factors are continually changing, and can also affect the abiotic factors in the ecosystem. Conditions in any ecosystem are therefore never constant. Understanding the dynamics of an ecosystem is one of the main tasks of ecology.

Some important ecological terms

It is important that you use ecological terms accurately, so let's summarise the meaning of the main ones:

- **Ecosystem** A group of interrelated organisms and their physical environment in an area that has fairly uniform conditions, such as a pond, desert or forest.

- **Habitat** The part of an ecosystem in which particular organisms live. The mud on the bottom of a pond and the surface layer of water are both habitats.

- **Population** All the organisms of one species living in a particular habitat, such as all the pond snails or water lilies in a pond. Sometimes the term is used to mean all the members of a species in a much larger area, such as the human population of the world or the rabbit population of Australia.

- **Community** All the living organisms of all the species that live together in a particular ecosystem or habitat. The pond community comprises all the plants, snails, insects, frogs and fish living there, as well as the microscopic algae, bacteria and so on.

- **Abiotic factors** The non-living, physical conditions in an ecosystem, such as temperature, light and pH.

- **Biotic factors** The effects of the activities of living organisms on other organisms. Food availability, predation and competition are examples of biotic factors.

1 Which term correctly describes each of the following:
a all the oak trees in a wood;
b the surface of the bark of an oak tree;
c the Siberian tundra;
d the salt concentration of a rock pool;
e the organisms living in a rock pool;
f the effect of snails grazing on pondweed.

2 Explain why are there are fewer predators than primary consumers in a community.

Communities and niches

The pond community shown in Fig 12.2 contains many different species of plant and animal, many more than can be shown in the diagram. Each of these species is a specialist in some way. There are examples of every trophic level in the food chain, some producers, some primary consumers, and so on.

The total size and richness of the community depends on the resources available to the producers. A pond which has few mineral nutrients dissolved in the water will support a limited amount of plant life, and hence relatively few consumers.

Different species are not evenly distributed throughout the pond. The greater the variety in the physical environment, such as shallow bays, deep water, shaded banks and so on, the greater the diversity is likely to be. Those plants that must have their roots in the soil can grow only near the margins and in shallow water. Others, such as the water lilies, float and can therefore extend across the surface of the pond. Swan mussels lie on the bottom and filter food particles from the water that they suck through their body, whereas pond skaters are fast-moving predators that can literally walk, and run, on water.

A pond skater, *Gerris lacustris*, on the surface of water (right). A freshwater swan mussel showing frilly edge of siphons projecting between the valves on the right of the picture (below).

The concept of the ecological niche

In the community, each species is adapted to a set of conditions, and it is only successful where the abiotic and biotic factors in an ecosystem are suited to its way of life.

The part of the habitat in which a species lives and the environmental conditions that it requires form what is called its **ecological niche**. Let's look at the ecological niche of the swan mussel, which lives predominantly on the bed of shallow ponds, as an example.

The body structure of the swan mussel obviously rules out a place for it with the pond skater; it could not easily chase insects across the top of the water. Instead, it uses its siphon and cilia to draw a current of water through its body and filter out microscopic organisms for food. This may seem very lazy, but is an energy efficient way of obtaining food, as long as the pond water contains a good supply of microscopic food particles. This is more likely in shallow ponds than in

deep ponds, since microscopic plant plankton need light. Very deep water would also contain less oxygen and more silt, which could clog the delicate filter system. All these factors contribute to the specific requirements of the mussel and determine its niche in the pond.

Niches within a habitat

In a particular habitat every species has its own niche. This prevents organisms of different species from competing for exactly the same resources. Even species that live in the same habitat and that appear to be very similar often have different ways of life. For example, several snail species live in pond habitats, but different species are part of different food chains, and the smaller and lighter ones can live on the more delicate plants shunned by their heavier neighbours.

Snails are often found in habitats with chalky soils; they need the calcium in the chalk to build their shells.

Similarly, different species of humming bird have very slightly different shaped beaks that enable them to feed from one flower, but not another.

Rufous humming birds drink nectar from the scarlet gilia, pollinating it at the same time

Common mole (top) and Marsupial mole (bottom)

Competing for the same niche

When two species occupy exactly the same niche, one usually out-competes the other, either by being better able to use the food supply, or being better at protecting itself from predators. In the end the less successful competitor is driven out of the habitat.

Interestingly, similar niches in different ecosystems in different parts of the world may be occupied by different species. Australia used to have marsupial species that grazed on the vegetation, but when rabbits were introduced they out-competed the marsupials because of their more efficient method of reproduction. Similarly, when the grey squirrel was introduced to Britain from North America, it was able to exploit woodland food sources such as nuts and acorns more effectively than the native red squirrel and largely supplanted it.

3 The common mole is adapted to burrow through soil and feed on organisms such as earthworms. It has powerful clawed front legs, a pointed snout and eyes buried in its fur. In Australia there is a marsupial mole which occupies a very similar niche and which has very similar behaviour and adaptations. However, the two animals have totally different ancestors.

Use your knowledge of evolution to explain how both the common and marsupial mole could have evolved from quite different ancestors to have similar features, such as powerful clawed front legs and a pointed snout.

12.2 Populations

A family decides to have a small pond in their garden. They dig a big hole, put in a plastic liner and fill it with water. Most families would want an instant community in their new pond and would add water plants, fish and so on. But this very patient family waits to find out what develops naturally. They wait to see which species may reach the pond in very small numbers by chance, for example in the wind or on the feet of birds. One early arrival might well be a single-celled alga, which is able to photosynthesise and which reproduces asexually. In the virgin territory of a new pond, this newcomer would be able to develop a population without competition.

Fig 12.3 shows the results of an experiment in which a culture of single-celled algae was grown in a laboratory beaker rather a pond. At first the population grows slowly, but then, after a few days, the rate of growth increases rapidly. However, in a small beaker, this rise in numbers is soon restricted by a shortage of resources. Once the surface is covered by algae, there is less light lower down for other cells to photosynthesise. Also, the algae might have absorbed most of the mineral ions that they need for the synthesis of proteins and chlorophyll. In the beaker, population growth stops and starts to fall as some cells die.

This is an example of intraspecific competition. 'Intra' means 'within', and this describes competition between members of the same species.

4 Suppose that ten algal cells were originally put into the beaker and that they all survived after every division.

a How many cells would there be after each of the first ten generations? Show your results in a simple table.

b Draw a graph showing the growth of this population and describe the shape of the curve.

c How does the theoretical population growth compare with actual growth in Fig 12.3?

d Which abiotic factors probably limited the actual growth?

In real situations changes in population size are much more complex, because a species would hardly ever live in total isolation from other species. In the family pond it is unlikely that the algal species would continue to grow until it reached its maximum possible size. Other species would undoubtedly arrive and either compete with it or feed on it.

Fig 12.4, below, and Figs 12.5 and 12.6 on the next page show the results of an experiment originally done by a Russian ecologist to investigate competition between two species. The species chosen were both single-celled protoctists; *Paramecium aurelia* and *Paramecium caudatum*. Both feed on bacteria and yeast cells.

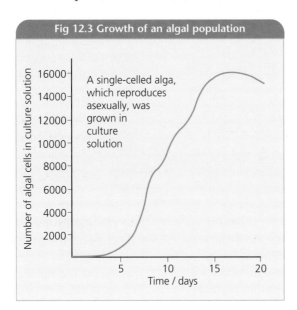

Fig 12.3 Growth of an algal population

A single-celled alga, which reproduces asexually, was grown in culture solution

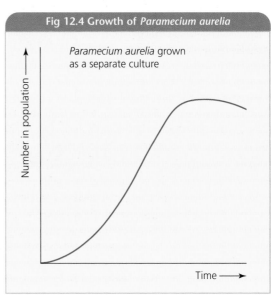

Fig 12.4 Growth of *Paramecium aurelia*

Paramecium aurelia grown as a separate culture

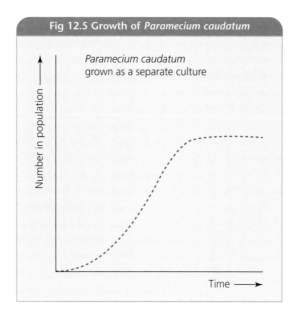

Fig 12.5 Growth of *Paramecium caudatum*

Paramecium caudatum grown as a separate culture

Number in population →

Time →

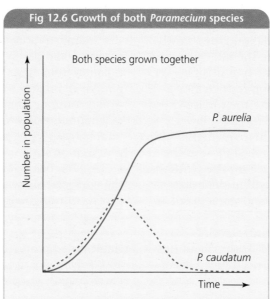

Fig 12.6 Growth of both *Paramecium* species

Both species grown together

Number in population →

P. aurelia

P. caudatum

Time →

As Fig 12.6 shows, when both species were grown together in the same culture, both species grew equally well at first. Then, once the food became more scarce *P. caudatum* was less successful at obtaining food. Its numbers declined while those of its competitor species, *P. aurelia*, increased.

When two populations of different species compete for the same resources in an ecosystem, this is called **interspecific competition**, because it is between ('inter') species.

You can remember what the two terms inter specific and intraspecific mean using the memory aid; 'Fighting *between* families is **ter**rible; fighting *within* families is **tra**gic'.

Stability of populations

So far we have considered simple situations in which populations are becoming established in a new habitat. Once a pond has an established community, there will be many interacting species and there will be little opportunity for the population of one species to increase rapidly. In fact, it is likely that the numbers of each species will remain fairly stable, unless some new factor, such as pollution, arises.

What determines population size?

The most important factor is the total amount of producers that can grow in a particular location. This, in turn, is limited by abiotic factors such as light. In a pond, once the surface of the pond is completely covered, no more plants grow because there is no space for them to receive enough light. Plants growing in shallow water can maximise the amount of light they get by growing upwards, but those that float on the surface in deeper water inevitably have a lower mass per unit area. In good soils, trees are able to grow to considerable heights and thus make best use of the incident light.

Other abiotic factors, such as water and mineral ion availability, wind or current speed, may also limit the producer populations. In most ecosystems, abiotic factors are not constant throughout the environment, and the plants themselves create diversity. The variation in conditions means that many niches develop with the result that many different species of plant can live together in the same area.

5 Suggest which abiotic factors are likely to be most important in limiting the growth of plants in each of the following habitats:

a a desert;

b the summit of a high mountain in Scotland;

c a mountain stream;

d a sandy shore;

e peat moorland.

The size of the populations of consumers depends on the productivity of the ecosystem. The greater the biomass of the producers the more consumers it can support. The low efficiency of transfer of energy from one trophic level to the next means that the total biomass of producers must be much greater than that of the consumers, as we explained in Chapter 10. Also, the greater the diversity of plant species, the greater the variety of consumers there is likely to be. The size of the population of each species varies according to the amount of available food for its particular niche. On the whole, very productive ecosystems such as tropical forest support the greatest variety of primary consumers, and these in turn sustain a large variety of secondary consumers.

Reaching a balance

Given time, most ecosystems reach a balanced situation in which the populations of most species remain fairly constant. However, the interactions between organisms in an ecosystem are highly complex, and quite small changes can alter the balance quite rapidly.

Obviously, animals that feed on plants damage the plants, but most plants have a remarkable capacity to withstand damage without individuals being killed off. An oak tree in summer may have many thousands of insects of many different species busily feeding on its leaves. Yet, it can generate enough new growth to maintain itself for hundreds of years.

The most successful herbaceous plants, the grasses, are adapted to tolerate almost continuous grazing, because the growing point of the stem is tucked away at the base of the leaves, very close to the ground. Grasses will only suffer serious losses if numbers of herbivores escalate excessively, as occurred with rabbits in Australia.

Normally, excessive growth of the herbivore populations is kept under control by predators. If numbers of herbivores start to increase, there will be more food for predators, so their numbers increase too. The increase in predation then brings down the population of herbivores again. If the herbivore population falls too low the predators fail to find enough prey, so the predator population falls again.

This means that there may be a regular fluctuation in numbers of predators and prey, as shown in Fig 12.7. Notice that the rise in population of the predators is always rather later than the rise in the prey population, and similarly there is a delay before it starts to fall.

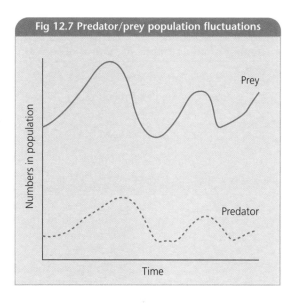

Fig 12.7 Predator/prey population fluctuations

Human influence can affect the natural balance

It is not in the long-term interests of predators to be too successful at killing their prey, because they run the risk of eliminating their own food supply. Natural selection has favoured a sort of arms race in which the defences of the prey have more or less matched the attacking capabilities of the predators. Prey with inadequate defences and predators that wiped out all their prey would both become extinct.

Human activities have disrupted this balance in many places. For example, by removing wolves and lynx and other predators, populations of large herbivores such as red deer have soared in areas like northern Scotland and have greatly reduced the diversity of vegetation, especially woodland.

The introduction of new predators such as cats and rats to New Zealand has almost exterminated many of the flightless birds, including the national emblem, the kiwi.

Table 12.1 A study of a colony of rabbits	
Number of adult rabbits at start of observations	**70**
Number of breeding females	36
Total number of young emerging to feed	280
Number of young in colony at end of first season*	28
Number of adults in colony at end of first season	11

*A few of the young may have moved away to another colony, but the great majority were killed by predators in their first week above ground

6 Grazing rabbits are in constant danger from predators. One way in which they are protected is by living in underground burrows. Their acute hearing and 'all-round' eyesight enables them to sense danger and escape quickly when feeding above ground. However, narrow-bodied predators such as the weasel and polecat can follow them into their burrows.

Table 12.1 shows the results of a study of rabbit numbers in a particular colony.

a What would you expect to happen to the rabbit population in this colony if the same level of predation carried on? Explain your answer.

b How might the colony's numbers be restored by natural means?

Population oscillations

In productive ecosystems with very complex food webs, it is difficult to monitor and record the fluctuations in predator and prey populations. They are sometimes more obvious in more extreme conditions, where there are relatively few species and where a predator may be dependent on one prey species.

For some prey species it may be an advantage to have a cycle in which the population expands rapidly and then crashes to a low level. This avoids a possible build-up of predators because for much of the time there is an inadequate food supply for them. One of the most famous examples of this is the lemming, a small herbivorous rodent that lives on the Arctic tundra. Fig 12.8 shows population changes over a period of 12 years.

According to popular myth, lemmings deliberately commit suicide by jumping over cliffs in order to prevent their colleagues starving. Such public-spirited behaviour would defy the normal rules of competition and selection, and the reality is less romantic.

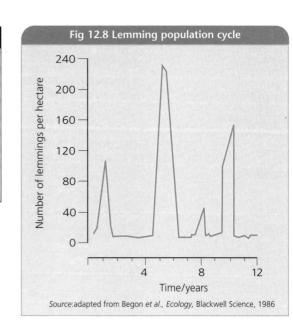

Fig 12.8 Lemming population cycle

Source: adapted from Begon *et al.*, *Ecology*, Blackwell Science, 1986

In years when the population explodes, rapid breeding occurs while the land is still snow-covered. The young lemmings consume large quantities of grass and other plants while still protected from predators by the blanket of snow. Then, once the snow melts, various factors work together to cause the population to crash:

- Predators move in to take advantage of the large supply of prey.

- The rising population consumes the most nutritious plant material first. This means that, when the lemming population is at its peak, the diet is short of key nutrients. This weakens the lemmings and makes them more susceptible to predators and disease.

- The high density of animals may lead to frequent aggressive encounters between individuals, which cause hormonal imbalances and reduce their reproductive capacity.

All of these factors cause the population to fall to a low level that is sustainable until the plants recover sufficiently for a new cycle to begin. Meanwhile some of the lemmings migrate and may populate new habitats that have not been over-exploited. It is during these migrations that the occasional spectacular mass drowning may occur.

7 The Arctic fox preys on lemmings. What pattern would you expect to find in the Arctic fox population over the same period as that shown in Fig 12.8?

- In the absence of competition, for example when a new species is introduced, the population of some species may grow rapidly until limited by the availability of food, space or other resources.

- Individuals of the same species will compete with each other for any resource that is in limited supply. This is called **intraspecific competition**.

- Members of different species may compete for the same resources. This is called **interspecific competition**.

- The number of primary consumers depends on the amount of food available and on the number of predators that feed on them.

- In a particular ecosystem the variety of consumer species generally depends on the quantity of producers and the number of different niches available. A greater biomass of producers means that more primary consumers can be supported.

- Populations of predators and prey interact. When prey populations increase, there is a corresponding increase in the predator population, and vice versa. In most ecosystems this results in minor fluctuations in population sizes, but in some extreme environments there may be much larger variations.

12.3 Succession

So far in this chapter we have looked at established ecosystems. But, how do ecosystems become established? Bare ground rarely stays bare for long. Every farmer and gardener knows that weeds soon take over any area of untended soil.

Suppose that a farmer stops using a field, either for grazing animals or growing crops. This is now happening regularly as a result of the 'set aside' policy, which aims to reduce usage of land not required for food production and to encourage the development of larger areas of natural habitat. Most agricultural land in Britain reverts to forest, which is the most stable type of community. Until about 3000 years ago most of Britain was forested, and

there were still large tracts of forest at the time of the Norman Conquest. Human activities, such as agriculture, charcoal burning and use of timber for fuel, ship-building and housing materials destroyed great swathes of woodland. The most stable type of community in an area is called a **climax community**. Once a climax community is established it remains in a similar state permanently, unless conditions change. Individual trees may die, but they are replaced by others. There may be temporary gaps that support 'unusual' communities, but overall the ecosystem remains stable.

The change from bare ground or grassland to forest takes place in a series of stages, called **succession**, as illustrated by Fig 12.9.

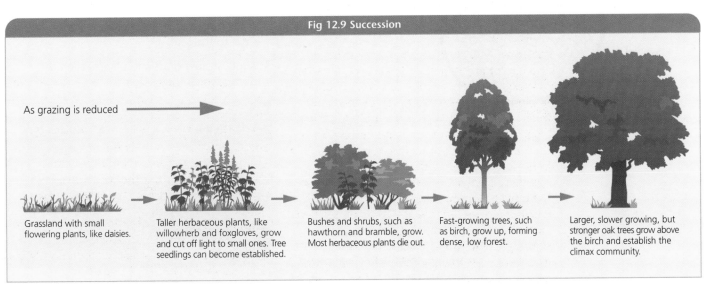

Fig 12.9 Succession

As grazing is reduced →

Grassland with small flowering plants, like daisies.

Taller herbaceous plants, like willowherb and foxgloves, grow and cut off light to small ones. Tree seedlings can become established.

Bushes and shrubs, such as hawthorn and bramble, grow. Most herbaceous plants die out.

Fast-growing trees, such as birch, grow up, forming dense, low forest.

Larger, slower growing, but stronger oak trees grow above the birch and establish the climax community.

Sand dune succession

Sand dunes

The photograph below right shows sand dunes at Luskentyre, Harris, in the Western Isles of Scotland. Prevailing winds blow sand up the beach. Just beyond the reach of most high tides the sand dries out and starts to pile up in dunes parallel to the shore. Very few species of plant can tolerate conditions in this dry, salty sand that is continually being shifted around by the wind. However a few specimens of marram grass may be able to take hold. These have a network of branching underground stems that help to stabilise the sand. As small mounds of sand build up, sand particles are deposited in the slightly more sheltered spots behind them because the wind speed is reduced. Ridges of sand accumulate in the same way as snow drifts. Within ten years these ridges may be three metres high and well covered by marram grass and with a few other species able to take advantage of the shelter that it provides.

As the humus content of the dunes increases, water retention is improved and mineral nutrients do not drain away so rapidly. Other grasses and grassland plants colonise the dunes. In these more favourable conditions the marram grass is out-competed and dies out. If you move inland from the beach, as you cross older and older dunes you will find a complete record of succession, until established woodland is reached.

1 Suggest four abiotic factors that make colonisation by plants particularly difficult in the sand just above the high tide line.

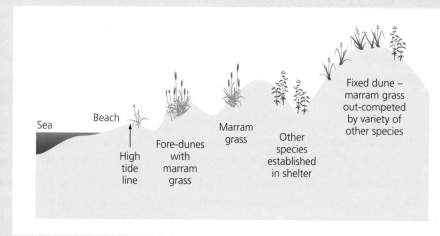

Marram grass

Marram grass is a particularly successful coloniser of dunes. It has xerophytic adaptations similar to those of desert plants, as we saw in the AS book (pages 188 and 189).

2 List and explain the adaptations of marram grass that enable it to colonise sand dunes next to the sea.

3 Suggest how grassland plants reach the dunes which they colonise.

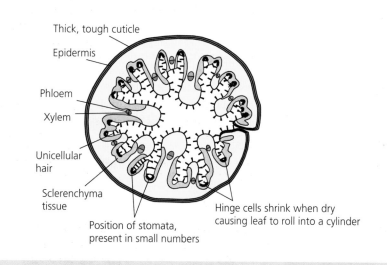

Marram grass usually grows on exposed sandy sites (see photograph right). The diagram above shows the intricate structure of the hinged leave of marram grass.

Why does succession occur?

Succession occurs because conditions within the habitat change. If a farmer removes grazing animals from a field, the grasses are able to grow taller. The tall grasses prevent smaller plants like daisies from obtaining enough light. However, the new set of conditions allows the growth of taller herbaceous plants that have different niches.

These plants are unable to withstand grazing because they are killed if their stem is cut near the ground, but once grazing stops they can grow amongst the grasses. By having leaves that extend sideways from high up on tall stems, they are able to obtain light for photosynthesis. Their extended leaves shade the ground and reduce the supply of light to the grasses, so these tend to die out. The tall herbaceous plants have deeper roots than the grasses, so they are able to access more mineral ions in the soil.

Other plants, such as shrubs and other low-growing plants, take over as conditions continue to change. Eventually, large trees start to appear. This process carries on until a **climax community** is reached. The changing conditions also alter the niches available for animals, so each stage of the succession has a characteristic community adapted to the available niches.

8 Describe the role of biotic factors in succession that occurs in an untended field.

Succession in a barren landscape

In natural conditions, succession may start from newly exposed bare rock or from sand dunes deposited on a shore. The first colonisers of rock are usually lichens. These slow-growing organisms consist of a fungus with algal cells living inside it. This double act provides mutual support, with the algae carrying out photosynthesis and the fungus producing organic acids that slowly break down the rock surface to provide essential mineral ions.

Eventually, enough dead material accumulates for other organisms such as mosses to grow and soil begins to form. As more soil and humus build up, more water can be retained. As the conditions change small plants can take hold and the process continues on its progress towards a climax community.

A few ancient hedges still survive in Britiain. A hedge like this could have been planted by mediaeval farmers to mark off their land and keep in livestock. Initially, the hedge may have been only a few hawthorn plants, but other plants soon colonised the spaces between them, and succession has happened constantly over the centuries, creating the rich mixture of plants that we see today.

KEY FACTS

- If cultivated land is abandoned it is colonised by a succession of communities until a climax community is developed.

- The climax community of most uncultivated land in Britain is oak forest.

- Succession occurs because the species in each community alter the biotic and abiotic conditions. This creates new niches for other species which out-compete the existing ones.

- The first colonisers on bare rock are usually lichens which gradually break down the rock surface and start the process of succession.

1 What is meant by each of these ecological terms?

a community (2)

b population (1)

c niche (2)

BY05 June 1997 Q1

Total (5)

2 An investigation was carried out into competition between two species of grass, *Bromus madritensis* and *Bromus rigidus*. Equal numbers of seeds of *B. madritensis* were sown in a number of different pots. In each pot, an equal number of seeds of *B. rigidus* was then sown a different number of days after *B. madritensis*.

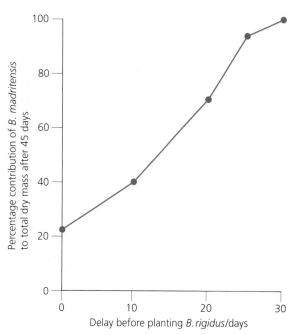

Fig 12.Q2

a What type of competition exists between the two species of grass? (1)

b Give two resources for which these grasses are likely to be competing. (2)

c
i Given that the total dry mass of plant material was the same in each pot, summarise the main conclusions that can be drawn from this investigation.
ii Suggest an explanation for the results where the delay before sowing *B. rigidus* was 30 days. (3)

BY02 February 1995 Q7

Total (6)

3 Barnacles are animals that live on rocky shores. The adults are fixed to the surface of rocks and do not move. The young larvae can swim freely in the sea. As they get older the larvae settle and attach themselves to a rock surface. Here they develop into adults which feed on microscopic plants and animals in the sea when the tide is in. In Britain two species of barnacle, *Chthamalus stellatus* and *Balanus balanoides*, commonly occur together on the same rocky shore.

The diagram shows the typical distribution of the two in relation to the tide levels on a rocky shore.

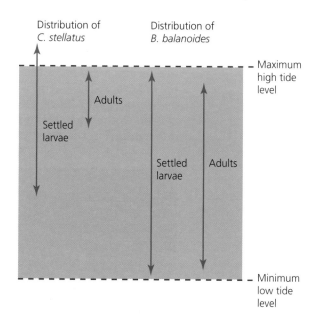

Fig 12.Q3

a In both species of barnacle few of the larvae which settle become adults. Explain how intraspecific competition could account for this. (1)

b Suggest how interspecific competition could account for the difference in distribution of the adults of the two species. (2)

c Suggest why there are larvae of *C. stellatus* above maximum high tide level, but no adults. (1)

d In an investigation, it was found that the presence of adult barnacles stimulated larvae of the same species to settle in the same area of the shore.
i Suggest a possible stimulus that encourages the larvae to settle. (1)
ii Suggest an advantage of larvae settling in the same area as the adults. (1)

BY02 February 1997 Q6

Total (6)

4 A particular species of fruitfly is a crop pest in Hawaii. Parasitic wasps lay their eggs inside the fruitfly larvae. The wasp larvae feed on the tissues of their host and kill it. They then emerge as adult wasps. An investigation was carried out to find out which of two different species of parasitic wasp would prove effective as a means of biological control. Both species were released into a trial plot at the same time. The graph shows the changes in the populations of both species of wasp in the period following their release.

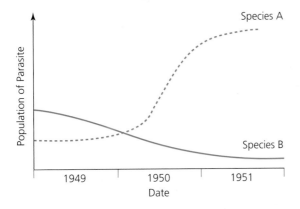

Fig 12.Q4

Explain the changes in population size of species A in terms of interspecific and intraspecific competition. (5)

BY02 June 1998 Q9

Total (5)

5
a Explain what is meant by an ecological niche. (2)

b Two species of beetle may be found in stored grain. Fig 12.Q5 shows the range of moisture content and temperature that each species can tolerate.

The temperature in different parts of a large grain store ranged from 14 °C to 20 °C. The moisture content of the grain was constant at 16%. Beetles of both species were introduced into the store. What would you expect to happen if
i species A were a more successful competitor than species B;
ii species B were a more successful competitor than species A? (3)

BY05 June 1999 Q3

Total (5)

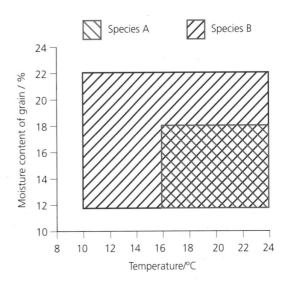

Fig 12.Q5

6 The diagram shows the profile of a sand-dune ecosystem. Samples were collected at points 1,2,3 and 4. The samples showed the trends indicated below the diagram.

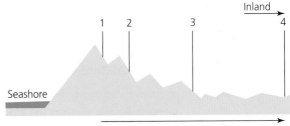

Fig 12.Q6

a One way in which mineral ions enter this ecosystem is by the action of microorganisms on organic molecules in the soil. Suggest two other ways in which mineral ions enter a sand-dune ecosystem. (2)

b Giving a reason for your answer in each case, at which of points 1 to 4 would you expect to find
i a climax community;
ii the lowest soil moisture content;
iii the highest proportion of plants which are wind-dispersed? (4)

BY05 March 1999 Q3

Total (6)

13 Human effects on the environment

When we talk about the effect of human activity on the environment, we tend to emphasise the more dramatic aspects, such as global warming, climate change, oil spills, etc. But people affect their environment in more subtle ways. Everything that humans do has some impact on their surroundings.

The fish in the photograph have been killed by something that most people would think was completely harmless – warm water. The heated water released as a by-product of many industrial processes is probably the most overlooked cause of damage to inland aquatic ecosystems. Fish and water-living invertebrates are killed by warm water, not because they are scalded directly, but because warm water carries much less dissolved oxygen than cool water. The fish that swim into its path 'suffocate' because they cannot extract sufficient oxygen to stay alive. Warm water in a river or stream can also encourage the growth of parasites that would otherwise not be a problem, and further fish can be affected by infection.

13.1 How humans have shaped the countryside

Farmland in the Vale of Clwyd, North Wales shows the typical patchwork appearance of countryside in Britain.

Typical, unspoilt British countryside, as most people perceive it, is an attractive patchwork of fields, growing a variety of crops and separated by hedges. But things have been changing over the last few decades – pasture fields have been ploughed and the mixture of native grasses and wild flowers that used to thrive has been replaced by a single fast-growing species of grass. The demise of the wild flower has also been helped along by regular use of fertilisers, which enhance crop growth but suppress recolonisation by wild flower species. Modern farming methods, which often remove hedges and give enormous areas of land over to a single crop are bad news for animal species too. More efficient harvesting machines mean that fewer seeds get left behind for birds and small mammals to feed on in winter, and autumn sowing of cereal crops brings earlier crops and earlier harvests, making it difficult for these animals to complete their breeding cycle in the fields. Birds like the skylark have disappeared from many areas.

There has also been increased pressure on the variety of habitat as a result of building development, roads, drainage schemes, forestry and other human activities. The bar chart in Fig 13.1 shows the habitat losses in various parts of just one English county. As you can see, there have been significant losses from a wide range of different types of habitat. In some areas, a very high proportion of the habitat that was present only 20 years ago has now has vanished.

How can we balance such damaging effects on the environment with the need for a reliable and inexpensive food supply, for increased demand for housing, for recreation and so on? In this chapter we look at some examples of the impact of farming on the environment, and consider how pressures for food production can be balanced against the demand for conservation.

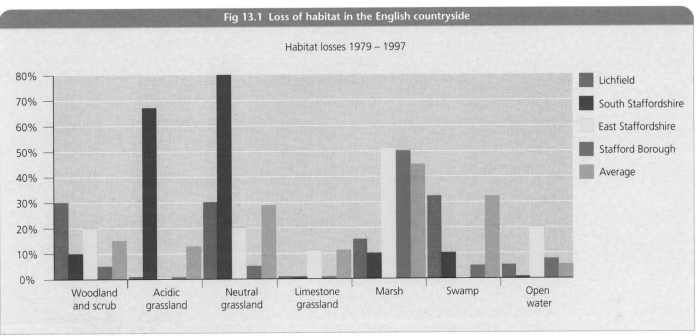

Fig 13.1 Loss of habitat in the English countryside

Habitat losses 1979 – 1997

Legend:
- Lichfield
- South Staffordshire
- East Staffordshire
- Stafford Borough
- Average

Categories: Woodland and scrub, Acidic grassland, Neutral grassland, Limestone grassland, Marsh, Swamp, Open water

Hedges and farming

A farmer's first priority is to make the best possible use of the land, either for growing crops or raising animals. Traditionally, farmers produced food for themselves and for the local community by growing a variety of different crops and keeping a range of different animals. In many parts of the world, subsistence farmers are still doing this. For this type of mixed farming, it is an advantage to divide the land into small fields to allow animals to be separated from crops, and for crops and stock to be rotated between fields. Hedges and walls were a commonplace feature of the landscape.

Today, there is increasing pressure on farmers to specialise and grow only a single crop, or maybe two or three, and to concentrate on one form of animal husbandry, such as dairy cattle or pig-breeding. This is more economical because better use can be made of equipment, and organisations such as supermarkets have fewer farmers to negotiate purchases with.

Wheat being harvested from a huge single field in the Vale of Pickering, North Yorkshire.

Also, transport is now much easier, so produce can easily be moved to much more distant markets. Consequently, in many parts of the country, large areas are used for single crops, such as wheat or oil-seed rape. This is called **monoculture**. In these areas most of the hedges, walls and fences have been removed. Removing field boundaries offers several advantages to the farmer:

- The space previously taken up by hedges can be used for growing the crop, which increases the yield per unit area;

- There is no need to cut and maintain hedges, which reduces labour costs;

- It is easier to manoeuvre large machines, such as combine harvesters, which speeds up sowing seeds, harvesting and spraying;

- It removes the shading effect of tall hedges;

- It removes places that might harbour pests.

However, there are also disadvantages in taking away hedges, both to the farmer and to the environment as a whole:

- When not covered with growing crop, the soil is much more exposed to wind erosion, and, if sloping, to erosion by rainwater. In drier parts of the country there can be considerable losses of the more fertile topsoil;

- There is reduced flexibility of land use on farms which keep some animals, since fences have to be erected to keep them separate. There is also less shelter for the animals;

- There is far less habitat for wildlife. For instance, birds have little cover and few nesting sites, and with fewer plant species and insects there is a much reduced food supply;

- Pressure to improve yields by cutting down competition with weeds leads to intensive use of herbicides. This further reduces the variety of food plants available for insects such as butterflies and for seed-eating birds and small mammals. Predators that normally keep insect pests under control lose their habitat, and crops are more exposed to large scale infestations by pests. As a result, farmers apply large quantities of pesticide, which tends to reduce natural populations even further.

- Growing the same crop on land for several years reduces the availability of mineral ions at the soil depth of the crop roots. With no animals on the farm, organic manure is not easily available, so the amount of humus in the soil declines. This affects the soil structure, for example by reducing its water-holding capacity, and lowers the bacterial and earthworm content. The soil dries out easily and is therefore more susceptible to erosion. Monoculture

farmers usually use large amounts of artificial fertilisers to counteract the loss of nutrients, but this does little to restore soil structure.

- Heavy machinery can compact soil and reduce the amount of air spaces, which ultimately slows down root growth.

Overall, therefore, monoculture can increase yields and offer significant economies, but in the long term there is liable to be a decrease in productivity. In the mid-west of the USA, where monocultural farming has been carried out on a huge scale for many years, the land in some areas has become so degraded that it is now an almost infertile desert.

A pine tree killed by the arid conditions of the encroaching desert in Colorado, USA.

1 Explain how each of the following may affect crop yield in a monoculture:

a reduction of air spaces in soil as a result of compacting by heavy machinery;

b reduction in the bacterial content of the soil;

c increased exposure of crops to wind.

2 Fig 13.2 shows the effect of a 2 metre high hedge on crop yield and on some abiotic factors at various distances from the hedge.

a Explain the effects of the hedge on soil moisture and air temperature.

b How far from the hedge is the greatest increase in crop yield?

c Suggest why the yield close to the hedge is decreased.

d What is the evidence from the graph that the net effect is a gain in yield in the area within 40 metres of the hedge?

e Suggest why this gain in yield may not be found in practice.

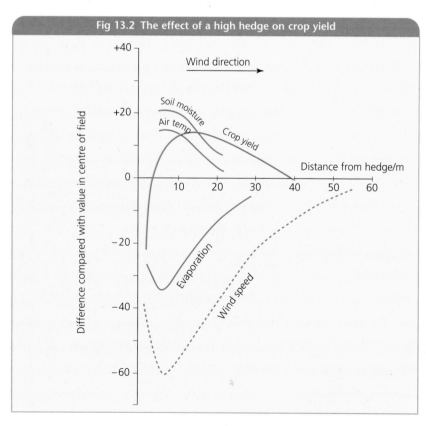

Fig 13.2 The effect of a high hedge on crop yield

Wind direction →

Difference compared with value in centre of field

Soil moisture
Air temp
Crop yield

Distance from hedge/m

Evaporation

Wind speed

- **Monocultures** are large areas of the same crop grown on the same land year after year.

- Monocultures are more economical than mixed farming, because they make more efficient use of equipment and labour costs are reduced.

- To improve efficiency, many hedges have been removed. This has reduced the amount of habitat available for wildlife. It has also increased soil erosion.

- The ecology of hedges is complex. Removal increases the area of land available for crops and makes use of machinery easier, but reduces shelter for crops and destroys the habitat of predators that can keep the number of pests down.

- Monocultures are particularly susceptible to pests, and large amounts of pesticide have to be used.

13.2 Farming and pollution

An algal bloom on water in a reservoir in Essex (right) and eutrophication in a stream overloaded with agricultural run-off (bottom right).

Cows produce awesome quantities of waste. The combined output of urine and dung from a dairy cow is about 60 litres a day – enough to half fill a bath. When cattle are out in the fields all of this manure gets spread around and of course acts as fertiliser for the growth of new grass. However, in winter dairy cattle are often kept indoors in large barns, and the disposal of their waste, called slurry, has to be carefully controlled. Sometimes it is mixed with the straw used as bedding. The semi-solid manure can then be kept in piles until it is convenient to do some muck-spreading. Alternatively the liquid slurry may be drained directly into large tanks before being sprayed onto the fields.

Eutrophication

In well-managed farms, these systems cause no problems, but it is easy for some of the waste to find its way into streams and rivers, either from leaking stores or as a result of leaching from neighbouring fields after slurry spraying. In the water this **organic effluent**

can cause problems. The nitrogen compounds are broken down to ammonium compounds and nitrates in the processes of the nitrogen cycle (see Chapter 10). Other mineral ions such as phosphates are released by saprophytic bacteria. The nitrates, phosphates and other nutrients from the effluent encourage excessive growth of plants in the water, a process called **eutrophication** (derived from Greek words meaning 'good feeding').

In shallow water vegetation growth increases vastly, and ponds become overgrown and waterways blocked. In lakes and slow rivers there is often very rapid growth of single-celled algae, often called phytoplankton, which can turn the water into the consistency of pea soup. This most often happens in the summer when conditions for growth are favourable, and the

185

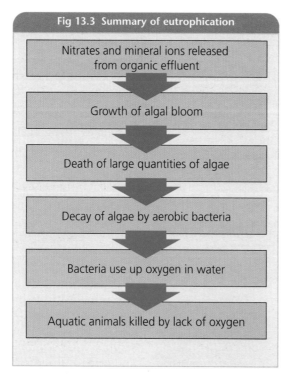

Fig 13.3 Summary of eutrophication

Nitrates and mineral ions released from organic effluent

⬇

Growth of algal bloom

⬇

Death of large quantities of algae

⬇

Decay of algae by aerobic bacteria

⬇

Bacteria use up oxygen in water

⬇

Aquatic animals killed by lack of oxygen

result is an **algal bloom**. Some of the phytoplankton in a bloom are toxic and can be a serious threat to fish, and also to humans if the poisons get into drinking water.

The main problem with eutrophication is the effect of large masses of algae dying, sinking to the bottom and decaying. This causes a massive increase in the population of aerobic bacteria – as the bacteria reproduce and respire, they rapidly deplete the oxygen concentration in the water. This devastates the aquatic ecosystem. As fish and invertebrates

die because of the oxygen shortage, the decay of their bodies makes the situation worse.

If the amount of dead organic matter is very large, conditions may become anaerobic. Anaerobic bacteria can survive on the organic matter that has not decayed but they can only partially break down this material. The incomplete oxidation releases methane (CH_4) and the evil-smelling gas, hydrogen sulphide (H_2S). Once a pond, lake or river reaches this state it is almost devoid of life, and it may take a long time to recover.

3 The concentration of nitrogen compounds in aquatic ecosystems is not influenced only by pollution. There is natural variation in concentration at different times of year. Fig 13.4 shows the nitrate and ammonium ion concentrations in a small lake over a twelve-month period.

a Suggest explanations for the following:
the decline in nitrate concentration during the spring and summer;
the rise in concentration during the autumn and winter;
the steep increase in ammonium concentration early autumn;
the slow decline in ammonium concentration through the late autumn and winter.

b From the evidence in the graph, suggest whether this lake is seriously polluted by organic effluent from surrounding farms.

Fig 13.4 Variations in nitrate and ammonium nitrate concentrations

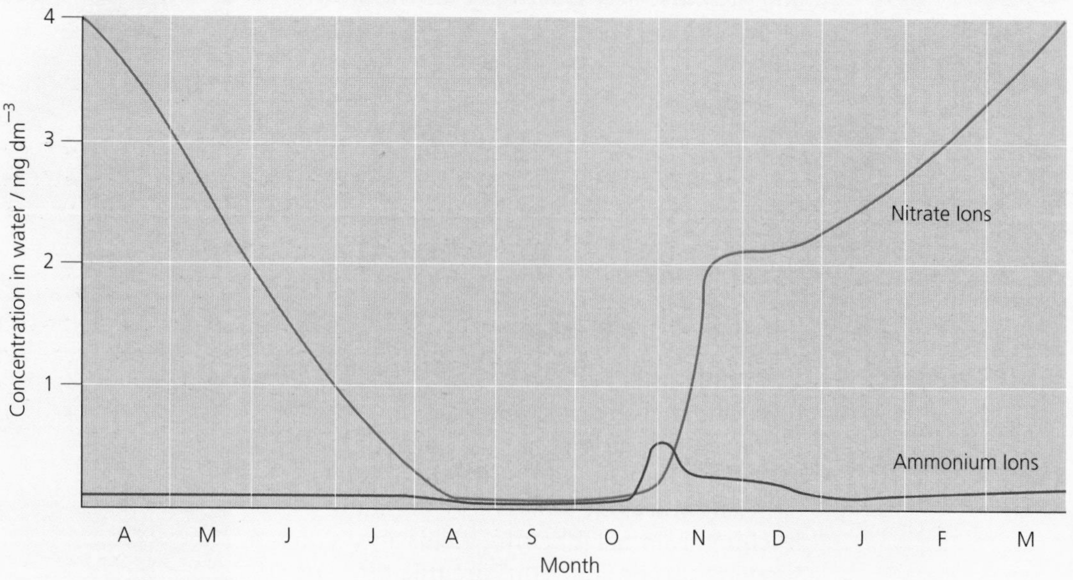

Concentration in water / mg dm⁻³

Nitrate Ions

Ammonium Ions

Month: A M J J A S O N D J F M

Biochemical oxygen demand

Large escapes of slurry into a lake or river can massively increase the amount of organic matter in the water. So also does a large release of effluent containing human sewage, or industrial effluent from some food factories. River authorities need to monitor the amounts of organic matter in their waterways very carefully in order to ensure that amounts do not exceed a critical level.

This is done by measuring the biochemical oxygen demand (BOD) of the water or of effluents being discharged into the water, for example from a sewage works. The greater the amount of organic matter in a water sample, the greater the number of aerobic bacteria that will grow in it. The more bacteria there are, the larger the amount of oxygen they will use, and so the higher the biochemical oxygen demand.

BOD is normally measured by:

- collecting two water samples from the same site;

- measuring the oxygen concentration of one sample with an oxygen meter;

- sealing the second sample in an air-free container and incubating it in darkness at 20 °C for five days;

- measuring the oxygen concentration of the second sample at the end of this incubation period.

The difference in oxygen concentration is the standard measure of BOD.

4

a Explain why the second sample is kept in darkness when doing a BOD test.

b The BOD test can underestimate the amount of organic matter in effluent. Suggest two possible reasons for this.

5

a What is the main nitrogen compound in urine?

b Explain why nitrates are important for the rapid growth of algae.

c Give two uses of phosphates in algal growth.

6

a Explain why living algae do not decrease the oxygen content of water.

b Suggest why lakes that are not polluted by farm effluents do not normally develop algal blooms in summer.

c Why is it dangerous to swim or bathe in water with an algal bloom?

KEY FACTS

- Farm animals, especially cattle, can produce large quantities of organic effluent. When organic effluent gets into aquatic ecosystems it can cause rapid growth of algae and plants. This is eutrophication.

- Other sources of nitrate and phosphate ions, such as sewage and excess fertilisers, can also cause eutrophication.

- When excess algae and plants die, the bacteria that make them decay severely reduce the oxygen content of the water. This causes the death of aquatic animals.

- Biochemical oxygen demand is a measure of the amount of oxygen removed from water by bacteria in a given time and is therefore an indicator of the amount of pollution by organic matter in water.

Sewage effluent

Most human sewage is treated in sewage works, but these also discharge organic matter into rivers. In winter this may cause little problem, because the river contains a lot of fast-flowing cold water. In summer, however, there may be less water, a slower current and warm water. These three factors can significantly increase biochemical oxygen demand in the river.

The graph shows the conditions in summer in a river below a point at which there is a continuous discharge of diluted sewage.

1 Explain how and why the following factors change as you go down the river from the sewage discharge:
   a oxygen concentration;   **c** number of bacteria;
   b nitrate concentration;   **d** number of algae.

2 Explain why the curve for BOD does not follow the same pattern as the curve for oxygen concentration.

3 Explain why summer conditions in the river make sewage pollution more serious.

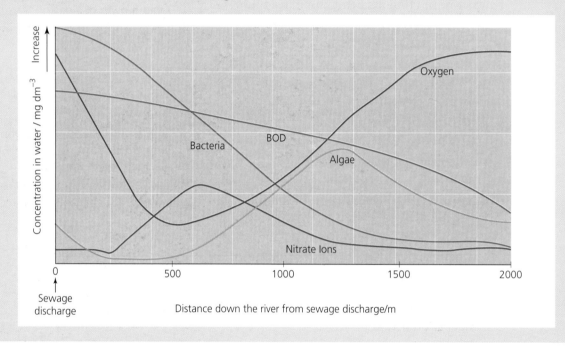

Distance down the river from sewage discharge/m

13.3 The pest problem

A villager in Madagascar tries to scare away a swarm of locusts (*Locusta migratoria capito*). This swarm, in May 1997, contained over a billion locusts.

Pests are no different from other plants and animals; they are simply organisms that compete with humans for their crops, but their effects can be spectacular. A swarm of locusts may consist of several billion insects and can destroy the crops round an African village in a matter of hours. In Britain, tiny aphids, only a few millimetres long, can breed at an immense rate under the right conditions and wreak havoc on crops such as tomatoes and roses. In the middle of the nineteenth century the history of Ireland was changed by potato blight, a fungal pest. This destroyed the entire potato crop and set in motion the emigration of a massive proportion of the Irish population.

Controlling pests

The practice of growing crops in monocultures has produced ideal conditions for pests to thrive, since they have an almost unlimited food supply and can spread easily. Controlling pests is vital for the economic success of farmers. Even partial damage to plants by an insect pest can seriously reduce yield in a crop and reduce profits. From a global perspective, pests have a major impact on the world's food supply. For example, over a quarter of rice yield is lost to insect pests, and at a time of rapidly rising population that is bad news for the ever increasing numbers of people that regularly go hungry.

Pesticides

The main weapons in the farmer's armoury against pests are chemical pesticides. Pesticide production is, therefore, a huge multi-national industry. Pesticides include:

- **insecticides**, which kill the largest group of animal pests, the insects. Many thousands of species of insect pest are known and many carry viral and other diseases that also weaken crops;

- **fungicides**, which kill fungal infections of plants, such as potato blight;

- **herbicides**, which are weedkillers. Weeds are simply plants that happen to grow alongside crops and compete with them for resources such as mineral ions and light.

There are, of course, plenty of chemicals that will kill pests, but that does not mean that they are all suitable as pesticides. It is, for example, rather important that a pesticide does not kill the farmer, gardener or people eating the crop as well. The ideal pesticide kills the pest being targeted without causing any harm to anything else in the environment. An insecticide being used in an orchard, for instance, should not also kill

insects such as bees that are important for pollinating the flowers, nor should it last so long that it leaves a residue on the fruit which might be toxic to human consumers.

In practice, most pesticides represent a compromise between toxicity and specificity, and their use has to be carefully controlled. Few pesticides target one pest only without causing harm to any other species. The dose used needs to be just enough to destroy the pest and has to be applied accurately so that as little as possible gets into the wider environment. It is very easy for wind-blown herbicide spray to damage plants in adjacent fields or gardens, or for excess pesticide to leach into streams and rivers where it kills aquatic insects and hence the food supply of fish.

Pesticides should be biodegradable

It is very important that a pesticide should be **biodegradable** – broken down by decomposers such as bacteria after it has done its job, so that it does not persist in the environment and perhaps kill other beneficial organisms. A gardener who uses a herbicide to get rid of weeds does not want a chemical that remains in the soil and prevents the growth of other plants. Only perhaps on paths might it be useful to use a non-biodegradable weedkiller, and even then it would be important to ensure that it does not spread to neighbouring flower beds. To make life difficult for manufacturers, a biodegradable pesticide must be sufficiently chemically stable for it to have a reasonable shelf life before it is used. Otherwise it is liable to be ineffective at the recommended dose.

Biodegradable pesticides break down at different rates. Some natural insecticides, such as pyrethrin, obtained from the flowers of a plant from the daisy family, break down rapidly. This makes them particularly good as insecticides for use in household sprays. Some synthetic compounds take many years to degrade. Particularly slow to decompose are the organochlorines, many of which are now banned in Britain. Organochlorines kill by damaging the membranes and fatty sheaths of neurones and inhibiting the transmission of nerve impulses. Because they are soluble in lipids, they tend to accumulate in fat storage tissues.

The capacity to be stored in fatty tissue leads to a particular problem with organochlorines, and also with fungicides containing mercury compounds. When first

Fig 13.5 Bioaccumulation in a food chain

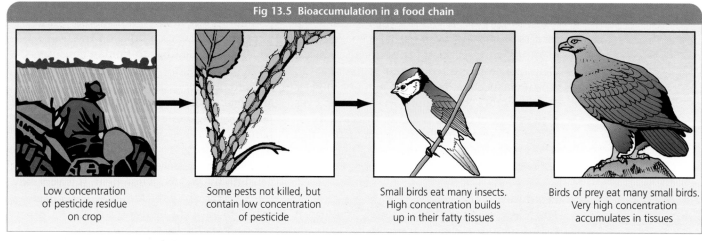

Low concentration of pesticide residue on crop

Some pests not killed, but contain low concentration of pesticide

Small birds eat many insects. High concentration builds up in their fatty tissues

Birds of prey eat many small birds. Very high concentration accumulates in tissues

discovered these were widely used because they were fairly cheap and very effective. The fact that they were slow to break down made them particularly useful for treating soil pests and for coating seeds so that they would be protected after sowing. However, not all pests received a lethal dose from feeding on treated plants or seeds. Some of these pests were eaten by predators, which retained the pesticide in their fat stores. Because a predator would eat many prey organisms, the amount of pesticide stored could become quite large. Consumers higher up the food chain, including humans, that fed on these predators could accumulate high concentrations of the pesticide, as shown in Fig 13.5. This process is known as **bioaccumulation**.

The introduction of persistent pesticides, such as DDT, resulted in major reductions in the populations of many top predators, particularly birds of prey such as buzzards and eagles. In some situations their use could actually be counterproductive, because the pesticide was even more effective at wiping out the natural predators of a pest than the

pest itself. Once the problem of bioaccumulation was appreciated, restrictions on their use were put in place, but nevertheless they are still commonly used in some parts of the world. Bioaccumulation can mean that the danger is not confined to the immediate area where pesticides are used. Even penguins confined to Antarctica, hundreds of miles from the nearest place where crops grow, have been found to contain significant amounts of organochlorines in their fatty tissue.

7 Fig 13.6 shows a pyramid of biomass for the organisms in an estuary. The figures give the mean concentration of DDT in the tissues of organisms at each trophic level, as measured in the 1960s.

a Calculate the number of times that the DDT was concentrated between each trophic level.

b The mean concentration of DDT in the water was only 0.00005 parts per million. By how many times was the DDT concentrated between the water and the tertiary consumers?

c A large carnivorous fish feeds on small plant-eating fish. The concentration of DDT in the predator is ten times as great as the concentration in its prey, even though the predator has eaten several hundred fish. Give two reasons why the concentration in the predator is not several hundred times the concentration in the prey.

Fig 13.6 Pyramid of biomass showing bioaccumulation of DDT

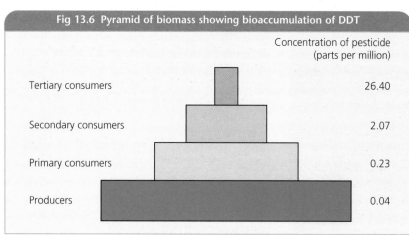

Concentration of pesticide (parts per million)

Tertiary consumers	26.40
Secondary consumers	2.07
Primary consumers	0.23
Producers	0.04

- Pesticides are used to kill insect and other invertebrate pests, fungi that cause disease in crops and weeds that compete with crops.

- Pesticides should target the pest without causing harm to other organisms in the environment. They should be biodegradable, so that they do not persist in the environment after they have destroyed the pests.

- Pesticides can build up in food webs as a result of bioaccumulation. Although concentrations in plants and in the pests that eat the plants may be quite low, the concentrations increase in organisms higher up the food chains because predators consume large numbers of their prey. Some pesticides, such as organochlorines, that are slow to break down cause particular problems for predators.

13.4 Food production versus conservation

A typical supermarket basket (near right) with a mixture of foods, mostly mass-produced and produced by intensive farming and processing. A selection of organically-grown vegetables (far right), which are often relatively expensive, but which may be better for us and the environment.

Modern supermarkets offer a massive range of choice of foods. People have become used to being able to buy most types of high quality fresh vegetables, fruit and meats all year round. Although food may seem expensive, the proportion of income that most people spend on food is much lower than it was thirty or forty years ago. This extension of choice and quality has come about partly as a result of improved efficiency in agricultural practices and partly because modern transport means that products can be rapidly moved around the world.

Some of the improved efficiency in agriculture in Britain has been at the expense of wildlife and the environment. For politicians there is a dilemma. Most people, and that means most voters, want continued access to cheap food. On the other hand there is an increasingly vociferous minority campaigning for more 'organic farming' and for conservation of the environment.

We have already seen in this chapter some of the ways in which modern intensive farming can have an impact on the environment. There has been economic pressure on farmers growing crops to:

- concentrate on a small number of crops and grow these as large areas of monoculture;

- remove hedgerows and field boundaries to make maximum use of land area;

- drain marshy areas and remove unprofitable pockets of woodland;

- use large quantities of chemical fertilisers to obtain maximum yield;

- use pesticides to deal with the increased damage from insects, plant diseases and weeds resulting from growing large areas of the same crop on the same land for many successive years.

Corresponding pressures on farmers keeping animals for meat and dairy produce have resulted in:

- improvement of pastures with fertilisers, thus reducing the variety of plant species growing in them;

- overgrazing on more marginal land, especially by sheep in upland areas, preventing regeneration of woodland and scrub;

- cattle being kept indoors through the winter and the associated problems of disposing of their waste;

- escape of effluent from slurry tanks, manure heaps and silage stores into watercourses;

- widespread movement of animals around the country for optimum pasturage and for slaughter, with the attendant risks of spreading disease.

What can be done?

Is it possible then to reconcile improved efficiency and at the same time reduce the effect on the environment? Would people accept slightly more expensive food and perhaps less choice in return for preserving a greater range of habitats and wildlife? Or would it be possible to obtain just as much variety using more sustainable methods of farming? There is little doubt that many people are becoming suspicious of the overuse of fertilisers and pesticides. However it seems unlikely that there could be a return to the sort of mixed farming that used to be the norm.

Some measures that might be taken to make farming sustainable and reduce the impact on wildlife include:

- making as much use as possible of organic manure, which improves soil structure by providing more humus and retaining water;

- delaying application of chemical fertilisers in spring until a crop is starting to grow, to reduce the chances of fertiliser being washed into streams;

- leaving crop stubble over winter and not ploughing grasslands to reduce the time that soil is left bare and thus reduce soil erosion;

- rotating crops, so that different crops are grown from year to year, making better use of minerals in soil at different depths and avoiding the build-up of pests that are specific to a particular crop;

- including nitrogen-fixing crops, such as clover, peas and other legumes in the rotation, to help restore nitrates without the use of fertilisers;

Skylark

House sparrow

Lapwing

- reducing the density of grazing by sheep in upland areas to allow vegetation to regenerate;

- stopping the removal of hedges and setting aside areas of land for wildlife.

The populations of many previously common birds have declined steeply in recent years. The house sparrow was one of our commonest birds, but it is a seed-eater that depended for much of its food in winter on the seeds left behind after harvesting crops. This source has been much reduced by the practice of ploughing in autumn soon after harvesting and planting winter wheat which improves yields because it has a head start and grows more rapidly than spring-sown wheat. Skylarks and lapwings both nest on the ground in long grass, and in many parts of the country their populations have plummeted due to ploughing of grassland. Also, farmers often cut grass early to make silage, rather than leaving it until later in the summer and then harvesting the hay. This often destroys nests before the young have hatched. Changes like these in bird populations are often the most visible signs of much greater changes taking place in the ecosystems of the countryside.

8 The partridge is a pigeon-sized bird that lives on farmland where there is good cover from hedges, long grass, bushes and ditches. Partridges nest in thick vegetation, and produce large broods of 12 to 15 young. The chicks leave the nest within a few hours of hatching. They feed on a wide range of things, including seeds, buds, insects, spiders and slugs.

The Table 13.1 shows the results of an investigation to compare the effects of spraying crop fields with pesticide on the success of partridges during the breeding season. In one area the whole field was sprayed. In the control area a 6-metre wide strip next to the hedges was left unsprayed.

a The parents depend more on insects, spiders and slugs when feeding chicks than at other times of year. Suggest why.

b Suggest why more chicks survive when a 6-metre strip is left unsprayed.

c Suggest explanations for the differences in distance moved each day and area searched.

d Explain what the data for statistical significance show.

e Suggest farming practices that could help to conserve partridges.

Table 13.1 The effect of crop spraying on the partridge population			
	Whole field sprayed	Strip left unsprayed	Statistical significance (P)
Chicks surviving to 21 days / %	59.7	97.7	<0.05
Mean distance moved by parents and chicks each day / m	102.3	43.5	<0.05
Mean area searched for food / ha	2.1	0.8	<0.10

■ There has to be a balance between the demands for economical food production and the need to conserve the environment.

■ Intensive farming methods have much reduced the diversity of wildlife in many parts of Britain.

■ Changes in some of these practices, such as greater emphasis on organic farming, could help to restore the balance.

1 Over most of the last 2000 years, agricultural practices in Britain have resulted in an increase in the number of species compared to the original climax forest. Modern intensive agriculture, however, is leading to a reduction in the number of invertebrate species such as insects.

a Explain how each of the following activities associated with modern farming might reduce the number of species of invertebrate animal.

   i the use of herbicides;
   ii using large areas for the growth of single crops. (4)

b Intensive agricultural production in the European Community resulted in a surplus of some crops. One solution to this has been to pay farmers to 'set aside' some of their land by neither planting crops nor grazing animals on it. Describe what will happen to an area of land which is set aside and not returned to agriculture. (4)

Total (8)

BY02 June 2000 Q6

2 The table below shows some differences between two areas of grassland. Site **A** was an area of natural grassland situated on a nature reserve. Site **B** was a field on nearby agricultural grassland. The vegetation at site **B** was mown twice a year and removed to make hay.

	Site **A** Natural grassland in nature reserve	Site **B** Agricultural grassland
Nitrogen added in fertiliser /kg per hectare per year	0	300
Percentage dead plant material and humus in top 2 cm of soil	5.9	0.3
Mean number of plant species per m²	6.8	2.4
Mean number of woody shrubs per m²	0.3	0
Mean number of insect species caught in traps on soil surface	18.3	4.1

a Suggest an explanation for the difference in the percentage of dead plant material and humus at the two sites. (1)

b There are fewer plant species per square metre at Site **B**. How could each of the following help to explain this difference?

   i mowing; (1)
   ii the use of fertiliser. (2)

b Give two reasons why there was a greater number of insect species at Site **A**. (2)

Total (6)

BY02 June 1998 Q5

3 Read the following passage

Wetlands – Water, water everywhere?

Wetlands are areas where land and water meet. They are found in almost every country in the world and vary enormously in size from a small pond to the vast 10 million hectare bays in the Canadian Arctic. The movement of water is slow in the wetlands, allowing sediments to settle to the bottom. Wetland plants, and the bacteria associated with them, absorb and break down substances, such as organic waste, that would otherwise pollute rivers, ponds and lakes downstream.

However, there is a limit to how many pollutants wetlands can absorb. In some areas, excessive amounts of sewage, slurry and fertilisers are being dumped into the water. Air pollution falls on wetlands as acid. Sediments from road-building and construction block out the light, and heavy metal ions accumulate.

Many flat, low-lying wetlands have been drained for development or the animal communities living there severely depleted through overhunting or overfishing. One of the greatest threats to UK wetlands has been excessive extraction of peat. Nearly 100 wetlands of international importance have been identified in the UK and many conservation

(Reproduced from an article by permission of The Guardian)

a Describe how the following pollutants could affect wetland ecosystems.

   i fertilisers; (6)
   ii heavy metal ions. (3)

b Explain the benefits of conserving wetlands. (3)

Total (12)

BY05 March 1998 Q7

4 Dieldrin is an organochlorine pesticide. It was used to treat wheat grain before planting. An investigation was carried out to find the effect of treated wheat grain on the dieldrin concentration in the tissues of mice living in wheat fields. Mice were trapped before and after the treated wheat was planted. One line of traps was in the grass border of the field. Another was in the area planted with wheat.

The results are shown in the table.

Period	Location of traps	Number of mice caught	Number of mice analysed	Mean dieldrin content of mice /ppm
Before sowing	In grass border	11	9	0.15
Before sowing	In planted area	15	4	0.23
After sowing	In grass border	18	2	6.49
After sowing	In planted area	18	7	10.96

a i Calculate the percentage change in mean dieldrin concentration in the tissues of mice from each of the two areas. Show your working. (2)

ii Suggest **one** explanation for the different dieldrin content of mice trapped in the two areas after sowing. (1)

b Suggest **one** reason why the results of the investigation might be unreliable. (1)

c Suggest an explanation for the fact that the use of dieldrin is now banned in this country. (2)

Total (6)

BY07 March 1999 Q7

5 The passage below was printed on a beer mat.

Why beer gives farmers a headache

Brewers specify that very low levels of nitrate fertiliser should be used when growing barley for making beer. This makes it harder for farmers to get a good yield. But "low nitrate" barley helps the flavour of the beer as well as being less harmful to the environment. In East Anglia, the very top grade barley is still said to be "good enough for beer".

a Describe and explain the relationship between the yield of a cereal crop such as barley and the amount of nitrate fertiliser added. (5)

b Explain how the use of large quantities of nitrate fertiliser might be harmful to the environment. (7)

Total (12)

BY07 February 1996 Q8

6 Otter to make a comeback in ambitious species revival.
Plans have been published by a group set up to advise the government on implementing the Biodiversity Convention agreed at the Earth Summit in 1992.
One of the most ambitious projects is to restore otters to all rivers where they existed in 1960, before pollution and removal of bankside vegetation wiped them out from almost all of the Midlands and South-east England.
Otters are mammalian carnivores that feed mainly on fish.

a Suggest ways in which pollution may have contributed to wiping out otters. (8)

b Suggest how you might measure the size of a local otter population in order to see whether conservation measures were working. (4)

Total (12)

BY05 June 1997 Q8

14 Principles of investigation

It is almost certain that some of the information in this book is wrong, and not just because of mistakes made by the authors (for which we apologise, but we are only human!). Biology is about living organisms, and living organisms are extremely complex. As in all science, knowledge and understanding is based on the best interpretation of the available evidence. But, scientists have to accept that new evidence may emerge that requires ideas to be modified, or occasionally be completely discarded.

This does not mean that we should throw up our arms in despair and decide that no explanations are worth the paper they are written on. People that adopt this attitude often come up with completely wacky explanations that have even less basis in evidence, such as that the development of a child depends less on its genes than on the movements of the planets and stars. Genetics is a good example of an area of biology where knowledge and understanding are changing almost daily. These new discoveries do not mean that fundamental principles have to be changed. The principles relating to the control of characteristics by genes, first put forward 100 years ago (see Chapter 7), have not been overturned. The intensive research to identify the order of all the bases in the DNA of the human genome has, however, produced some surprises. For example, humans do not have as many different genes as expected – probably only 30 to 40 thousand, which is only two to three times as many as tiny worms and fruit flies. We used to assume that since we are so much more complex and so much more clever, we must have many more. In fact, we share a huge proportion of our genes with other organisms. Only 1% are unique to humans.

It may now be necessary to refine our understanding of how genes provide the instructions. The traditional assumption was that a particular section of DNA, that is a gene, coded for a particular protein or polypeptide, as we saw in the AS book (Chapter 6). Now it seems that the gene code may be even cleverer, and that by transcribing different sections to mRNA a single gene can code for several different proteins. Nevertheless the basic transcription process is the same – the secret lies in the instructions that determine the sections to be transcribed.

As we learn more and more about how genes work, we can understand more clearly how a fertilised egg turns into a human baby. This does not mean that we could or should control the process artificially and 'create' a baby. It does, however, open up the possibilities for treating genetic defects and improving the quality of life for the considerable proportion of children born with faulty genes.

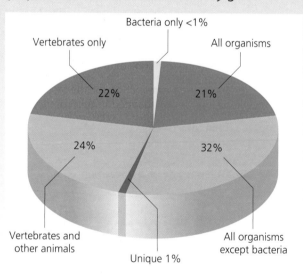

Percentage of human genes similar to those in other organisms

The importance of observation and experiment

In this chapter, we look at how biological understanding advances by a combination of observation and experiment, and at how the evidence gathered can be analysed to derive reliable conclusions. During your study of biology, you will have carried out experimental investigations and you will already be familiar with many of the basic principles used by scientists in their research. Here we emphasise those rules that should be applied to any scientific investigation. This is to help you in answering 'synoptic' examination questions about investigations and the methods used in science (see Chapter 16 for some examples of synoptic questions).

Designing an investigation
Many people 'believe' that they can read someone's mind. We've probably all experienced the situation where we feel

something is just about to happen in the moments before it does. Many scientists dismiss the whole idea of mind-reading, or telepathy, as nonsense and not worth investigating, probably because there is no obvious explanation of how it could work. But some people have carried out experiments to try to establish whether the phenomenon really does exist. Many have consisted of getting one person (the 'sender') to look at a picture or drawing and asking someone else (the 'receiver') to describe or draw what they think the sender is looking at.

Results have been unconvincing and often the experimental methods have been open to criticism. For example, the experimenters may not have excluded all possible means of communication, conscious or unconscious, such as faint nods. With drawings, it may be difficult to decide how close to the original a receiver's version is, or to eliminate the possibility of guessing likely subjects, or sheer coincidence. Some experiments have been exposed as definite frauds.

Read the following account of an experiment designed to ensure that there is no possibility of cheating.

The receiver is isolated in a small room with thick, sound-proof walls. He or she is blindfolded, and meaningless 'white noise' is played through headphones. The sender sits in another room about 25 metres away. The sender concentrates on a photograph that has been selected by a computer from a choice of 100 possibilities.

The receiver describes any impressions about the photograph that he or she experiences. The description is relayed by microphone to an experimenter outside the room, who is unaware of the photograph selected. The receiver is then shown four photographs, one of which is the actual target and the other three randomly selected by the computer. The receiver selects the photograph that seems to be the closest match to the impressions experienced.

In this investigation, the aim of the experimenters was to find out whether people really can communicate by telepathy. To do this scientifically, they have tried to:

- eliminate other possible means of communication using recognised senses;
- prevent possible bias on the part of the experimenters;
- eliminate the possibility of the receiver obtaining unintentional clues;
- make sure that the sender and receiver could not cheat, or predict results from knowledge of each other's preferences;
- obtain enough results for statistical analysis.

Results of this and similar experiments have so far been inconclusive. One sender/receiver pair had a success rate of 47% out of 128 attempts. Statistically this is significantly greater than would be expected. Others have scored no better than chance. Overall, the combined results of experiments involving a considerable number of pairs of receivers and senders have shown no statistically significant relationship. However, this could be because only a small proportion of people have the ability to communicate by telepathy, or possibly because telepathy is only possible when people are in a particular, relaxed state of mind.

1 Explain how the experimenters designed the investigation described on this page in order to achieve each of the aims shown in the bullet points.

14.2 Hypotheses and theories

One day in 1928 Alexander Fleming came back from a two-week holiday and noticed a mould growing in a Petri dish containing a bacterial culture on a plate he had left lying on his desk. No bacteria grew around the mould. From this observation it occurred to him that the mould might be producing some substance that was killing the bacteria. He embarked on the series of experiments that led to the discovery of the first antibiotic for medical use, penicillin.

This is one of the most famous examples of a chance observation leading to a major scientific breakthrough. Fleming's brilliance was to realise the possible significance of his observation and to propose a suggested explanation. A suggested explanation that can be tested by experiment is called a **hypothesis**. Fleming's hypothesis was that the mould secreted a substance that killed the bacteria in the dish. He set up experiments to determine whether the secretions really did

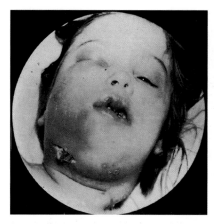
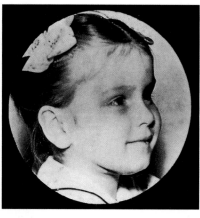

This little girl was seriously ill with a massive infection and would have died without antibiotics. She was one of the first people to receive penicillin. The second photograph was taken six weeks later

kill bacteria, for example by taking samples of agar medium from around growing mould and testing their effect on bacterial cultures. This led to many more experiments with different substances extracted from the secretions, different types of bacteria, different concentrations. Once the anti-bacterial activity of the substance produced by the penicillin mould had been established, it was a long time before the penicillin could be used as a drug. Alexander Fleming had neither the expertise nor the interest to purify the substance and work on it further, and it was then up to other scientists, notably Howard Florey and Ernst Boris Chain, to carry the research to its next stage. Within 15 years of Fleming's initial observation, a vast pharmaceutical industry had grown up and antibiotics found widespread use against many previously incurable infections.

Testing a hypothesis

Fig14.1 summarises the stages in scientific research.

Progress in science is made when a hypothesis is tested by an experiment. Contrary to popular belief, scientists do not just do experiments to see what happens. Fun though it might be, they don't just mix chemicals together and watch the results. An experiment must be designed to test one possible explanation of an observation. A good hypothesis is one that an experiment can either support or disprove. Strictly, experiments can never prove that a hypothesis is absolutely definitely correct. There is always the possibility that some other explanation that nobody has thought of could fit the evidence equally well. However, an experiment can prove a hypothesis to be definitely wrong.

In the case of the telepathy investigation described above, there have been relatively few scientific experiments, so that it is still not clear whether 'extra-sensory' communication does exist. The hypothesis being tested is the suggestion that people can communicate without using sight, sound, smell or any other of the recognised senses. If experiments showed that such communication can happen, it would be necessary to do experiments to eliminate other possible means of communication, such as by detection of changes in electro-magnetic fields. If a possible means of communication could be found, or at least could not be excluded, the next step would be to formulate a hypothesis as to how this method of communication might work and then to test this by experiment.

Unfortunately, people are often tempted to bypass these stages and go straight to an

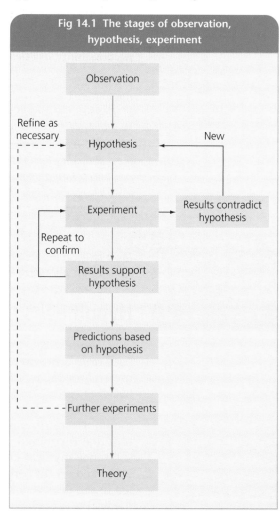

Fig 14.1 The stages of observation, hypothesis, experiment

Observation

Refine as necessary

Hypothesis — New

Experiment — Results contradict hypothesis

Repeat to confirm

Results support hypothesis

Predictions based on hypothesis

Further experiments

Theory

explanation without the experimental evidence. Humans seem to be uncomfortable when they are unable to find an explanation for a phenomenon. Even scientists have a tendency to be biased towards finding evidence to support their hypothesis. As a student doing an investigation you may well have been disappointed to get results in an investigation that disproved your hypothesis or were not what was expected. When this happens students often suggest that their experiment has 'gone wrong', but, in scientific research, negative results are just as important as positive ones.

When a hypothesis becomes an accepted theory

When a hypothesis is supported by experimental results, it may be accepted as the best explanation of an observation. The explanation may suggest predictions that, in turn, can be tested by further experiments and observations. Other scientists try to think of alternative interpretations of the results. It is normal practice for one scientist to be critical of another's published results. To ensure that published work is of sufficiently high quality, journals practise peer review – a submitted paper is reviewed by 2 or 3 other experts in the field to make sure the experiments have been carried out well, and that the interpretations of the results are reasonable.

It should also be possible to repeat an experiment and get the same results. Only after many confirmatory experiments is it

likely that a new idea will be accepted. For example, for many years it was thought that cell membranes have a structure rather like a sandwich with protein 'bread' and phospholipid 'filling'. After many experiments this hypothesis was shown to be false and it has been replaced by the fluid-mosaic explanation that you came across in the AS course. This idea is now so well supported that it is described as the theory of plasma membrane structure.

A **theory** is a well-established hypothesis that is supported by a substantial body of evidence. The Theory of Natural Selection, for example, is based on huge numbers of observations, predictions and experiments that support the underlying hypothesis.

2 If you breathe in and out of a large plastic bag several times, so that you keep re-breathing the same air, your rate of breathing increases. You probably already know why, but give three different hypotheses that could explain this observation.

3 Suggest hypotheses that could explain each of the following observations:

a having a hot drink can make one sweat, even when it is very cold;

b only sunflower seeds can germinate in the area close to a sunflower plant;

c cats have narrow vertical pupils in their eyes, rather than round ones as humans do.

KEY FACTS

■ A **hypothesis** is a suggested explanation of an observation.

■ A hypothesis should be based on scientific knowledge and understanding and should be sufficiently precise to be tested by experiment.

■ An experiment can either support or disprove a hypothesis, but it cannot prove that is certainly true.

■ Once a hypothesis has been confirmed by many experiments and by alternative forms of evidence it is established as a theory.

14.3 Variables and controls

The way to test a hypothesis is to do experiments. You will almost certainly have carried out experiments with enzymes to investigate a hypothesis such as that rate of reaction changes when temperature or pH changes. With an enzyme such as catalase, which breaks down hydrogen peroxide to water and oxygen, this is relatively straightforward. To investigate the effect of temperature you set up water baths at a range of temperatures, mix the catalase and hydrogen peroxide and measure the amount of oxygen released at each temperature. There are of course practical difficulties to be overcome, such as collecting the oxygen without letting any escape, but in principle the experiment is quite simple. The key to this and all similar experiments is that you do three things:

- Select and set up a range of different values for the factor whose effect you are testing, in this case temperature or pH. This factor is the **independent variable**;

- Measure the change in the factor that you are testing, in this case the rate of oxygen production. This is the **dependent variable**;

- Keep all other factors, such as enzyme and hydrogen peroxide concentrations, the same. These are the **controlled variables**.

So, in an experiment:

- The independent variable is the one the experimenter changes;

- The dependent variable is the one the experimenter measures;

- All other possible variables are kept constant.

Including a control

One other precaution is to carry out a **control experiment**. This is not the same as keeping other variables constant. Its purpose is to ensure that changes made to the independent variable have not in themselves changed any other factor, and that the results really are due to the factor being tested. For example, when testing the effectiveness of different antiseptics at killing bacteria, paper discs soaked in the antiseptic might be placed on a bacterial lawn in a Petri dish as shown in Fig 14.2.

In this experiment four of the discs were soaked in different antiseptics. The fifth disc was the control. The control disc should not be just a plain paper disc, but a disc that has also been soaked in sterile water, or whatever solvent was used in the antiseptics. This would prove that the results obtained were really due to the antiseptics and not perhaps to something that could dissolve from the paper disc. In a control experiment it is always important to include something that is an exact replacement for the factor being tested, rather than just having the factor absent. For example, when testing new drugs on human patients, it is not good enough to give some patients the new drug and give nothing to the control group. The patients in the control group should get a pill that is exactly the same as the one with the new drug except for the absence of the active ingredient. A pill without any active ingredient is called a **placebo**.

What happens when not all the variables can be kept constant?

In an experiment with an enzyme it may be quite straightforward to control all the major variables, but when experimenting with living organisms, things are rarely so simple because living things are themselves are so variable. If investigating the response of an animal to a stimulus, such as a woodlouse to light, you can never be sure that all specimens will respond in the same way. Although most woodlice may move away from light, some might not. Even the simplest of organisms

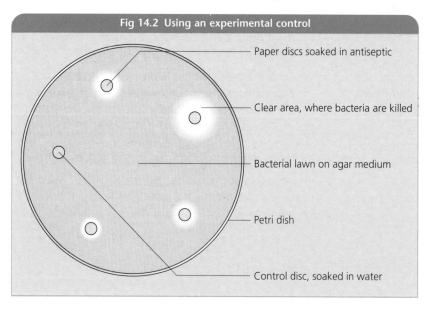

Fig 14.2 Using an experimental control

Paper discs soaked in antiseptic

Clear area, where bacteria are killed

Bacterial lawn on agar medium

Petri dish

Control disc, soaked in water

respond to many stimuli. An individual may behave untypically according to how well fed it is, its age, the time of day, sexual maturity, or just because it is genetically different from most.

The only way to deal with this uncontrollable variability is to repeat an experiment several times and to use a large number of different organisms. Even in an experiment like the one using catalase it would be necessary to repeat the procedure several times for each value of the independent variable. For example, you would make several measurements of rate of oxygen production at 35 °C, several at 40 °C. Each repeat is called a **replicate**. Repetition increases the reliability of the results, and this increases the likelihood of being able to draw useful conclusions.

For students, there is nearly always a limit to the number of times an experiment can be repeated. Even researchers have time and resource constraints, and it is necessary to use judgement about the likely reliability of a set of data. If the results from replicates are all very similar, it is more likely that the results are reliable. In some experiments it is easier to be sure that all the major factors have been controlled. If investigating the effect of a plant growth hormone on a small section of root, you can ensure that all root sections are the same length, all from plants of the same age, and that the temperature and pH are kept constant. The root sections can be supplied with solutions of known concentration (the independent variable), and the measurements of change in root length can be accurately made (the dependent variable). On the other hand, determining the effects on growth in whole plants is much more difficult. Roots will vary in length, amounts of hormone absorbed may differ,

measurements will be more difficult to make. Determining the effects of a growth hormone in humans would be even more difficult, since it would be totally unethical to experiment by giving different doses to different individuals, irrespective of the great variability between people. It is essential, therefore, to think carefully about the degree to which variables can be controlled in assessing the reliability of results. In Chapter 15, we look at ways of using statistical analysis to assess the reliability of results.

4 In an experiment to test each of the following hypotheses, give the independent and dependent variables, and suggest the major factors that should be controlled.

a Temperature affects the permeability of the cell membranes of beetroot cells (which have a purple pigment in the cytoplasm).

b Nitrate fertiliser increases the rate of growth in wheat plants.

c Drinking coffee increases urine production in humans.

5 A gardener is plagued by slugs eating his lettuces. He experiments in his greenhouse with various 'folk' remedies. Give suitable controls for each of the experiments.

a A piece of rope soaked with creosote placed on the soil around the plants.

b Small pots filled with beer, sunk into the soil around the plants.

c Small piles of tea leaves treated with powdered metaldehyde and placed among the plants.

d A cardboard model of a blackbird hung above the plants to act as a 'scare-slug'.

14.4 Accuracy and limitations

There is a limit to the accuracy of any measurement made in an experiment. One reason is, of course, the limitation of the measuring instrument. A second is the care with which the instrument is used. But in biological experiments there is often a practical limit to the accuracy that it is worth trying to achieve. Although instruments exist which can measure length to a fraction of a micrometre, there would be no point in such accuracy when measuring tail length in mice in an investigation of variation. In fact, with a wriggling mouse, it might be difficult to measure even to the nearest millimetre. This difficulty would be compounded by having to decide exactly where the base of the tail actually starts.

It is important, therefore, to consider the accuracy that might reasonably be expected from a set of data. Accuracy is often confused with reliability. Consider the data in Table 14.1.

Taking measurements from several specimens increases the reliability of the results, but it does not make them more accurate. For plant A, all the results are reasonably similar, which suggests that the value for the mean is likely to be somewhere in the same area. However, if another five leaves were measured, it is highly unlikely that exactly the same mean would be obtained. It is clearly absurd to give a value for the mean that is more precise than the accuracy of the measurements. Calculators give answers to many places of decimals, but judgement has to be used about the number of significant figures that can sensibly be given in data for means, or other calculations based on manipulating raw data.

The mean for plant B looks even more dodgy. The result for leaf 1 is very different from all of the others, so the mean comes well below all the other results. It may be that this result was a mistaken reading of the balance. On the other hand the anomaly may have been because the leaf was atypical, e.g. much smaller, with fewer stomata than normal, or half-dead. Without information about the original masses from which the losses were calculated it is impossible to guess. Expessing the results as percentage loss rather than as total loss would make comparison more reasonable.

Table 14.1 Comparing loss in mass of leaves from two different types of plant		
Leaf	Loss in mass over 24 hours / g	
	Plant A	Plant B
1	1.03	0.28
2	0.96	0.72
3	0.89	0.74
4	1.05	0.69
5	0.94	0.77
Mean	0.968	0.64

Using statistics to interpret results

The likely accuracy of a mean can be assessed statistically. This test is based on measuring the standard deviation of the results (for details of standard deviation see Chapter 15). Provided enough measurements have been made, when the standard deviation is small, it is likely that the calculated mean is close to the value that would be obtained if more results were obtained. The results of this test are called the **standard error**. Standard errors are often shown as a line on a graph, as in Fig 14.3. The standard error line indicates that it is 95% certain that the true mean is between its two extreme values. Notice that in Fig 14.3 the standard error lines for seed numbers of 100 and 1000 overlap, so there is no significant difference between them.

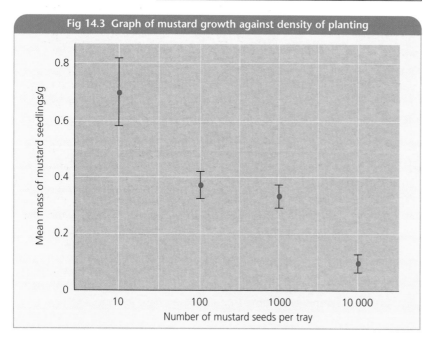

Fig 14.3 Graph of mustard growth against density of planting

Mean mass of mustard seedlings/g

Number of mustard seeds per tray

When we assess the limitations of an experiment, we consider those aspects which could not be avoided however accurate and careful we were. Dropping or misreading a thermometer is a limitation of the experimenter, not the experiment! Common limitations are the natural variability of living organisms and the impossibility of controlling certain environmental conditions, such as soil texture.

For example, in the experiment for which the results are shown in Table 14.1, it would be very difficult to find leaves that were all of exactly the same area. This could be allowed for by calculating loss in mass per unit area, but it is possible that leaves of different sizes would have different thickness and different numbers of stomata per unit area. It might also be difficult to seal the broken end of the stalk. The assumption was that loss in mass was due to loss of water, but some loss could be due to respiration or loss of other substances. For an experiment to be **valid** it must measure what it is aiming to measure. Otherwise, no matter how accurate the measurements are, the conclusions will still be wrong.

6   Fig 14.3 shows the results of an experiment to find the effect of planting density on the growth of mustard seedlings.

a   Judging from the standard error lines, suggest which planting density produced the greatest variation. Suggest a reason for this variability.

b   The seeds were planted in soil in the trays. To measure growth, the plants were cut at the base after 21 days. 50 plants from each tray (all from the tray with only 10) were weighed. Suggest what limitations this method might have.

c   Using a sample size of 50 should eliminate variability due genetic variation between seeds. However, this could be a problem in the tray with only 10 seeds. Suggest how this possible source of error could be reduced.

Standards and assays

When counting beans, or weighing them, an experimenter can be sure of obtaining an accurate and repeatable result. However, in many experiments it is necessary to make a subjective judgement. For example, Benedict's test for reducing sugars gives a range of colours from greenish through to orange-red depending on the concentration of the sugar. To use the test as a means of determining the concentration of sugar in, say, a fruit juice, a series of standard solutions can be made with known concentrations of sugar. The colour obtained by testing a sample of the juice can then be compared with those of the standard solutions to find the best match.

The same principle can be used with other coloured solutions, such as indicators. The principle is also used in bioassays, in which an effect of a substance on 'standard' living tissue, or an extract from it, is used. The test illustrated in Fig. 14.2, on page 200, is an example of a bioassay. The 'standard' sample is the bacterial lawn. Since the bacteria are of the same species and evenly spread across the medium in the Petri dish, the effectiveness of different antiseptics can be compared. A similar technique can be used to compare antibiotics, or enzyme activity (see AS book, p 78). An extract of the substance that makes the tails of fireflies, which are really types of beetle, glow luminously in the dark can be used to assay the concentration of ATP in a tissue. The substance only glows when supplied with energy from ATP. To assess the amount of ATP in different tissues, samples can be added to equal amounts of the extract and compared according to how long the extract emits light.

7   The straight shoots (coleoptiles) of young cereal seedlings are stimulated to grow by plant growth hormone. The rate of growth is sufficiently rapid for a measurable increase in length of a cut coleoptile to be seen within 48 hours. Suggest how you could use cut sections of coleoptile to estimate the concentrations of plant growth hormone in plant tissues, such as seeds, potatoes or buds.

- The accuracy of a measurement depends on the accuracy of the instrument being used. Means and other calculations from data should not be given with greater precision than the raw measurements.

- Finding the mean of several readings of the same measurement increases the reliability of data, but not the accuracy. Calculation of the standard error indicates the range of values that a mean is likely to be within.

- For conclusions from an experiment to be valid, the data must be measures of what was intended.

- Standard solutions or samples can be used where subjective judgements have to be made, for example of colour.

- Bioassays are used to determine the quantity or activity of a substance in biological material by comparing its activity with that of a standard sample.

14.5 Associations and correlations

Many biological investigations depend on a combination of observation and data analysis rather than on actual experiments. This is because it is often not practical to carry out proper controlled experiments with living organisms in the field, sometimes because of the complexity of interrelationships between organisms and the environment and sometimes for ethical reasons. It is, for example, not possible to remove the whole population of one species in an ecosystem in order to find the effect on the food web. Similarly you can't experiment on the effects of smoking by taking two groups of people and make one group smoke while keeping all other factors the same.

Investigators, therefore, have to look for **associations** that occur in the normal course of events. However, care needs to be taken when drawing conclusions. The number of fish may decline in a lake affected by acid rain or some other pollutant, but this association does not necessarily prove that the pollution has caused the decline, or even that the two are connected. Further investigations could look for data on natural populations of particular fish species in water of different acidity. It would also be possible to carry out laboratory experiments to determine fish survival rates in water of different acidity. Results might well show that the lower the pH the lower the survival rate. In this case there would be a **correlation** between pH and fish survival. This would still not prove that the decline in fish numbers in the lake was actually caused by the acidity.

If you counted, say, the number of night-clubs and pubs and the number of churches in a several towns and cities and then plotted a graph of one against the other you would almost certainly find a correlation. But this would obviously not prove that churches cause night-clubs and pubs to be built, or the other way round. The correlation is likely to be the result of a completely separate factor, i.e. the size of the town or city.

Similarly the decline in fish numbers might be due to some other factor, which might or might not be due to acidity. There could be an indirect association, caused by the effect of acidity on the food supply or the acid-related release of toxic mineral ions. The laboratory experiment would be unable to mimic the complex interaction of abiotic and biotic factors in the real situation of the lake. Nevertheless it is only by searching for correlations and investigating them further that biologists can increase their understanding of ecology. A correlation may be either positive or negative. When one factor increases as another increases it is a positive correlation; when one increases while another decreases it is a negative correlation. In the next chapter we consider in more detail how correlations in data can be analysed.

Epidemiology

Links between human afflictions and factors such as environmental pollutants, diet, smoking and other aspects of lifestyle are equally hard to establish by experiment. Most associations have been established by studies of the incidence of disease or disorders in large groups of people. Looking for patterns in the occurrence of disease in human populations is called **epidemiology**. Many of the suggested links have been matters of controversy and some have caused considerable confusion in the minds of the public. Consider issues like the dangers of using mobile phones; the possible link between taking contraceptive pills and various cancers; vaccination and autism in children; fat consumption and heart disease. There are still some people who refuse to accept the association between smoking and lung cancer, despite the overwhelming statistical evidence.

The stages in establishing the cause of a non-infectious disease are:

- searching for a correlation between a disease and a specific factor;
- developing hypotheses as to how the factor might have its effect;

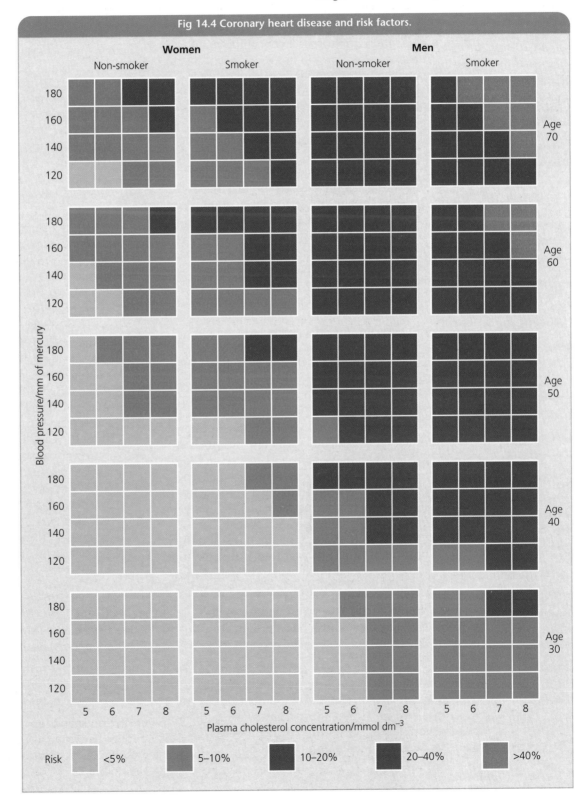

Fig 14.4 Coronary heart disease and risk factors.

- testing these hypotheses to determine whether the factor can induce the disease.

To establish a correlation means collecting data from large numbers of people. Because of the huge variability between people and their lifestyles, it requires comparisons to be made as far as possible between matched groups. For example, suppose you were looking for a correlation between beer consumption and heart disease. It would not be sufficient just to compare the rates of heart disease between 1000 beer drinkers and 1000 non-drinkers. The ideal comparison would be between groups of people where the only difference in lifestyle was whether or not they drank beer. In practice this would be virtually impossible to achieve, but at least a much more valid comparison could be made between groups matched for age, sex, amount of exercise taken and major features of diet. The difficulty is to eliminate the possibility that any correlation found is not due to some other linked factor, such as that people who are tempted to indulge in beer-drinking are also consumers of excessive quantities of fish and chips, or simply that they have some genetic predisposition to heart disease. The latter is a particularly difficult argument to refute, and has regularly been used as an excuse for shedding doubt on the smoking/lung cancer correlation.

Once a correlation has been found, the next stage is try to determine how exactly the factor actually causes its effect. This is often much more difficult. Many diseases, such as cardiovascular disorders and cancers develop as a result of several interacting factors. The correlation between smoking and incidence of lung cancer has been established for many years. The search to isolate a specific carcinogen in cigarette smoke has still not been successful. However the tar inhaled into the lungs contains a massive cocktail of organic compounds, many of which may have carcinogenic properties. Some of the effects may be additive, i.e. it may be a combination of substances and other factors that is the main cause. Also, individuals differ in their susceptibility, probably due to genetic factors. Research has involved detailed chemical analyses of tar, experiments on animals and with tissue cultures, and comparisons between many genetically distinct groupings. Until a precise mechanism is discovered, the arguments will no doubt continue, and only after that will it be possible to produce effective countermeasures, apart, of course, from not smoking!

8 The chart in Fig 14.4 shows the risk of developing coronary heart disease during the next ten years in relation to a number of risk factors.

a Which risk factors have been taken into account in this chart?

b According to the chart, what are the characteristics of the people with the highest risk of developing coronary heart disease?

c A group of 500 men aged between 40 and 50 are studied. They all have high blood pressure of over 180 mm of mercury, and a plasma cholesterol concentration between 7 and 8 mmol dm^{-3}. They all smoke. How many of these men would be expected to suffer from coronary heart disease over the next 10 years? How many would suffer if they were all non-smokers?

d Explain the limitations of using the chart as a way of predicting whether an individual will develop coronary heart disease.

e The data used to construct the chart have a number of limitations as a means of predicting risk. Suggest three weaknesses in the data.

KEY FACTS

- An **association** in data is where there appears to be a link between one factor and another, such as between the numbers of fish in a lake and its acidity.

- Where a change in one factor is associated with a corresponding pattern of change in another factor, the two factors are **correlated**. For example, one factor may increase as the other increases (a **positive correlation**), or one may increase while the other decreases (a **negative correlation**).

- A correlation is not proof that a change in one factor is the direct cause of the change in the other. This can only be supported by experimental evidence.

- In complex situations, such as in ecosystems and human populations, it is difficult to establish causes and effects because many factors may interact.

- In human populations **epidemiologists** look for associations between factors and try to establish the likely causes of diseases by studying data from matched groups.

15 Interpreting data

In this chapter we look at the skills required when interpreting unfamiliar data. These may be the results of actual experiments, or information collected together from many investigations

15.1 Calculations

The calculations in A2 may be more difficult than those that you met in the AS exam. You need to be able to calculate percentage changes and rates. For some calculations, you may need to transform formulae.

Percentage change

It is useful to calculate a percentage change when a difference occurs in one of the variables investigated by an experiment. For example, suppose we were investigating the effect of hormone concentration on the growth of plant roots. It would be almost impossible to find roots that were all the same length. If the roots have different lengths to start with, then simply reporting the increase of length of each root would be meaningless. In cases such as this we measure the percentage increase in length of each root. Table 15.1 shows some typical results.

At first sight, it looks as though the roots in the 0.03 μM hormone solution have grown faster than those in the 0.02 μM hormone solution. But the roots were different lengths to start with, so we cannot tell which grew faster simply by looking at the increase in length. Instead, we have to calculate how much each of them grew per unit of length

during the experiment. The best way to do this is to measure the length before the experiment starts, and again at the end, and then calculate the percentage increase in length. We do this by using the equation:

$$\frac{\text{Increase in length} \times 100}{\text{Original length}}$$

For the root in 0.02 μM hormone solution:

$$\frac{14 \text{ mm} \times 100}{16 \text{ mm}} = 87.5\%$$

For the root in 0.03 μM hormone solution:

$$\frac{16 \text{ mm} \times 100}{20 \text{ mm}} = 80.0\%$$

So, in fact, the rate of growth of the shoot in the 0.01 μM hormone solution was the greater.

Do not be surprised if you get results that are greater than 100%. The data for a root placed in 0.01 μM hormone solution are: original length 15 mm, final length 33 mm; increase in length 18 mm. The percentage increase in length for this root is therefore:

$$\frac{18 \text{ mm} \times 100}{15 \text{ mm}} = 120\%$$

Table 15.1 Percentage change

Concentration of hormone/μM	Initial length of root/mm	Final length of root/mm	Change in length of root/mm
0.02	16	30	14
0.03	20	36	16

Table 15.2 Results of the Dieldrin experiment

Period	Location of traps	Number of mice caught	Number of mice analysed	Mean dieldrin content of mice/ppm
Before sowing	In planted area	15	4	0.23
After sowing	In planted area	18	7	10.96

Let's look at a typical question:

1 Dieldrin is a pesticide that was used to treat wheat before planting. An investigation was carried out to find the effect of treated wheat grain on the dieldrin concentration in the tissues of mice living in wheat fields. Mice were trapped before and after the treated wheat was planted. The results are shown in Table 15.2.
Calculate the percentage change in mean dieldrin concentration in the tissues of mice.

Here is a worked example to show how to answer this. To calculate the percentage, first calculate the actual increase:

$$10.96 \text{ ppm} - 0.23 \text{ ppm} = 10.73 \text{ ppm}$$

Now calculate 10.73 as a percentage of 0.23:

$$\frac{10.73 \times 100}{0.23} = 4665\%$$

Significant figures

The actual display on the calculator at the end of the above calculation is 4665.217391. Clearly, since the data for the mice is in **integers** (whole numbers), the answer should be given to the nearest whole number: 4665.

You should not write down more numbers after the decimal point than the number of figures given in the data. It is a good practice, however, to show the number given by your calculator display, *then*, round up or down as appropriate.

Estimating

A good way of checking the magnitude of your answer is to do the calculation again, but using whole numbers where possible.

You could check the above calculation by finding 11 × 100 / 0.25.

The answer is 4400, so the answer 4665 is clearly of the right magnitude.

Suitable calculations

When looking at data, we must decide which mathematical technique to use. For example, what is the best technique to use when presented with the data in Table 15.3?

The rhinoceros beetle is a pest that damages coconut palms growing on South Pacific islands. One method of control is to introduce a virus which kills the beetles. The

Table 15.3 Results of the Tonga surveys	
1971	
Number of palm trees examined	**Number of palm trees damaged by beetles**
289	48
1978	
Number of palm trees examined	**Number of palm trees damaged by beetles**
302	23

virus was first used on the island of Tonga in 1971. Table 15.3 shows the results of surveys of rhinoceros beetle damage to palm trees carried out at two sites in 1971 and 1978.

2 Look at the results in Table 15.3. Was the introduction of the rhinoceros beetle-killing virus successful in Tonga?

To approach this question properly, you need to support you answer with suitable calculations from data in the table. Because the samples are not of equal size, you must calculate the percentage of damaged trees in each of the years:

The percentage of trees damaged in 1971 is:

$$\frac{48 \times 100}{289} = 16.6$$

The percentage of trees damaged in 1978 is:

$$\frac{23 \times 100}{302} = 7.6$$

The percentage of trees damaged fell from 16.6% in 1971 to 7.6% in 1978, a reduction of 9%.

The beetle *Delphastus pusillus* (right) is used in the UK for biological control of whitefly, a common plague on greenhouse tomatoes. The beetle kills larvae as well as adult flies, and so is an effective method of control.

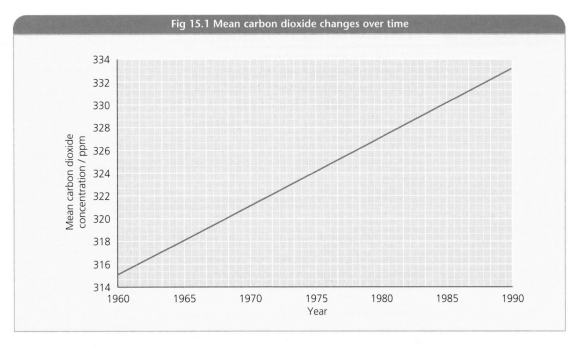

Fig 15.1 Mean carbon dioxide changes over time

Rate of change

You also need to be able to use the gradient of a graph to calculate the rate of change. The same principle applies to working with graphs in biology as it does in physics or chemistry. You divide a reading from the vertical axis by the corresponding reading on the horizontal axis. Fig 15.1 shows how the mean concentration of carbon dioxide in the atmosphere changed above a Pacific island between 1960 and 1990.

Since this is a 'straight-line' graph we can use it to calculate the rate at which the carbon dioxide concentration rose. It is much easier if you choose whole numbers. For example the graph crosses intersecting gridlines at 1965 and 1975.

Read off the carbon dioxide concentrations in these two years – 318 ppm and 324 ppm. The carbon dioxide concentration rose by 6 ppm in 10 years, so the rate of increase is:

6 ppm/10 years = 0.6 ppm year^{-1}.

Let's look at another typical question:

3 The graph in Fig 15.2 shows the effect of temperature on the mean number of red spider mites eaten by two predatory mites, *Amblyseius fustis* and *Typhlodromus occidentalis*.
Calculate the mean rate of increase in the number of red spider mites eaten per day by *A. fustis*.

The increase in mean number of mites eaten as the temperature rises from 20 °C to 30 °C is 0.4. The rate of increase is therefore:

0.4 mites/10 °C = 0.04 mites °C^{-1}

Do not forget to give the unit when answering this type of question.

Now here is a question to do on your own:

4 Calculate the rate of increase in the mean number of mites eaten by *T. occidentalis* as the temperature rises from 25 °C to 30 °C.

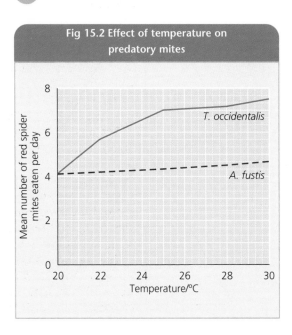

Fig 15.2 Effect of temperature on predatory mites

15.2 Transforming formulae

You probably learned the 'magic triangle' method for transforming formulae at GCSE. The 'magic triangle' for the formula A = B × C is shown in Fig 15.3a. From the triangle:

$$B = \frac{A}{C}$$

and

$$C = \frac{A}{B}$$

A good example of how a magic triangle formula can be used is the relationship between actual size, observed size and magnification (Fig 15.3b):

Observed size (O) = actual size (A) × magnification (M)

Suppose the you are given a photograph on which a mitochondrion has an observed width of 20 mm and you are told that the magnification is 800 000. You are asked to calculate the actual width in μm.

Using the triangle:

$$A = \frac{O}{M} = \frac{20\,\text{mm}}{800\,000} = 0.00025\,\text{mm}$$

Divide this by 1000 to convert to μm. The answer is therefore 0.25 μm

The following question, which you can try on your own, requires you to do two separate things: read data and transform a formula.

5 An individual's estimated average requirement for energy (EAR) can be determined by multiplying the basal metabolic rate (BMR) and the physical activity level (PAL).

EAR = BMR × PAL

Table 15.4 gives the average PAL values for males with different levels of activity and Fig 15.4 shows the effect of age on EAR values of males with low levels of activity. Use the graph to calculate the basal metabolic rate of a 35-year-old man with a low level of activity. Show your working.

Table 15.4 Average PAL values	
Level of activity	**PAL**
Low	1.4
Moderate	1.7
High	1.9

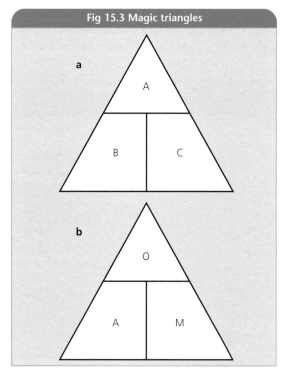

Fig 15.3 Magic triangles

a

b

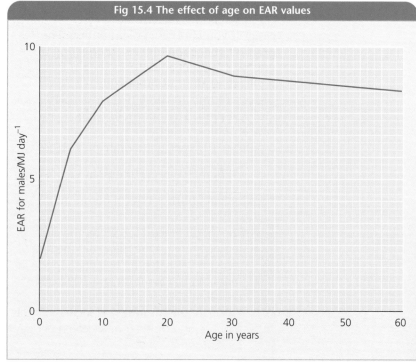

Fig 15.4 The effect of age on EAR values

Patterns in data

Sometimes it is not possible to do an experiment in which one variable, the **independent variable**, is altered so that the effect of this change on another variable, the **dependent variable**, can be investigated. For example, in an ecological investigation on predation, it would not be possible to change the number of predators or prey in a habitat. Instead the scientist needs to measure two or more variables to see if there is any pattern that might relate them. If there is a pattern, the scientist will suggest that the two variables are **correlated**, or related to each other. In this case the scientist would count the number of predators and prey over a period of time, then look for patterns in population sizes.

Using scattergrams

Data collected from experiments that look to see if two variables are related often does not show a direct relationship. Instead it is often indirect. Results are usually plotted on a scattergram, as shown in Fig 15.5. This scattergram shows the results obtained by an ecologist who collected data about the predation rate by weasels on great tits and the population density of great tits.

As you can see, the data does not conveniently fall into points on a straight line or a curve, rather it is more scattered – hence scattergram.

However, if you look more closely, you will notice that there *is* a pattern in the data. The greater the population density, the higher the predation rate. But this does *not* mean that a high population density *causes* a higher

predation rate, merely that there is a correlation between the two. What it does mean is that a change in one variable is *linked* with a change in another variable.

Explaining relationships

Once a correlation is found, we need to think of possible explanations. Further investigations can then help to find whether a suggested explanation is true. The first step, which you may be asked for, is a suggestion, or **hypothesis**. In this case we might suggest that at high densities, more great tits are killed by weasels, reducing the great tit population, making it more difficult for weasels to locate and then kill great tits. To check this, it would be necessary to find whether weasels really do kill more great tits at high densities by, for example, examining weasel faeces for indigestible remains of great tits.

Sometimes the relationship is negative, as Fig 15.6 shows. This graph shows the relationship between the population density of mice and the rate of predation of great tits by weasels.

The correlation here is negative: the greater the mouse population, the lower the rate of predation by weasels on great tits. In this case the hypothesis might be that weasels find it easier to catch mice than great tits, so when the mouse population is high, the weasels obtain most of their food from mice rather than great tits. Further investigations, again using faecal examinations, would be done to find what was happening in the real ecosystem.

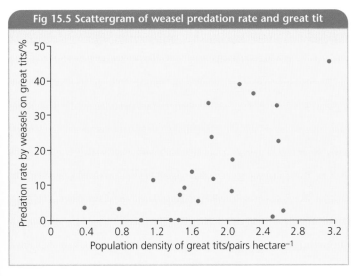

Fig 15.5 Scattergram of weasel predation rate and great tit

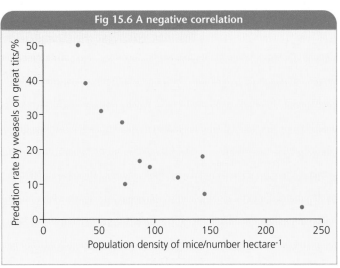

Fig 15.6 A negative correlation

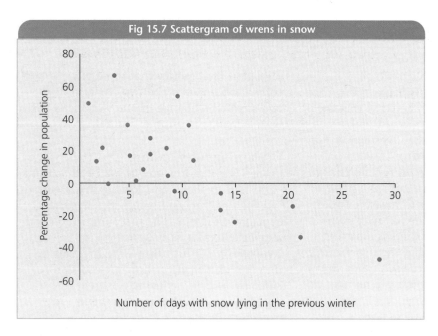

Fig 15.7 Scattergram of wrens in snow

Percentage change in population

Number of days with snow lying in the previous winter

The results of such investigations often show that food webs are not simply a collection of 'straight' food chains, but have much more complex feeding relationships.

In other investigations, variables may be correlated for some values but not for others. The scattergram in Fig 15.7 shows the relationship between the population size of wrens and the number of days that snow covered the ground in the previous winter. You might be asked this sort of question on these data:

6
a Describe the relationship between the number of days with snow lying and the change in population size.
b Suggest and explain a reason for this relationship.

The answer to part 'a' is that these data show no correlation between number of days of snow and change in the wren population when the number of days of snow is less than 13. However, when there are more than 13 days of snow, there is a negative correlation between the number of days of snow and the population size.

When you answer the second part of the question, you need to remember that the data are about snow cover and population change. A reasonable hypothesis is that there are fewer birds left to breed in the following summer because some birds starved when their food supply was covered by snow for longer periods.

Looking for patterns

Correlation data are often presented in tables. Again we look for patterns in the columns of data that might suggest a hypothesis that relates two of the patterns.

Table 15.5 shows the relationship between the northern limit of tree growth and the resistance to freezing of winter buds.

7 Look at Table 15.5 and describe the patterns in the data.

There are three columns of data, so we refer to all three. For example:

- The northern limit of the trees is positively correlated with the mean minimum temperature.

- The northern limit of the trees is positively correlated with the temperature at which the buds are damaged by frost.

- The mean temperature at the northern limit is greater than the temperature at which the buds are damaged by frost.

Table 15.5 Tree growth and resistance of buds to freezing			
Species	Northern limit /°N latitude	Mean minimum temperature at northern limit /°C	Temperature below which the winter buds are damaged by frost/°C
Oak	32	–6	–7
Magnolia	35	–11	–17
Liquidambar	40	–19	–27
Poplar	48	–33	<–80
Willow	48	–33	<–80
Elm	52	–42	–45
Birch	60	<–46	<–80

Table 15.6 Woods inhabited by different bird species

Species	Food	Typical body mass / g	Percentage of woods of each size inhabited by named species				
			0.001–0.01 ha	0.01–0.1 ha	0.1–1 ha	1–10 ha	10–100 ha
Blackbird	Wide range of insect and plant food	90	13	34	63	72	91
House sparrow	Weed and grass seeds	30	9	21	44	35	22
Great tit	Insects and nuts	20	0	3	12	16	73
Treecreeper	Insects	10	0	0	2	8	25
Great spotted woodpecker	Insects	130	0	0	0	1	26

Now let's look at another example. This time the question is for you to answer.

8 Table 15.6 shows the percentage of woods of different sizes that were inhabited by different species of birds.

a Describe the relationship between the size of wood and the diversity of the birds it contains.

b Use data in the table to explain the different distribution of treecreepers and greater-spotted woodpeckers.

Blackbird feeding its young

Experimental investigations

In an experimental investigation the scientist manipulates one variable and then measures the effects of this manipulation on other variable.

If the scientist finds that whenever variable A is changed, then variable B changes, then the conclusion is that A influences B. Only experimental data can conclusively demonstrate that the change in one variable is *caused* by the change in the other variable.

Independent variables are those that the experimenter changes whereas dependent variables are the ones that change as a result of the experiment.

Line graphs

Most data obtained from experimental investigations can be plotted on a line graph. Conventionally the independent variable is plotted on the horizontal axis (also known as the x-axis) and the dependent variable on the vertical axis (the y-axis).

Line graphs include both those where a straight line can be drawn through the data points and those where a curved line is more appropriate. Data points often give curves that change direction abruptly at one point.

The graph in Fig 15.7 shows the effect of light on the rate of photosynthesis of a crop plant at different light intensities. In this investigation the experimenter changed the light intensity, so this is the independent variable. The rate of photosynthesis was

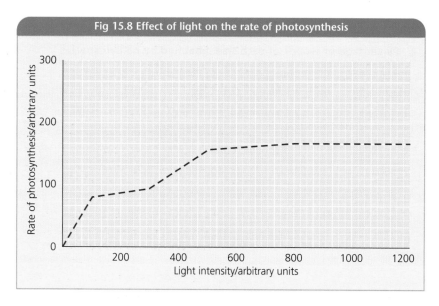

Fig 15.8 Effect of light on the rate of photosynthesis

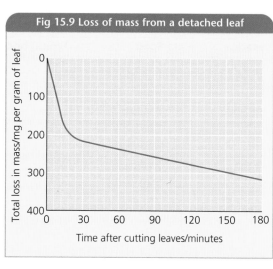

Fig 15.9 Loss of mass from a detached leaf

measured at each light intensity chosen, so this is the dependent variable.

The plotted line for the crop plant levels off at a light intensity of 800 arbitrary units. This means that the rate photosynthesis remains constant at the rate of 160 units, *not* that photosynthesis stops.

For light intensities between 0 and 800 units, light intensity is the factor that limits the rate of photosynthesis. At light intensities above this, some other factor such as carbon dioxide concentration is limiting the rate, since increasing light intensity beyond 800 units has no further effect.

Reversing the axes of a line graph
Sometimes it may be better to show data on a graph with axes that are reversed. An example is shown in Fig 15.9. This graph shows the changes in total water loss from a detached leaf over 180 minutes. By having the axis for mass loss going downwards, it shows the actual loss of mass more clearly.

The rate of mass loss in any period can be calculated from the gradient. Thus, in the first ten minutes after being detached, the rate of mass loss from the leaf is:

100 mg per gram per 10 minutes

= 10 mg per gram of leaf per minute

Let's have a look at a question:

9 Look at Fig 15.9 and calculate the rate of mass loss between 60 and 150 minutes.

A good description of the data would be:

'The leaf lost mass at a high constant rate for the first 25 minutes then continued to lose mass at a slower constant rate for the rest of the time.'

Some data give graphs in which the rate of change is exponential for part of the time. This means the increase in rate becomes more and more rapid. The graph in Fig 15.10 shows the light absorption of a colony of microbes.

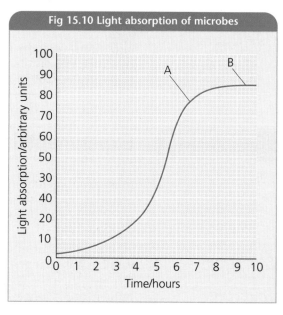

Fig 15.10 Light absorption of microbes

As the number of microbes increases, more light is absorbed.

For the first six hours there is an exponential increase in numbers – the rate of at which numbers increase gets larger. Again, the population does *not* decrease after 8 hours, it remains at a high, constant level.

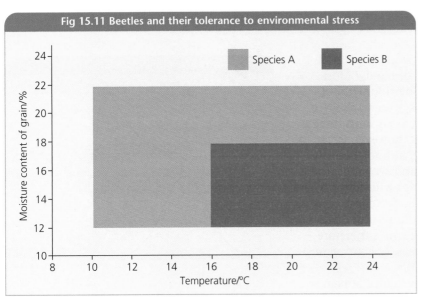

Fig 15.11 Beetles and their tolerance to environmental stress

11 What conclusions can be drawn by comparing the results for

a treatments A and B?
b treatments B and C?
c treatments C and D?

The differences between treatments A and B, and between B and C are so small they are likely to be due to variation; they are too small to be significant. Therefore, in part 'a' light does not affect the total amount of auxin; and in part 'b' equal amounts of auxin diffuse into the two blocks when the two halves of tip are separated. In part 'c', the difference in concentration between treatments C and D is significant. A reasonable hypothesis would be that the cover glass in C prevented diffusion of hormone away from the illuminated side of the tip.

Using area graphs

Data may also be presented as area graphs.

Two species of beetle are commonly found in stored grain. Fig 15.11 shows the range of moisture content and temperature that each species can tolerate. The ecological ranges of the two species overlap. Where their ranges overlap, the beetles will compete, but there will be no competition in the part of the range occupied by only one of the beetles.

10 Look at Fig 15.11. The temperature in different parts of a large grain store varied from 14 °C to 20 °C. The moisture content of the grain was constant at 16%. Beetles of both species were introduced into the store. What would you expect to happen if:

a Species A were a more successful competitor than species B;
b Species B were a more successful competitor than species A?

Significance

When asked to draw conclusions from data we need to be careful to include only significant differences. This is because living organisms are variable, so minor differences may not be due to changes brought about by the experiment.

A good example is shown by these data on plant auxins. Fig 15.12 shows the results obtained from experiments that investigated the effect of light on auxin distribution in shoot tips. The figures are mean values derived from several experiments.

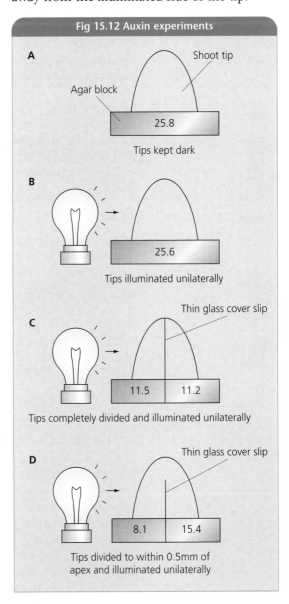

Fig 15.12 Auxin experiments

A — Agar block — Shoot tip — 25.8 — Tips kept dark

B — 25.6 — Tips illuminated unilaterally

C — Thin glass cover slip — 11.5 | 11.2 — Tips completely divided and illuminated unilaterally

D — Thin glass cover slip — 8.1 | 15.4 — Tips divided to within 0.5mm of apex and illuminated unilaterally

15.5 Using statistics

How many people in the world have more than the average number of hands? Most people who answer this question without thinking will say 'none' or 'very few', since most of us don't know anybody with three hands. The correct answer, however, is 'nearly everyone'. This is because, although hardly any people have more than two hands, there are unfortunately quite a lot with fewer. There are, for example, those who have lost arms in accidents or were born without them. The arithmetical average, or mean, is therefore rather less than 2.0, whereas, of course, most people do have exactly 2.0.

This illustrates the importance of being very careful when interpreting data. Common sense and statistics don't always go together.

Probability

Because living organisms are variable, we need to test whether differences we measure are significant, or just down to chance variation. To do this we use statistical tests. Most statistical tests give us an answer in terms of the **probability** of our observed differences occurring by chance.

There are several ways of expressing probability:

1 in 10
1 to 2
0.1 (or 1 in 10)
$\frac{1}{2}$ (1 in 2)

Note that '1 in 2' is not the same as '1 to 2' (1 in 2 is a 0.5 chance and 1 to 2 is a 0.33 chance).

Thus, the probability of a Y sperm fertilising an egg can be expressed in three ways:

0.5
$\frac{1}{2}$
1 in 2

Normal distribution

Statistical tests usually depend on the **normal distribution**. The exact shape of the normal distribution depends on the **mean** and the **standard deviation** of the distribution. The standard deviation is a measure of how much measurements are spread out from the mean.

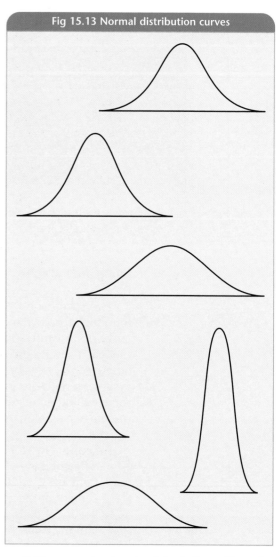

Fig 15.13 Normal distribution curves

Differences in standard deviation affect the shape of the distribution. All the curves in Fig 15.13 represent normal distributions. Although the distribution is symmetrical in all the curves shown, the distribution changes as the standard deviation changes. When the SD increases, the curve becomes flatter; if the SD decreases, the curve is taller.

In a normal distribution:

- measurements greater than the mean and measurements less than the mean are equally common.

- small deviations from the mean are much more common than large ones.

- 68% of all the measurements fall within a range of ± standard deviation from the mean and 95% within ± 2 standard deviations.

An example of normal distribution

Fig 15.14 shows the normal distribution of diastolic blood pressure for a sample of males.

The mean blood pressure is 82 mm Hg and the standard deviation is 10 mm Hg. This means that 68% of the sample have blood pressures between 72 and 92 mm Hg and 95% of the sample have blood pressures between 62 and 102 mm Hg. It follows that if we sample, there is only a 0.05 (1 in 20 chance) of selecting a male with a blood pressure less than 62 or greater than 102 mm Hg.

In Chapter 12 you looked at data on the number of earthworms in quadrats. As well as calculating the mean number of earthworms per quadrat, it is useful to have a measure of how much the data is spread out.

The formula for calculating the standard deviation of a sample of a population is

$$S = \sqrt{\frac{\sum x^2 - (\sum x)^2 / n}{n - 1}}$$

where s = the standard deviation of the population
Σ = the sum of
x = each measurement
n = the number of measurements

The first step is to write the number of earthworms found in each quadrat, square each one and write them all down in a table. Table 15.7 gives an example.

Table 15.7 Calculating a standard deviation		
Quadrat	Number of earthworms x	x^2
1	12	144
2	14	196
3	11	121
4	15	225
5	13	169
6	12	144
7	16	256
8	11	121
9	14	196
10	12	144
Σ	130	1716

Now substitute the totals in the equation:

$$s = \sqrt{\frac{1716 - (130)^2 / 10}{10 - 1}} = 1.7$$

The mean number of earthworms per quadrat is 13.

The standard deviation of 1.7 is quite low, meaning that the normal distribution curve would appear tall and narrow.

The standard deviation result also means that the number of earthworms in 68 per cent – about two thirds – of the quadrats could be expected to contain between

$$(13 + 1.7) = 14.7 \text{ earthworms}$$
or $$(13 - 1.7) = 11.3 \text{ earthworms}$$

This is a very narrow range.

12 Look at Table 15.8. What is the range of the concentration of zinc:

a within 1 standard deviation at 4 km?
b within 2 standard deviations at 22 km?

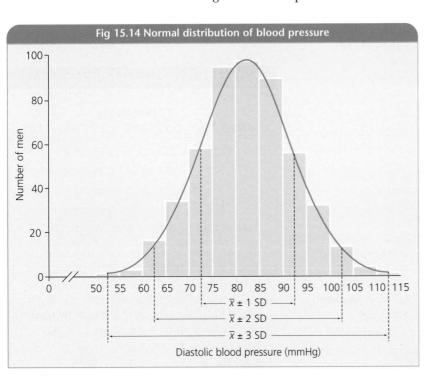

Fig 15.14 Normal distribution of blood pressure

Table 15.8 Zinc concentration	
Distance from pollution source	Zinc concentration /mg dm⁻³ (mean and standard deviation)
3	3.0 ± 2.5
4	1.6 ± 0.9
10	1.3 ± 0.6
13	0.8 ± 0.2
22	0.4 ± 0.04

The chi-squared test

In Chapter 12 you learned that the chi-squared test can be used to find if there is a significant difference between two sets of data. You also learned that the chi-squared test is used to test the null hypothesis.

Look again at the data collected for four plant species in fertilised and unfertilised areas (Table 15.9).

Table 15.9 Plant species data		
Species	Total number in 20 quadrats	
	Fertilised area	Unfertilised area
A	0	182
B	2	51
C	88	124
D	91	102

It seems fairly certain that fertilising the fields affected species A and B, but the results are less clear for species C and D.

Before calculating chi-squared we need a null hypothesis. The null hypothesis in this case is that:

Fertiliser does *not* affect the distribution of the plant species.

In the chi-squared test the observed number in each category is compared with an expected number.

The expected number can be calculated according to a theory, as in the case of genetics experiments.

It can also calculated by using the means of the observed numbers in the case of environmental investigations.

The formula for the chi-squared test is:

$$\chi^2 = \sum \frac{(O - E)^2}{E}$$

where χ^2 is the symbol for chi-squared
O is the observed number
E is the expected number.

So, chi-squared tests variance, which is the difference between observed and expected numbers.

If we take the result for species C, the observed numbers are 88 for the fertilised area and 124 for the unfertilised area. The expected number in each area, if the null hypothesis is true, is the mean of the number of plants.

The mean number per quadrat is:

$$\left(\frac{88 + 124}{2}\right) = 106$$

We can now put our observed and expected results into a table, as Table 15.10 shows.

Table 15.10 Observed and expected results			
	Fertilised area	Unfertilised area	Total
O	88	124	212
E	106	106	212
$(O - E)$	−18	18	
$(O - E)^2$	324	324	
$\dfrac{(O - E)^2}{E}$	3.06	3.06	6.12

So chi-squared value for plant species C is 6.12. We now need to find if this value for chi-squared confirms or rejects the null hypothesis.

If the value shows that the observed numbers would occur by chance only five times out of a hundred times or less, we consider it unlikely that the results occur by chance and we reject the null hypothesis. However, we are still *not* certain that the null hypothesis is not true – only that there is a very good chance that it is not true

We compare the computed result, 6.12, with values in a table of chi-squared (Table 15.11).

Table 15.11 Some values for chi-squared						
Degrees of freedom	Probability					
	0.50	0.25	0.10	0.05	0.02	0.01
1	0.45	1.32	2.71	3.84	5.41	6.64
2	1.39	2.77	4.61	5.99	7.82	9.21
3	2.37	4.11	6.25	7.82	9.84	11.34
4	3.36	5.39	7.78	9.49	11.67	13.28

To use Table 15.11, we have to select the probability we are using and the number of degrees of freedom in the data. Biologists usually choose the 5% probability level. This means a probability of 5 times in a hundred, so we select the 0.05 probability column.

The number of degrees of freedom in the data = (number of categories – 1). In this case there are 2 categories, fertilised and unfertilised. There are therefore (2 – 1) = 1 degree of freedom.

In Table 15.11, the chi-squared value for a probability of 0.05 and 1 degree of freedom is 3.84. The calculated value of chi-squared is 6.12. Since the calculated value, 6.12, is greater than the table value, 3.84, the null hypothesis is rejected.

This means that the observed results would occur by chance less than five times in one hundred.

 13 Use Tables 15.9 and 15.11 and now calculate chi-squared for the results for plant species D.

Another way of calculating expected numbers

In one of his experiments, Mendel crossed true-breeding long-stemmed pea plants with true-breeding short-stemmed pea plants. All the F_1 plants had tall stems. When he self-pollinated the F_1 plants 787 of the F_2 plants had long stems and 277 had short stems.

There was a total of 1064 plants. If Mendel's hypothesis is correct we would expect a 3 : 1 ratio of tall : short plants, i.e., 798 tall plants and 266 short plants. We can set up a table (Table 15.12).

Table 15.12 Mendel's results			
	Tall plants	**Short plants**	**Total**
Number observed	787	277	1064
Number expected	798	266	1064

Using a computer or calculator, χ^2 for these data = 0.607. Look back at Table 15.10 for some values for chi-squared

In this case there are two categories, long stem and short stem, so the number of degrees of freedom is (2 – 1) = 1.

The null hypothesis is that the difference between the observed and the expected results is significant, i.e. greater than would be expected by chance.

For χ^2 = 0.607 the probability is somewhere between 0.5 and 0.25. This means that there is a probability that the observed results would differ from the expected results by the amounts shown in the data in between 25 and 50% of

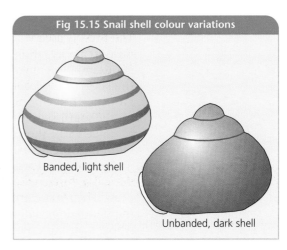

Fig 15.15 Snail shell colour variations

Banded, light shell

Unbanded, dark shell

cases. The null hypothesis is therefore rejected: the difference between the observed and the expected results is not significant.

Using the mean of the observed numbers to calculate χ^2

Cepaea nemoralis is a species of snail that lives in woods and fields. It is prey to birds such as thrushes. The snails show several different colour variations, such as yellow with dark bands and brown with no bands. Fig 15.15 shows two of these forms of the snail.

In an investigation, samples of the snail were collected from two sites, one in a beech wood and the other under a hedge. The results are shown in Table 15.13.

Collection site	Number of snails collected		
	Yellow banded	**Brown unbanded**	**Total**
Beech wood	32	88	120
Hedges	49	27	76

Table 15.13 Snail data

14

a Suggest a null hypothesis for the data shown in Fig 15.12.

b How many degrees of freedom are there in the data?

c What is the overall mean number of type of snail per location? This is the expected number of snails (E)

d Calculate χ^2 for the data.

e Look up the probability for this value. What do you conclude?

The t-test

The t-test is used when we make a range of measurements rather than counting numbers. For example we might wish to compare the thickness of the leaves of a species of plant growing on the north side with those growing on the south side of a wall.

Table 15.14 shows the results of one such set of measurements.

The statistical test you can use to find if there is a difference between two means is the t-test. The t-test compares both the mean and the standard deviation of two populations whose distribution curves overlap as shown in Fig 15.16.

Table 15.14 Comparing leaf thickness	
Thickness of leaves on south side of wall/μm	Thickness of leaves on north side of wall /μm
300	180
270	210
220	220
250	160
210	210
250	190
290	160
190	180
220	200
270	210

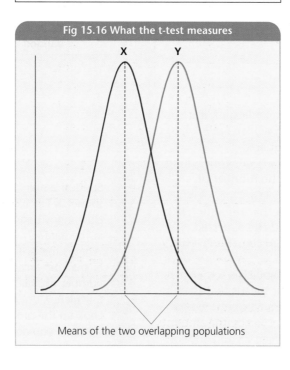

Fig 15.16 What the t-test measures

X   Y

Means of the two overlapping populations

Note that you would not be asked to calculate a t-test in the examination so you need not learn the formula. But you may need to use a t-test in an investigation.

The t-test compares the means and standard deviations of two populations. The t-test calculates:

Difference in means of two populations

Variability of the two populations.

The variability of the population is the square of the standard deviation, so the formula for the t-test is:

$$t = \frac{|x_1 - x_2|}{\sqrt{\dfrac{\sigma_1^2}{n_1} + \dfrac{\sigma_2^2}{n_2}}}$$

where t = t-test value

$|x_1 - x_2|$ = the difference between the mean value of population 1 (x_1) and the mean value of population 2 (x_2)

σ_1^2 = the variance (square of the standard deviation) of population 1

σ_2^2 = the variance (square of the standard deviation) of population 2

n_1 = the number of measurements in population 1

n_2 = the number of measurements in population 2

You can see that this formula takes into account both the size of the differences and the size of the sample.

In this example, the null hypothesis is that there is no significant difference between the thickness of leaves on the north and south facing walls.

First calculate the mean thickness of each population of leaves:

Mean thickness south facing leaves (x_1) = 247 μm
Mean thickness north facing leaves (x_2) = 192 μm

$|x_1 - x_2|$ = 247 μm – 192 μm = 55

Now calculate the standard deviation of each population of leaves:

Standard deviation south facing leaves = 36.2
Standard deviation north facing leaves = 21.5

$$\sigma_1^2 = (36.2)^2 = 1310.4$$

$$\sigma_2^2 = (21.5)^2 = 462.25$$

$$\frac{\sigma_1^2}{n_1} = \frac{1310.4}{10} = 131.04$$

$$\frac{\sigma_2^2}{n_2} = \frac{462.254}{10} = 46.22$$

$$t = \frac{55}{\sqrt{131.04 + 46.22}} = 4.131$$

Degrees of freedom	t-value					
	P = 0.2	P = 0.1	P = .05	P = 0.02	P = 0.01	P = 0.001
1	3.078	6.314	12.706	31.821	63.657	636.619
2	1.886	2.920	4.303	6.965	9.925	31.598
3	1.638	2.353	3.182	4.541	5.841	12.941
4	1.533	2.132	2.776	3.747	4.604	8.610
5	1.476	2.015	2.571	3.365	4.032	6.859
6	1.440	1.943	2.447	3.143	3.707	5.959
7	1.415	1.895	2.365	2.998	3.499	5.405
8	1.397	1.860	2.306	2.896	3.355	5.041
9	1.383	1.833	2.262	2.821	3.250	4.781
10	1.372	1.812	2.228	2.764	3.169	4.587
11	1.363	1.796	2.201	2.718	3.106	4.437
12	1.356	1.782	2.179	2.681	3.055	4.318
13	1.350	1.771	2.160	2.650	3.012	4.221
14	1.345	1.761	2.145	2.624	2.977	4.140
15	1.341	1.753	2.131	2.602	2.947	4.073
16	1.337	1.746	2.120	2.583	2.921	4.015
17	1.333	1.740	2.110	2.567	2.898	3.965
18	1.330	1.734	2.101	2.552	2.878	3.992
19	1.328	1.729	2.093	2.539	2.861	3.883
20	1.325	1.725	2.086	2.528	2.845	3.850
21	1.323	1.721	2.080	2.518	2.831	3.819
22	1.321	1.717	2.074	2.508	2.819	3.792
23	1.319	1.714	2.069	2.500	2.807	3.767
24	1.318	1.711	2.064	2.492	2.797	3.745
25	1.316	1.708	2.060	2.485	2.787	3.725
26	1.315	1.706	2.056	2.479	2.779	3.707
27	1.314	1.703	2.052	2.473	2.771	3.690
28	1.313	1.701	2.048	2.467	2.763	3.674
29	1.311	1.699	2.045	2.462	2.756	3.659
30	1.310	1.697	2.042	2.457	2.750	3.646
40	1.303	1.684	2.021	2.423	2.704	3.551
60	1.296	1.671	2.000	2.390	2.660	3.460
120	1.289	1.658	1.980	2.358	2.617	3.373
??	1.282	1.645	1.960	2.326	2.576	3.291

Table 15.15 Values of t

In the t-test, the degrees of freedom is the sum of the number of measurements in both groups minus 2. In this case, the number of degrees of freedom = (10 + 10 – 2) = 18.

We now look up compare our values for t with the values of t in a table (see Table 15.15, above).

The table value for 10 with a probability of 0.05 and 18 degrees of freedom is 2.101. Our calculated value of t is 4.131. Since this is greater than 2.101, the null hypothesis is rejected.

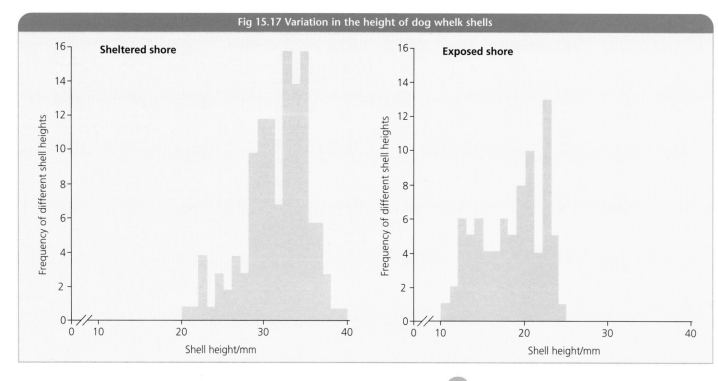

Fig 15.17 Variation in the height of dog whelk shells

For the t-test for independent samples you do not have to have the same number of data points in each group. We have to assume that the population follows a normal distribution. The t-test can be performed knowing just the means, standard deviation, and number of data points.

The graphs in Fig 15.17 show the heights of the shells of dog whelks living on exposed and sheltered shores.

Try this question for yourself.

15

a What would be the null hypothesis when using a t-test to compare the two populations?

b For a sample of 15 dog whelks from each population, how many degrees of freedom would you use in a t-test?

c The calculated value of *t* for the sample is 2.8. Would you confirm or reject the null hypothesis? Give your reason.

KEY FACTS

- Most statistical tests give an answer in terms of the probability of the observed differences occurring by chance.

- **Standard deviation** is a measure of how much the individual data points are spread out from the mean.

- The **chi-squared test** is used to find out if the difference between observed and expected results is significant.

- The **t-test** is used to find out if the difference between the mean values for two sets of data is significant.

- In biology, we use the 5 per cent significance value when doing statistical calculations. In the t-test, results that give a p value of less than 0.05 are considered significant.

16 Synopsis

At the end of your A2 course you will sit tests on module 5(a) (Environment), and *either* Module 6 (Applied Ecology) *or* Module 7 (Microbes and Disease) *or* Module 8 (Behaviour and Populations). The tests on these modules are different from the tests on all the other modules in that they contain not only questions on the content of the particular module, but also questions testing understanding of principles from earlier modules. They may also contain questions testing experimental and investigative skills.

This retesting of principles and skills is known as **synopsis**. It is very important since it accounts for forty percent of the total marks available in the A2 course.

Principles are retested in two different ways:

● Questions on principles in the context of a module;

● Essay questions.

16.1 Retesting principles in the context of a module

Principles are retested in the context of Module 5 and of Modules 6, 7 or 8 in AQA, Specification B. Examples of principles that could be examined in the context of these modules are shown in Table 16.1 on the opposite page.

Some principles, for example, the tertiary structure of proteins in relation to their function, could be retested in:

● Module 5, in the context of pesticides;

● Module 6, in the context of pollution by heavy metals;

● Module 7, in the context of the immune response;

● Module 8, in the context of ageing.

The synoptic parts of questions are marked by an 'S' in the margin next to the question.

Some examples from Module 5

One example of plant succession is sand dune development. Sand dunes first develop when sand blown from the seashore accumulates around obstacles such as driftwood, forming hillocks. Plants such as couch grass can grow in these embryo dunes and more sand accumulates around them, increasing the size of the hillocks.

The next stage in dune development is characterised by the growth of marram grass, which produces numerous underground stems called rhizomes. Sand continues to accumulate and dunes often reach a height of 15 metres.

The final stage involves colonisation of the dune by a variety of plants that eventually completely cover the sand of a mature dune.

1

a The graph in Fig 16.1a shows changes in the humus content of sand dunes with age. Explain why the humus content of dunes changes with age.

b Explain why there is a greater diversity of organisms in the mature dunes than in the embryo dunes.

S c One of the reasons why marram grass can live in embryo sand dunes is that it can roll its leaves during dry weather as shown in the drawings in Fig 16.1b. Explain the advantage to the marram grass of being able to roll its leaves.

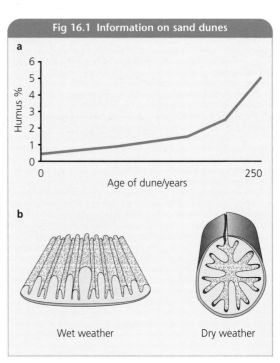

Fig 16.1 Information on sand dunes

a

Humus %

Age of dune/years

b

Wet weather   Dry weather

Parts a and b of this question relate to Module 5. Part c is marked with an 'S'. This means that it relates to the content of another Module, in this case Module 3. Part c is testing understanding of transpiration and xerophytic modifications of plants. You would be required to explain that rolling the leaves reduces the surface area from which water is lost by transpiration, thus conserving water.

Another example from Module 5 is Question 2, which tests understanding of the significance of surface area to volume ratio for the exchange of heat from Module 1.

2 Warming of the climate in Arctic regions, such as Northern Canada, could lead in the long term to a change in the mean body size of small mammals living there. Explain how.

You would be required to explain that very small mammals have a large surface area to volume ratio resulting in a large rate of heat loss per unit of body mass. This makes it difficult for them to survive in the cold of the Arctic. If the Arctic becomes warmer, then smaller mammals may be able to survive there.

Table 16.1 Principles that could be examined in the context of modules		
Module	**Module topic**	**Examples of synoptic principles that could be retested**
Module 5 **Environment**	Energy flow through ecosystems.	ATP, photosynthesis and respiration from Module 4.
	Nutrient cycles.	Biological molecules, enzymes and extracellular digestion from Module 1.
	Adaptation to abiotic factors.	Surface area to volume ratio from Module 1 and xerophytic modifications from Module 3.
Module 6 **Applied Ecology**	Pollution of aquatic ecosystems.	Eutrophication and BOD from Module 5.
	Physiological adaptation.	Kidney function from Module 4.
	Crop rotation.	Nitrogen cycle from Module 1.
Module 7 **Microbes and Disease**	Commercial biotechnology.	Enzymes from Module 1.
	Protection against disease.	Proteins and enzymes from Module 1.
Module 8 **Behaviour and Populations**	Reproductive behaviour.	Survival, coordination and homeostasis from Module 4.
	Pregnancy.	Circulation from Module 3. Kidney function from Module 5.
	Human population and health.	Proteins and enzymes from Module 1. Transport systems from Module 3.

16.2 The essay

Section B of the test on Modules 6, 7 and 8 requires you to write an essay. This is to assess your ability to bring together principles from different areas of biology. There is a choice of one from two essay titles.

The instructions for the essay question make clear the skills that must be used to obtain high marks. Below are the instructions from the specimen paper for this specification:

Write an essay on one of the topics below.

EITHER

> a **The process of diffusion and its importance in living organisms.**

OR

> b **Mutation and its consequences.**

- **In the answer to this question you should bring together relevant principles and concepts from as many different modules as possible.**

- **Your essay will be marked not only for its scientific accuracy, but also for the selection of relevant material.**

- **The essay should be written in continuous prose.**

Maximum marks available for an essay

The maximum number of marks that can be awarded is:

- Scientific content   16
- Breadth of knowledge   3
- Relevance   3
- Quality of written communication 3

Although 16 of the 25 marks are given for scientific content, high marks can be awarded only for relevant content. You should include material from as many topics as possible from Modules 1 to 5 so that you cover the whole specification.

It is therefore essential to *plan* the essay. The examination allows 45 minutes for preparing and writing an essay: you should spend approximately 15 minutes on the planning stage.

Scientific content

The first stage in planning an essay is to 'brain storm' all the topics from Modules 1 to 5 that might be relevant to the topic.

Let's take one of the titles from the specimen paper, 'Mutation and its consequences', as an example.

Brain storming might produce the following list of topics:

From Module 2, section 11.1

- A definition of mutation;
- Types of gene mutation (addition, deletion, substitution);
- What causes mutation (spontaneous event, radiation, mutagenic chemicals);
- The effect of mutation on protein synthesis;
- A change in base sequence may result in change in amino acid sequence of a polypeptide;
- The resulting change in polypeptide may result in change in structure of protein and the way it works;
- The possibility of resultant metabolic blocks.

From Module 2 section 11.4

- Mutation in gene for producing CFTR results in malfunctioning CFTR;
- The relationship between malfunctioning of CFTR and symptoms of cystic fibrosis.

From Module 4 Section 13.11

- The role of mutation in evolution;
- Mutation as a source of genotypic variation;
- How natural selection operates on mutations leading to changes in population, changes within a species, the formation of a new species.

It is possible to gain one or two marks for each of the bulleted topics. There might not be time to write about all of them, but if you have to make a selection, be sure that your choices contain topics from *every* relevant area of the specification. It is *not* necessary to refer to all the above topics to gain full marks for scientific content. However, it is wise to include at least 8 to 10 well explained points. It is therefore best to select the topics you are most confident with.

Breadth of knowledge

To gain the maximum three marks available under this category, you need to show that you can bring together material from different areas of biology. In the example essay, although a mark for scientific content could be obtained by good explanation of the topics from just Module 2, section 11.1, these three marks can only be obtained by also including topics from 11.4 and 13.11.

Relevance

To gain the maximum three marks, all the material presented must be clearly relevant to the essay title. Because mutation may lead to variation, you might be tempted to include other factors relating to variation such as details of meiosis and the random fusion of gametes. Since the essay title is 'mutation' rather than 'factors affecting variation', you would not achieve full marks if you included irrelevant material on meiosis.

Quality of written communication

To gain the maximum three marks, all the topics selected must be logically presented in clear, scientific English. You must use technical terminology effectively and accurately.

After selecting your topics, you should write them in a sensible sequence. Think in terms of 'telling a story'. Each major idea should be the basis for a paragraph. Use bullet points and diagrams only if they make your explanations clearer. If you do use bullet points, remember to use punctuation, and use it consistently.

Try making an essay plan for questions 3 and 4.

3 What problems are associated with an increase in size of an organism? How are these problems solved?

4 How is ATP produced and used in living organisms?

For the essay in question 3, you should ensure that you include reference to plants as well as to animals. You should also refer to problems associated with temperature control as well as problems of absorbing and distributing materials such as oxygen.

For the essay in question 4, you should include the production and use of ATP during photosynthesis by plants as well as the obvious topic of respiration.

16.2 Testing synoptic skills

You are assessed on Experimental and Investigational skills in your coursework. You are retested on those skills both in Module 5 and particularly in section B of Module 6, Module 7 or Module 8, where 25 marks are at stake.

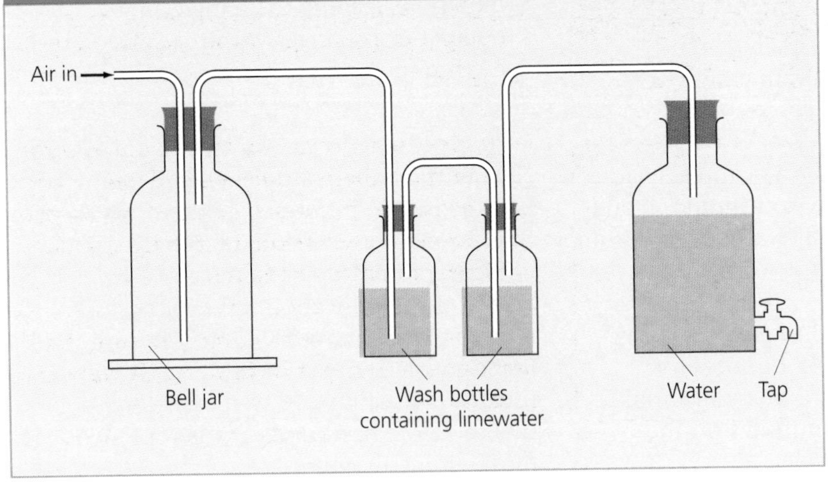

Questions may require you to:

- devise and plan experimental and investigative activities;
- interpret, explain and evaluate the results of experimental and investigative activities.

Some questions will involve both planning and interpreting skills. Some questions will test your knowledge and understanding of basic laboratory skills. Question 5 gives an example of a synoptic question that covers sections 13.2 and 13.3 of the specification – photosynthesis and respiration.

The preamble to the question explains that a series of experiments was performed using the apparatus shown in Fig 16.2. Living organisms were placed in the bell jar. The wash bottles were filled with fresh limewater and a standard volume of air was drawn very slowly through the apparatus. As air passed through the limewater carbon dioxide was absorbed and formed a precipitate of calcium carbonate. The

Fig 16.2

Air in →

Bell jar

Wash bottles containing limewater

Water   Tap

amount of carbon dioxide present in the air was calculated from the mass of precipitate. Below, we look at individual parts of the question, giving hints on what you should include in your answer:

5 a Describe how you would determine exactly the amount of precipitate present in the limewater at the end of one experiment.

This shows that you need to remember basic laboratory techniques such as filtering and then drying the filtrate to constant mass.

b Suggest a reason for the use of two wash bottles containing limewater in these experiments.

This shows that you need to remember ways of producing reliable data. (The second bottle ensures that all the carbon dioxide is absorbed.)

c Explain how you would draw a standard volume of air through the apparatus shown.

Again, understanding of basic laboratory technique is required. (Allow a standard volume of water to leave via the tap, i.e. the volume of water between the two marks.)

The apparatus was used to study respiration at different temperatures. Several experiments were carried out with each organism. In every case a standard volume of air was drawn through the apparatus in the same period of time. The results are shown in Table 16.2.

Table 16.2 Respiration of different organisms at different temperatures

Organism and conditions	Mass of carbon dioxide/mg at temperature of:		
	10 °C	20 °C	30 °C
Control with no no organism	8	8	8
Blowfly larvae	13	18	27
Geranium in light	7	6	4
Geranium in dark	8.5	9	10

d i What, was the purpose of the 'control' experiment?
ii How much carbon dioxide was released by the blowfly larvae at 10 °C?

In part i, the purpose is to measure the amount of carbon dioxide in the air entering the apparatus and also to check that changes in the carbon dioxide content are due entirely to the organisms and not to any other factor. Part ii is a simple table reading exercise – do not forget to give the unit.

e 40 g of larvae were used and the experiment lasted for 40 minutes. How much carbon dioxide was produced per kg per hour at 10°C? Show your working.

You will frequently be given problems such as this. The key is to do the calculation in two stages: first convert the mass of carbon dioxide produced by 40 g to the mass produced by 1 kg (multiply 15 mg by 1000/40); then multiply this answer by 60/40 to convert from 40 minutes to 1 hour. Again, do not forget the unit.

The effect of temperature on the rate of processes such as respiration may be expressed as the temperature coefficient, Q_{10}.

$$Q_{10} = \frac{\text{rate at } (t + 10)° \text{ C}}{\text{rate at } t° \text{ C}}$$

f Calculate the Q10 for the rate of respiration of the blowfly larvae when the temperature increases from 20 °C to 30 °C.

You may be given formulae that are not in the specification – you will only be required to use these, not to explain them. In this case Q_{10} = rate at 30 °C divided by rate at 20 °C, i.e. 19/10.

g The value of the Q10 for photosynthesis across a given temperature range is often around 2, but may be much lower under certain environmental conditions. Suggest why this may be the case.

Some factor other than temperature, e.g. light intensity, might be limiting the rate of reaction.

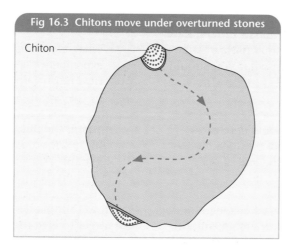

Fig 16.3 Chitons move under overturned stones

Chiton

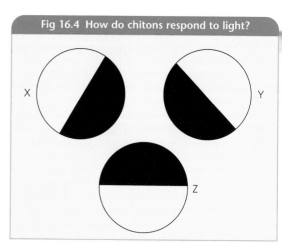

Fig 16.4 How do chitons respond to light?

X

Y

Z

Some questions will test experimental design and ask you to draw conclusions. The following example is a question that is synoptic based on section 13.4, Survival and response.

The preamble to the question explains that chitons are small animals that live on the seashore. When the tide is out they are found on the lower surfaces of stones. When stones are turned over deliberately, the chitons move to the new lower surface, as shown in Fig 16.3.

6

a Suggest two advantages to the chitons of this response.

'Suggest' indicates that you are not expected to know about chitons, so use the information given in the preamble. This behaviour occurs when the tide is out so sensible suggestions are that it prevents desiccation, and that helps the chiton to hide from predators.

b Give two factors, other than light, to which the chitons might be responding.

The chitons move downwards, so gravity is a good suggestion; and since the underside of the stone will be damp, water is a second feasible suggestion.

c A student investigated the response of chitons to light. Three dishes, X, Y and Z, were arranged as shown in Fig 16.4. One half of the top of each dish was painted black, the other half was transparent. The dishes were placed on a table outside at noon on a bright, cloudy day. Ten chitons were placed in the light half of each dish. The number of chitons in each half of the dishes was recorded every five minutes for the next hour.

i Suggest why the dishes were arranged as shown in Fig 16.4.

ii The results of the investigation are shown in Table 16.3. What conclusions may be drawn from these results?

Table 16.3 Results from the chiton light response experiment						
Time/minutes	Number of chitons					
	Dish X		Dish Y		Dish Z	
	Light	Dark	Light	Dark	Light	Dark
0	10	0	10	0	10	0
5	9	1	7	3	7	3
10	6	4	7	3	7	3
15	5	5	7	3	6	4
20	3	7	5	5	5	5
25	3	7	4	6	5	5
30	3	7	3	7	5	5
35	3	7	3	7	5	5
40	2	8	3	7	4	6
45	1	9	3	7	4	6
50	1	9	2	8	4	6
55	1	9	3	7	2	8
60	1	9	1	9	1	9

Part i is about experimental design. If the student is investigating the effect of light/dark on the behaviour of the chitons he or she should control as many variables as possible. This arrangement of the dishes is a control for direction of light.

Like part ii, many section B questions ask you to draw conclusions from the data. In this case, the conclusion is that the chitons continue to move until they reach darkness, then they tend to stop moving.

You may also be required to design simple investigations, as the following example shows:

7 The highland midge is a tiny bloodsucking insect that is the scourge of many a holiday on the west coast of Scotland. Scientists are investigating claims that an extract from bog myrtle plants acts as a natural midge-repellent. Fig 16.5 shows apparatus used in one of their investigations. In a series of tests more than 80% of the midges flew into branch Q.

a Suggest why the apparatus was illuminated only from above.

The answer here is straightforward – this is done as a control for directional light.

b Outline an investigation to test the effectiveness of bog myrtle extract in preventing human volunteers from being bitten by midges.

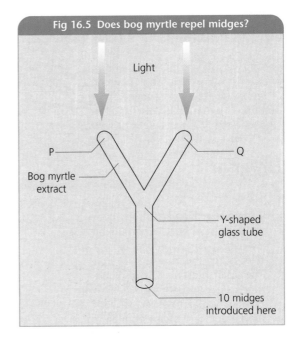

Fig 16.5 Does bog myrtle repel midges?

In this type of investigation you should refer to the independent variable – administering the extract to volunteers; the control – volunteers with no extract; the dependent variable – the number of bites; and the need for large numbers of volunteers to obtain reliable data.

The other types of questions that will appear in section B of the tests on Modules 6, 7 and 8 will be of the types already described in Chapter 15. You should prepare particularly for questions involving formulating hypotheses, and testing those hypotheses.

Answers to Questions

The answers to text questions and questions within application boxes are given below. Please note that when the question is intended for discussion or extended study, no answer is provided.

Chapter 1

1

a The most active parts of the body produce most heat. When the body is exercising, large amounts of heat are released by the muscles.

b The small intestine where soluble foods are absorbed; the kidneys where glucose and ions are reabsorbed.

c Production of proteins from amino acids; production of glycogen from glucose; production of lipids.

2 It has pigments to absorb light energy and membrane systems that create a large surface area, ensuring that light hits as much pigment as possible.

3 The supply of ATP and reduced NADP; once supplies of these are exhausted, they cannot be replenished until the light is 'switched on ' again.

4

a Reduced NADP → NADP.

b Glycerate 1,3-diphosphate → glyceraldehyde 3-phosphate.

c ATP → ADP + P$_i$.

5

a ATP, since ribulose bisphosphate has two phosphate groups per molecule whereas glycerate 3-phosphate has one.

b The process might be limited in Group A by either the amount of ribulose bisphosphate to act as acceptor for carbon dioxide, or by the supply of ATP and reduced NADPH. Alternating light and dark periods allows regeneration of these three compounds; they will not be limiting in Group B.

6

a It is converted into lactic acid.

b In anaerobic conditions, glycolysis is limited by the amount of NAD available. By accepting electrons from reduced NAD, NAD is regenerated to accept further electrons from glyceraldehyde 3-phosphate during glycolysis.

7 Each enzyme is specific to one substrate because the shape of each substrate is complementary to the shape of the active site of its specific enzyme.

8 38:
Glycolysis (substrate phosphorylation)   **2**
Krebs cycle (substrate phosphorylation) **2**
Reduced NAD (oxidative phosphorylation)
(6+ 2 + 2) = 10 x 3 = **30**
Reduced FAD (oxidative phosphorylation)
2 x 2 = **4**

9 Only 2 ATP molecules are produced by glycolysis, therefore only 2 would be produced in anaerobic respiration. This is much less than aerobic respiration, and life on Earth could probably not evolved in its current form if organisms could respire only anaerobically.

Application boxes

Why the colours in light are crucial to plants

1

a Blue and orange.

b Because it reflects light from the middle region of the spectrum (rather than absorbing it).

c Yellow to red (they absorb light at the violet - blue end of the spectrum, they reflect all other colours).

2

a The action spectrum for chlorophyll a should be the same shape as its absorption spectrum.

b Having several different pigments allows the plant to absorb a wider range of wavelengths of light, increasing the efficiency of photosynthesis.

3 Grind up tissue from green leaves and from the brown seaweeds using an organic solvent to extract the pigments. Mark the starting line on a piece of chromatography paper. Concentrate several drops of each extract on the starting line. Run the chromatogram in an organic solvent different to the one you used for extraction. Wait until the solvent front almost reaches the top of the paper. See if any of the pigments from the seaweed have the same colour and have moved the same distance as chlorophylls a and b from the green plant.

They changed the atmosphere

1 The cyanobacterium is very similar in size to the chloroplast; like the chloroplast, it is bounded by a phospholipid membrane and contains chlorophyll *a*.

2 It is not cost-effective at the moment. Living organisms require constant attention; the cyanobacteria would need constant supplies of nutrients and gases. There would be problems recycling or disposing of waste products.

The Calvin cycle

1 Y – glycerate 3-phosphate, since this is the first compound to be formed in the light-independent reaction, and will be the first to contain radioactive carbon from the carbon dioxide.
X – glyceraldehyde 3-phosphate. This is formed by reduction of glycerate 3-phosphate, which why it is not there on the 5-seconds chromatogram.

2

a It will fall as ribulose phosphate accepts radioactive carbon dioxide to form glycerate 3-phosphate. However, this cannot be reduced to glyceraldehyde 3-phosphate since there is no supply of reduced NADP and ATP from the light-dependent reactions. So, no glyceraldehyde 3-phosphate molecules are available for recycling to ribulose bisphosphate.

b It will rise as ribulose phosphate accepts radioactive carbon dioxide forming glycerate 3-phosphate. However, this cannot be reduced to glyceraldehyde 3-phosphate since there is no supply of reduced NADP and ATP from the light-dependent reactions. It levels off when the supply of ribulose bisphosphate acceptor molecules runs out. This happens when no more glyceraldehyde 3-phosphate molecules are available for recycling to ribulose bisphosphate.

Fig 2.Ans1a

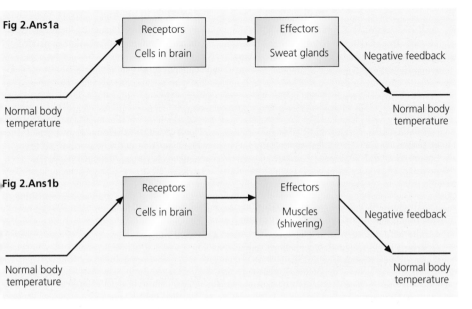

Fig 2.Ans1b

cold, the temperature of the tissues will fall causing a fall in the rate of respiration producing even less thermal energy.

10 Brown fat has the capacity to generate much more heat that white fat because it has far more mitochondria, the site of respiration in the cell. 80 per cent of the energy transferred by respiration is transferred as thermal energy.

11 Its fur is very long; this will trap a thick layer of insulating hair; it has a small surface area to volume ratio and therefore a relatively low surface area through which heat is lost; its ears are small, again reducing the surface area for heat loss.

Chapter 2

1
a see Fig 2.Ans1a.
b see Fig 2.Ans1b.

2 Production of digestive enzymes e.g. peptidases, amylase and lipase.

3
a Polysaccharide.
b The highly branched molecule gives it a compact shape.

4
a Hydrolysis.
b Condensation.

5
a The difference in concentration of the substance outside and inside the cell and the number of carrier protein molecules for that substance.
b Glucose molecules pass through cell membranes by facilitated diffusion that involves carrier proteins. The more carrier proteins, the more 'passages' there are for glucose through the membranes. (See AS Chapter 2.)

6
a Sugary foods do not need to be digested, or they are digested rapidly by intracellular enzymes in the villi. This leads to sharp increases in blood glucose concentration. Starchy foods take longer to digest because starch molecules have longer chains.

Absorption of the sugars produced by starch digestion takes place over a longer period and does not lead to sudden rises in blood sugar.
b Hypo results from low blood glucose levels. These result in less then 60 mg dm-3 sugar being delivered to the nerve cells in the brain. The symptoms are the result of brain malfunction caused by low blood sugar delivery.

7
a Circular muscles in their walls contract
b The circular muscles relax; blood pressure then brings about widening.

8 See Fig 2.Ans7

9 By the time the hypothalamus detects the fall, blood temperature will already have fallen. Blood temperature is maintained by thermal energy from respiration in all the body tissues. But if the blood entering the muscles is

Application boxes

What brings on puberty in girls?

1 Fertility drugs stimulate the production of mature eggs from the ovary, ensuring that eggs are available for fertilisation. Birth control pills work by tricking the body into thinking it is already pregnant; no mature eggs are released during pregnancy.

2 The effect of negative feedback is to bring about small changes; processes like childbirth need massive physiological changes to bring them to their eventual conclusion.

3 Negative feedback is about fine tuning. It helps to regulate blood glucose levels within fairly narrow limits. The processes that are controlled by positive feedback are dramatic, all or nothing events that need to run their course.

Fig 2.Ans7

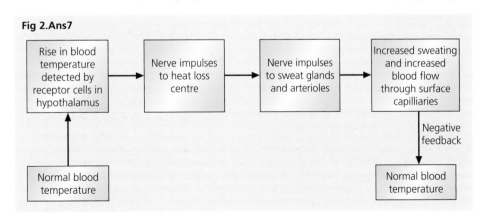

Insulin

1

a A chain of amino acids held together by peptide bonds.

b Endopeptidase, which hydrolyses peptide bonds deep within the molecule.

c Both the types of amino acid and their sequence.

d 81 amino acids x 3 nucleotides = 243

Football can be a dangerous game

1 Sweat is soaked up by the sandwiched fibres. Because the inner layer a good thermal conductor, it conducts heat from the body surface, cooling the body down. The conducted heat causes sweat in the fibrous layer to evaporate. The outer layer allows this evaporation. As heat is used to evaporate the sweat in this fibrous layer, more heat is conducted away from the body surface.

2 They have lots of muscle, so have a small surface area to volume ratio. This means they can lose less heat through their skin surface.

Treating hypothermia

1 Vasoconstriction – diverting blood away from the peripheries.

2 This will divert blood away from the core and may cause rewarming shock.

Fig 3.Ans10

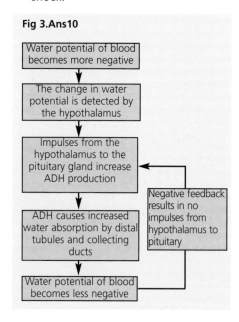

3

a A drop in core body temperature caused by treatment for hypothermia.

b Cold blood returning to the heart may cause heart failure.

4 Skin receptors detect increase in temperature, impulses sent to hypothalamus. Hypothalamus sends impulses to skin arterioles, diverting blood to skin. Less blood flows through muscles that are generating heat.

5 Warm air is breathed into the lungs. This will warm the blood flowing through the capillaries that surround the alveoli. Nothing is done to the outside of the body to induce vasodilation.

Chapter 3

1

a A: amino group, B: acid group.

b A group such as a hydrocarbon.

2 The bulk of a lion's diet is meat, which consists almost entirely of protein. A lion will therefore have a relatively higher proportion of excess amino acids than an herbivore or an omnivore.

3

a Ammonia molecules are added one at a time.

b Each of the reactions in the cycle is controlled by a different enzyme.

4 A gene mutation might result in a change in the amino acid sequence of the enzyme. This could alter the tertiary shape of the enzyme, so Arginine molecules would no longer fit into its active site. Ornithine molecules would no be regenerated, so there would be no acceptor molecules for the ammonia produced by deamination.

5 Small intestine, large intestine, anus as part of faeces.

6 There are no blood cells or large protein molecules in glomerular filtrate because they are both two large to pass through the basement membrane of the capillary.

7 The mechanisms are identical.

8 Carrier protein, by facilitated diffusion.

9 The high concentration of sodium ions gives the tissue fluid a more negative water potential than the filtrate, so water diffuses out of the tubule by osmosis.

10 See Fig 3.Ans10.

11 Lowering the amount of salt in the diet will reduce the ion content of the tissue fluid of the medulla. This will result in a less negative water potential, so less water will be reabsorbed from the collecting ducts and distal tubules.

Application boxes

Artificial livers?

1

a Water, plasma proteins, sugars, lipids, mineral ions.

b They could be damaged and induce clotting on their return to the body.

2 Absorption of benzodiazepines before they can affect liver cells.

3 In solution in the water.

4 Facilitated diffusion.

5

a New supplies from donors are required for each patient.

b Mitosis.

c Gene for cell division extracted from cells that normally continually divide (using endonuclease); gene inserted into plasmids using ligase; plasmids inserted into liver cells.

d Cell division may go out of control producing cancer.

Atrial Natriuretic Peptide (ANP)

1 Glucose and sodium chloride make the water potential of the blood plasma more negative. This causes more water to diffuse from the tissue fluid into the blood, causing an increase in blood pressure that could start ultrafiltration.

2 ANP causes dilation of arterioles supplying the glomeruli. This will increase the rate at which blood supplied to the glomeruli, causing ultrafiltration to begin.

3 84, since the codon for each amino acid consists of three nucleotides.

Reabsorption – facts and figures

1 Sodium 99.4, Chloride 18 000, Urea 28.

2 0.125 litres per minute.

3 1.5 litres.

4 140 mEq l^{-1} (25 2000 / 180)

5 Urea diffuses back along its concentration gradient until concentrations in the blood and filtrate are equal.

6 The microvilli provide a large surface area for absorption. Abundant mitochondria provide the energy for active transport via respiration. The carrier molecules in the symport, the sodium pump and the glucose permease systems bring about transport of glucose and sodium ions.

  The transport of glucose and ions into the blood, together with the presence of plasma proteins makes the water potential of the plasma much more negative than the water potential of the remaining glomerular filtrate. Water therefore moves from the filtrate into the blood by osmosis – from a less negative to a more negative water potential.

7
a Because there are no carrier proteins for mannitol.
b Mannitol will make the water potential of the filtrate more negative, so less water will be reabsorbed.

Adjusting the ion concentration of the blood

1 Aldosterone causes sodium pumps in the cells of the distal tubules and connecting ducts to pump sodium ions into the blood. The water potential of the blood will become more negative, resulting in water entering the blood from the tissue fluid by osmosis. This influx of water will increase the volume of the blood and thus its pressure.

Chapter 4

1 Electrical insulation.

2
a A neurone is an individual nerve cell; a nerve is a bundle of neurones.

bi Sensory neurone – information will not pass from the receptor to the brain.
bii Motor neurone – information will not pass from the brain to the leg.

3 The fibre between the cell body of the neurone and the synapse with the relay neurone, because an axon carries impulses away from the cell body.

4 Sodium, potassium and chloride.

5 Because of the impermeability of the myelin sheath, the neutral electrode would have to be positioned between the sheath and the cell membrane of the axon. This would be almost impossible to arrange.

6 Facilitated diffusion occurs along concentration gradients. The K^+ ATPase pumps produce a high concentration of Na^+ ions on the outside of the membrane and a high concentration of K^+ ions on the inside.

7 The Na^+ / K^+ ATPase pumps require ATP from respiration to operate. DNP inhibits respiration so there will be no ATP to operate the pumps. Without the pumps, the ions will only move through the channel proteins and then only until concentrations on each side of the membrane are equal. At this time there will be no net difference in the number of ions on each side of the membrane, so there will be no resting potential.

8
a D, C, A, B.
b 110 mV (change from –70mv to + 40 mV).
c 0.5 milliseconds.

9 The postsynaptic membrane would continue to depolarise and impulses would continually be transmitted along the postsynaptic neurone.

10
a The sino-atrial node (SAN).
b The molecules have a shape that will fit into the receptor molecules in the postsynaptic cells of the SAN. When noradrenaline is released by the nerve fibres, the molecules will not be able to bind with postsynaptic receptors and so will have no effect on the SAN.

11
a Because it has a complementary shape, caffeine binds to adenosine receptors at synapses and excites nerve cells.
b Too much caffeine stimulation might cause the brain to reduce the number of adenosine receptors. A person then might feel lethargic without caffeine and have the urge to drink more.

12 For example, they will not tear when partially cut as they might if contracted;
  or
  abdominal organs not under pressure.

Application boxes

Repairing nerves

1 It has several different genes controlling its development – the type of cell it develops into depends on which genes are switched on.

2 Promoter genes for sensory neurone growth are spliced into bacterial plasmids that are then introduced into the neural stem cells.

3 Discussion question, no answer provided.

Myelinated and non-myelinated nerves

1 30 m s^{-1}

2 10/15 x 100 = 66% increase.

3 100 / 10 – 80 times thicker.

4 One advantage is that they can be grouped together in nerves without risk of impulses passing laterally between fibres. Another is that because they are much thinner, many more fibres can be gathered together in a nerve, so a nerve can carry much more information.

Reversing paralysis?

1 The flow of electrons.

2 Receptor.

3 Motor neurones.

Chapter 5

1 The refractive index of water is equal to that of the cornea.

2 In the brightly lit area much of the rhodopsin has been broken down; time is needed to resynthesise it before the rods can become sensitive to light. The low light intensity does not stimulate the cones.

3 Snow reflects almost all the light so the light intensity will be very high. The pigment in the cones is broken down faster than it is resynthesised so the cones become inoperative and the person becomes temporarily blind since rods also don't work in bright light.

4 Most synthetic reactions require energy. Large numbers of mitochondria will provide, via respiration, the large amounts of energy needed to resynthesise rhodopsin or iodopsin.

5 Red and green.

6 All three types of cone are stimulated.

7 White light stimulates all three types of cone. Black objects do not reflect light, so none of the cones are stimulated.

8 These people lack red-sensitive cones, but the green-sensitive cones are stimulated by red light, so all the dots will appear green.

9 Mutation of the gene for rhodopsin could have resulted in a different nucleotide sequence in the DNA. This would add a different sequence of amino acids during protein formation. The resulting protein would have a slightly different shape and so would absorb different frequencies of light.

10 The pigment in the red cones becomes broken down faster than it is resynthesised. When you look at a white area, only the green and blue cones from this part of the retina send impulses to the brain, so the paper is seen as green-blue.

11
a Only the cones distinguish colours; the cones only work in bright light.
b Several rods synapse with one bipolar cell, so sufficient transmitter substance is produced to depolarise the bipolar cell. A cone cell would not produce enough transmitter substance to depolarise its bipolar cell.
c Each cone synapses with a single bipolar cell, so the information from it is discrete rather than being mixed with information from other cells as is the case with rod cells.
d In bright light we can see colours right to the edge of our field of vision, not just at the centre, so there must be cones in all parts of the retina.

12
a C since there is the highest density of cones.
b A-B and C-D because these have the highest density of cones.
c We would not see the image since there are neither rods nor cones. B is the optic disc – the region where the optic nerve leaves the eye.

13 In the spinal cord the grey matter is on the inside, surrounded by white matter.

14
a The skin on the fingertips and the lips.
b Both fingertips and lips actively 'explore' the environment. The more receptors, the more precise the information sent to the brain for interpretation.
c The retina has the highest density of receptors in the body. To distinguish fine detail visually, there are millions of receptors and therefore a large part of the sensory area of the hemispheres is needed to cope with the amount of information received.

15 Activities such as writing need very fine muscular control, which in turn requires generation of very large numbers of motor impulses. The left side of the cerebral cortex controls the right side of the body, and vice versa.

16
a The concentration of hydrogen ions in the blood.
b Stretch receptors in the air passages, chemoreceptors in the aortic bodies and carotid bodies, pressure receptors in the aorta and carotid arteries.

17
a Noradrenaline from sympathetic fibres.
b Acetylcholine from parasympathetic fibres.

18 Stretch receptors in the bladder wall. When the bladder fills impulses are sent to the medulla that, in turn, send motor impulses via the parasympathetic system. Acetylcholine release causes contraction of the muscles in the bladder walls and relaxation of the sphincter, resulting in urination.

19 Each half acts as a check on the activity of the other. For example, the sympathetic nervous system speeds up heart rate, but the parasympathetic system prevents it getting too high.

Application boxes

Repairing eye defects

1 Rejection is brought about mainly by the antibodies produced by white blood cells. Without white cells there is little risk of infection.

2 The molecules that cause the opaqueness refract the light rays so that the image is not clearly focused on the retina.

3 The lens does not change shape to bring about accommodation for near objects. so reading glasses are often needed. Colour vision is slightly affected.

4 Because most refraction occurs at the cornea, slight distortion of the surface will lead to objects being badly out of focus at the retina.

New techniques for diagnosing eye disease

1 Because they are in the third layer.

2
a This is the fovea where most of the cones have single connections.
b Fewer impulses would be coming from the fovea, so their vision would not be as acute.

Brain imaging

1 The auditory sensory areas would be receiving impulses from receptors in the ears, the auditory association areas would be receiving impulse from the sensory areas , processing them then forwarding impulses to the motor areas and thence to the hands. The visual sensory and association areas

would also be active as you part of the control of writing.

2

a Visual cortex → Wernicke's area → Broca's area.

b Auditory area → Wernicke's area → Broca's area.

Chapter 6

1 The fibre has many nuclei rather than one; the fibre is striped, the fibre is composed mainly of myofibrils; the fibre has an elongated shape.

2

a This is the region where actin and myosin filaments are found.

bi Myosin filaments only.

bii Actin filaments only.

3

a No; actin and myosin filaments neither contract nor expand.

b The actin filaments slide in between the myosin filaments so there is more overlap leading to a wider A band and a narrower area where there are just actin filaments.

4

a Nerve impulse arrives at neuro-muscular junction → acetylcholine released into synaptic cleft → action potential produced in plasma membrane → action potential transmitted down tubules into centre of myofibril → calcium ions released from endoplasmic reticulum → calcium ions bind to tropomyosin switch proteins → binding sites on actin filaments exposed → myosin processes bind to exposed sites on actin filaments → energy from ATP used to move actin filaments.

b To provide the abundant ATP required for muscle contraction; each swing of a cross bridge needs the energy from 1 mole of ATP.

5 Contraction of the gastocnemius pulls the heel up and the toes down, acting as the flexor. The tibialis anterior acts as the flexor, pulling the top of the foot upwards.

6

a When a muscle contracts, the contraction would extend the tendon rather than move the bone.

b The collagen molecule consists of three twisted polypeptide chains bound strongly together.

7

a Muscle X.

b Muscle Y.

Application boxes

Controlling muscle contraction

1 Temporal summation, since impulses are arriving more rapidly from the same neurone to the muscle fibre.

2 Increasing the frequency of nerve impulses to a muscle fibre increases the strength of contraction; for a nerve fibre the number of action potentials produced would increase, but every action potential would be the same size. The nerve fibre has a refractory period but the muscle goes into tetanus if the time interval between impulses is very short.

3 The association and motor areas of the cerebral hemispheres initiate impulses. Fine control of the sequence of impulses is coordinated by the cerebellum.

Fast twitch and slow twitch muscle fibres

1 The liver.

2 Mainly under the skin.

3

a Energy can be obtained from it very quickly.

b It is used up very quickly – there is not enough to sustain a long activity.

4 Lactic acid.

5 It dissociates in hydrogen ions and lactate ions. If hydrogen ions accumulate in the muscles they affect the tertiary structure of actin and myosin molecules, altering their shape and making contraction less efficient.

6 Slow twitch fibres obtain most of their energy from aerobic respiration. Mitochondria are the site of aerobic reactions in respiration.

7 Myoglobin provides an oxygen store

for the muscle fibres, decreasing the possibility of lactic acid formation and hence muscle fatigue.

Drugs and muscles

1 It does not alter the shape of the part of the hormone that binds to receptors on the target cells.

2 The mRNA produced is a copy (transcription) of the DNA code for the production of muscle proteins. The more the more mRNA, the greater the synthesis of muscle protein.

3 As well as increasing the amount of muscle, HGH causes fat breakdown, releasing energy.

Chapter 7

1

a 46.

b 23.

c 23.

2

a 4.

b

Stage	Number of copies of gene
Nucleus during prophase	4
Cell during metaphase	4
Each nucleus in telophase	2
Nucleus of a daughter cell	2

3 It enables mRNA to be formed on the genes when proteins are actively being produced, i.e. to give room for transcription to take place.

4 92.

5 They can then separate without becoming tangled together or broken.

6

a 16, i.e. 24 combinations.

b 223, i.e. 8 388 608.

7 Any three from: Chromosomes replicate in interphase or before the division starts.

Fig 7.Ans8

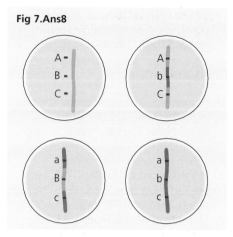

Chromatids are joined by centromeres.
Nuclear membrane disappears at end of prophase.
Centromeres attach to equator of spindle in metaphase.
Chromatids are pulled to opposite poles in anaphase.

8 See Fig 7.Ans8

9
a 3 normal : 1 with cystic fibrosis.
b 25%.
c 50%.
d 1/25 × 1/25 = 1 in 625 (0.16%).
e 1 in 4 (25%).
f 1 in 625 × 4 = 1 in 2500 (0.04%).

10 The recessive allele has a mutation in which the order of bases of the DNA is slightly altered. This causes one of the codons to differ, so the mRNA formed during transcription is different. As a result the CFTR primary protein structure formed during translation at the ribosomes has one amino acid missing. When the protein folds into its tertiary structure its three-dimensional shape is different from normal, and the channel protein produced does not allow chloride ions to pass through it.

11
a See Fig 7. Ans11a.
b There is no malaria in the USA. Resistance to malaria does not give people with the sickle cell trait a survival advantage. They are more likely to have fewer children that survive, as those with sickle cell anaemia often die young, before the can have children of their own.

12 A person with blood group O contains the antibody to antigen A in their plasma. This antibody will stick to the antigen on the red blood cell membranes and cause them to agglutinate.

13 Your genetic diagram should show you that children of parents who have blood groups AB and O have the genotypes I^AI^O or I^BI^O, in a 1 : 1 ratio. Children with genotype I^AI^O will be blood group A, those with genotype I^BI^O will be blood group B.

14
a The man with blood group A could be the father if his genotype is I^AI^O and the mother's genotype is I^BI^O. The other man could not be the father because the would have to receive either an IA or IB allele from him.
b Each of the four blood groups is common in the population, so many other men have the same group.

15
a TT.
b rr.
c In normal seeds the enzyme converts sugar to starch for storage. In wrinkled seeds this enzyme does not work, so sugar remains in the seeds.

16
a 3 in 16 (18.75%)
b 1 in 3; TTrr.
c See Fig 7.Ans16c.
d He should use seeds from plants that produced only tall plants after self-fertilisation. Any plant that produced a dwarf plant from its seeds should be rejected.

17
a Only those plants which have a desired characteristic are used for breeding. The alleles which give other characteristics are bred out, so that the crop plant will be pure-breeding.
b These stocks will have a much wider range of alleles. If conditions change, for example with the appearance of a new disease, or if breeders want to develop a new feature, the older breeds may contain the alleles needed for breeding.

18 BBDd would be seal: bbDd would be chocolate; BBdd would be blue; BbDd would be seal.

19
a The sperm, because it may have either an X or a Y chromosome; the Y chromosome determines maleness.
b Separate the X-carrying sperms from the Y-carrying sperms, and then use only the X sperms for artificial insemination. One possible method of separating the sperms is to use high speed centrifugation. Because the Y chromosome is smaller than the X, sperms with Y chromosomes are very slightly less heavy.
c Problems could include: imbalance of sexes in the population and social problems for those unable to find a partner; parents choosing a child's sex for selfish reasons, such as to provide help for themselves; rejection of a child where the technique failed and a child of the 'wrong' sex was born.

20
a 25% of children; 0% of girls; 50% of boys.

Fig 7.Ans11a

Parents	Mother	X	Father
Phenotypes	Sickle-cell trait		Sickle-cell trait
Genotypes	Hb^AHb^S		Hb^AHb^S
Gametes	50% 50%		50% 50%
Genotypes	Hb^A Hb^S		Hb^A Hb^S
Children			
Genotypes	Hb^AHb^A Hb^AHb^S	Hb^AHb^S	Hb^SHb^S
Phenotypes	Normal	Sickle-cell trait	Sickle-cell anaemic
Ratio of phenotypes	25% 1	50% 2	25% 1

Fig 7.Ans16c

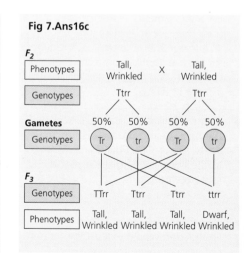

b A mother with genotypes XCXc or XcXc and a father who is XcY could produce a red/green colour blind girl.

c A boy receives his X chromosome from his mother, never from his father.

21

a XʰY.

b Mother XᴴXʰ and father XʰY. Haemophiliac girls are very rare and in the past have been unlikely to survive to adulthood to bear children.

Application boxes

Huntington's disease

1

a Two of Beatrice's children did not have Huntington's disease. She must, therefore, have carried the normal allele, which she passed on to these children. Since the normal allele is recessive, unaffected individuals must receive one normal allele from each parent.

b See Fig 7.AnsA1.

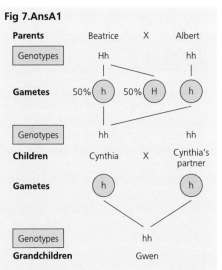

Fig 7.AnsA1

Parents	Beatrice X	Albert
Genotypes	Hh	hh
Gametes	50% h 50% H	h
Genotypes	hh	hh
Children	Cynthia X	Cynthia's partner
Gametes	h	h
Genotypes	hh	
Grandchildren	Gwen	

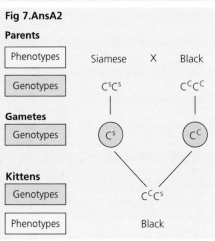

Fig 7.AnsA2

Parents		
Phenotypes	Siamese X	Black
Genotypes	CˢCˢ	CᶜCᶜ
Gametes		
Genotypes	Cˢ	Cᶜ
Kittens		
Genotypes	CᶜCˢ	
Phenotypes	Black	

c 50% chance, since he carries the abnormal allele.

d Discussion question; no answer provided.

2 People with the disease can have children before symptoms appear. The allele can therefore be passed on to the next generation. If the dominant allele caused death before the individual was old enough to breed, it could not be passed on.

Good breeding

1

a Siamese – CˢCˢ; Burmese – CᵇCᵇ.

b All blackish coated – see Fig 7.AnsA2.

2

a CᵇCˢ.

b Yes, because the heterozygote is different from either of the homozygotes.

c The proportions of the kittens would be 50% pale brown, 25% Burmese and 25% Siamese.

d She will have to breed a Burmese with a Siamese each time.

3

a 1 : 2 : 1.

b 50%. The Manx cat must have the genotype Mm, and the tailed cat MM. All the gametes of the tailed cat will have the genotype M, whereas the gametes of the Manx cat will be 50% M and 50% m.

Sex can be confusing

1

a 45, because there is only one X chromosome and therefore one fewer than the normal complement of 46.

b One, because there is only one Y chromosome.

2 XXY, XYY and XXXY might all be expected to have male characteristics, since all will possess the SRY gene. XXX would be female.

3

a PCR uses the enzyme DNA polymerase to replicate sections of DNA molecules that have been separated. For details of the method see the AS book, page 138.

b The presence of the SRY gene shows that male development should have been stimulated during embryonic development. Barr bodies might not be visible if, for example, the person has only one X chromosome or the second X chromosome has not been inactivated.

Chapter 8

1

a (c) because it shows four distinct phenotypes, corresponding to A, B, AB and O blood groups.

b (b) because it shows two distinct phenotypes, i.e. wet and dry.

c (d) because it shows continuous variation. Notice that the distribution curve is not quite normal; it is skewed to the right, meaning that there are more people with an extremely high mass than might be expected. This is due to the environmental factor of 'over-eating' being common in Western societies.

d (a) because it shows two distinct phenotypes, each showing a range of continuous variation. The continuous variation results from environmental factors affecting growth.

2 Factors such as light, water and nutrient availability; temperature; wind; grazing by animals; disease.

3 Siamese cats have an allele of the gene that produces an enzyme needed for synthesis of black pigment. This enzyme is denatured by temperatures above 37 °C. Only the parts of the body where the skin temperature is below 37 °C produce black pigment, e.g. the tail, ears and lower legs.

4

a A male can mate with several females and can successfully father many young. It may be a more economical use of available food resources for a population to contain a high proportion of females.

b It may become more difficult to maintain nests below 33 °C, so more males may be hatched. This may increase pressure on food resources and in the longer term reduce the population.

5 Gene mutation or environmental factors.

6 Environmental factors, such as differences in food intake, could cause differences during development. Also gene mutations occurring during the development of various parts of the body could cause these parts to grow differently. For example, a mutation affecting the gene controlling iris pigment could result different coloured eyes.

7 Each ovum has been produced from a different cell in the ovary by meiosis. As a result of independent assortment and crossing over, the ova will have received different combinations of alleles.

8 The amount of food available and space.

9

a The population would increase tenfold each year. There would soon be severe competition for food.

b Two.

10

a See Fig 8.Ans10a.

b At 2% - 4200 individuals; at 10% - 1800; at 50% - 100.

c It would decrease.

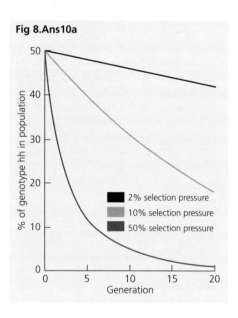

Fig 8.Ans10a

% of genotype hh in population (y-axis, 0 to 50)
Generation (x-axis, 0 to 20)

■ 2% selection pressure
■ 10% selection pressure
■ 50% selection pressure

11 Every individual with the dominant allele will show the unfavourable condition. Heterozygotes with the recessive allele will not show the unfavourable condition, so recessive alleles can be passed on by heterozygotes.

12 Tree trunks in industrial areas became blackened. Melanic moths were better camouflaged. Fewer of the melanic moths were eaten by predators, so a higher proportion survived. Therefore these melanic moths would pass on the melanic allele to their offspring. This process would continue over successive generations until most moths were melanic.

13 The melanic allele is dominant, so all moths with this allele would be black.

14 A higher proportion of melanic moths were recaptured in the polluted wood, suggesting that the black wing colour helped their survival. Conversely, a higher proportion of speckled moths was recaptured in the Dorset wood.

15 The proportion of the speckled form in the population is likely to increase again.

16 The range of variation in beak size was not great enough. None of the birds had small enough beaks, so that they could survive by selecting the smaller seeds of plants other than cacti.

Application boxes

Genetics and human history

1

a 0% of Native Americans have blood group B.

b B and AB. Genotypes $I^A I^A$, $I^A I^O$ and $I^O I^O$.

2

a No. For example Nigerian and Japanese people both have 23% with Group B, but their skin colour differs. On the other hand, both Nigerians and native Australians have black skin, but the percentage with group B is quite different.

b The black population derives from people of West African ancestry, such as Nigerians, whereas the white population is largely European in origin, where the proportion of group B is around 9%.

3

a They probably migrated to the area where they live from somewhere with a low proportion of group B in the population, such as from the population in Siberia from which some people moved east to North America.

b Information from DNA analysis, e.g. from comparing mutations in genes for substances such as haemoglobin.

Racial differences

1 People who are homozygous for the sickle cell allele misshapen red blood cells that are easily damaged and inefficient carriers of oxygen. People with this genotype are less likely to survive and have children.

2

a The extra red blood cells give more oxygen carrying capacity, which is an advantage at high altitudes where amounts of oxygen are low.

b Individuals with larger lungs would be able to inhale more air in each breath. Oxygen would pass into their blood more rapidly and they would therefore be able to work more actively. They would be better adapted to survival at high altitudes. They would be more likely have children who would inherit the large lung capacity, and in turn pass on the genes to their children.

Chapter 9

1 The parents have different numbers of chromosomes, so the sex cells will have different numbers too, 33 in a horse's egg and 31 in a donkey's sperm. The hybrid mule has different numbers of maternal and paternal chromosomes, so two chromosomes will have no partner with which to pair up during prophase of meiosis. The others may also be of different sizes and shapes and be unable to form bivalents. Mules are therefore unable to produce gametes by meiosis.

2 They lived in the sea where conditions may have stayed constant. Successful species would be able to survive largely unchanged while conditions stayed the same.

3 Species that are closely related are likely to have few differences in the amino acid sequence in the haemoglobin, or in the nucleotide bases in the DNA. More distant relatives are likely to have accumulated differences as a result of mutations.

Fig 9.Ans4

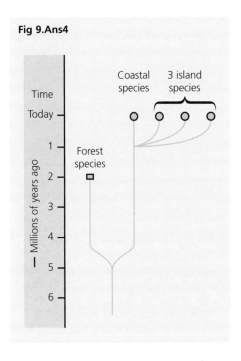

4   See Fig 9.Ans4.

5
a   Prokaryotae, Protoctista, Fungi.
b   Plantae, Protoctista.
c   Protoctista, Plantae.
d   Protoctista, Fungi, Plantae, Animalia.

Application boxes

Island isolation

1   You could check whether the finches could interbreed and produce fertile offspring.

2   On the island there were no other predators, and plenty of prey. The prey included quite large animals, such as pigs, so the largest 'dragons' could be the most successful at capturing these. They would then pass on alleles for large size to their offspring.

The naked ape

1   Within the hominid population there would be a range of hairiness. Those with the thinnest hair would cool quickest, and would perhaps be able to sustain pursuit of prey for longer, as well as requiring less water. As a result hominids with thin hair would be more likely to survive and pass on the alleles favouring thin hair to their

offspring. This process would continue for many generations until the bodies of hominids were largely hairless.

2   The active processes that maintain the brain need a continuous supply of energy from respiration, and this inevitably generates waste heat. The excess heat must be released in order to maintain the blood and body temperature within safe limits.

3
a   The fat could would provide buoyancy. It might also help insulation, although in warm waters this might not be necessary.
b   Aquatic vegetation is much softer. Also shellfish and other animal life found in water is less tough than meat from terrestrial animals.
c   Species with babies that drowned in water would clearly be at a significant disadvantage in an aquatic environment.
d   Wasting large amounts of water in urine would be disadvantageous on hot, dry grasslands, but not a problem in aquatic conditions.
e   They would be able to put their heads under water to search for food.

4   For example, other aquatic mammals living in shallow water are neither bipedal nor hairless (such as otters).

Chapter 10

1   Hibiscus (nectar) → humming bird → margay.
     Wood (from tree → termites → tamandua anteater.

2
For example:
a   Oak tree → caterpillar → titmice → weasel;
b   Other trees and shrubs → decomposers → earthworms → beetles → shrews;
c   Herbs → decomposers → soil insects → beetles → moles → tawny owls.

3   Titmice, parasites, spiders, voles, mice earthworms, soil insects and mites.

4   All of the consumer levels, since humans may feed directly on plants as primary consumers, or on other animals, which may be primary

Fig 10.Ans5

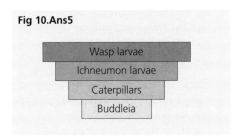

consumers, such as sheep, secondary consumers (or even tertiary or quaternary consumers) such as many species of fish.

5   See Fig 10.Ans5.

6   Your pyramid should look very strange. If you choose one tree, the bottom layer will contain one organism. Each tree has thousands of aphids, so the next layer up will be wide. The population of blue tits feeding of the aphids will be smaller, so the third layer up will be narrow, but not as narrow as the tree layer. The top layer will be wider as one blue tit could be infested by dozens of mites.

7   Take a sample of grass from a small area, such as a 10 cm square. Make sure that you have collected all parts of the grass, including roots, and cleaned off the soil. Weigh the grass sample and place it in an oven at about 100 °C for several hours. Weigh the sample again. This should be repeated until the weight stays the same, showing that all the water has evaporated. Other samples should be taken for a random sample of 10 cm squares in the meadow and the dry biomass found for each of these. From the mean of the results you can calculate the mean dry biomass per m^2, and from this the total biomass in the meadow.

8   Producers to primary consumers; 16%.
     Primary consumers to secondary consumers; 11%.
     Secondary consumers to tertiary consumers; 5.6%.

9   Animals use a high proportion of the available energy for respiration because they are active and move around.

10
a   Mammals lose more energy to the

environment as a result of respiration because they need energy to maintain their body temperature. Carnivores use more energy to move around and catch their food than herbivores do.

b Herbivores eat plants which contain large amounts of indigestible substances such as cellulose. The energy in these substances is not absorbed.

11 Glucose.

12 Higher temperatures increase the rate of enzyme activity and therefore the rate at which dead matter is digested. They also increase the rate of metabolism of decomposers and their rate of respiration.

13

a Protoctists (e.g. algae) and prokaryotes (some bacteria).

b ATP may be needed to provide energy for synthesis of compounds, e.g., for growth or seed production, for active transport of ions and for movement of organic compounds, e.g. in phloem.

14

a Mainly carbon dioxide and water. Small amounts of other gases such as sulphur dioxide and nitrogen oxides are formed from other elements in some carbon compounds.

b Trees contain carbon compounds in the wood that remain locked away throughout the life-time of the trees. When forest is burned, all the carbon in these compounds is released as carbon dioxide. When the forest is replaced by crops, only small amounts of carbon are used in their structure and much of this is recycled when the crops are harvested. There is, therefore, a large net increase in carbon dioxide concentration. Wood used, for example, in building and furniture-making would not release its carbon, but even so large amounts of carbon compounds may be destroyed from parts of the trees that are not usable.

15 There is much more growth of plants during the spring and summer in the northern hemisphere. During this period the carbon dioxide concentration falls as carbon is fixed by photosynthesis. In autumn and winter much of the plant growth dies off and is decomposed, so the rate of

respiration by decomposers and consumers exceeds the rate of photosynthesis. There is, therefore, a net increase in the atmospheric carbon dioxide concentration during the northern autumn and winter.

16 In the electron transport system, electrons are transferred from one acceptor to another and then to atmospheric oxygen, producing water. In the absence of oxygen gas, denitrifying bacteria pass the electrons to oxygen in the nitrite or nitrate ions. Energy released in this transfer can be used to synthesise ATP. The oxygen is then available to form water, and nitrogen gas is released.

17 Poorly drained soils become waterlogged and anaerobic denitrifying bacteria can thrive. These reduce the nitrate content of the soil, and hence its fertility.

18 Nitrogen-fixing bacteria in the root nodules of the clover would increase the amount of nitrogen compounds. When ploughed into the soil, these compounds would be decomposed into nitrates and increase soil fertility for crops.

Application boxes

Photosynthetic efficiency

1 5.5%.

2 23%.
3 59.8%.

4

a Large numbers of chloroplasts in palisade cells; several layers of mesophyll cells.

b Other pigments (carotenoids) absorb green wavelengths and transfer energy to chlorophyll.

c Chlorophyll molecules organised in layers in lamellae, which avoids random shading.

5 The rate of photosynthesis will be less than maximum for most of the time. Light intensity may only be at its optimum level for short periods during the day. Other factors, such as temperature and carbon dioxide concentration, may limit the rate of photosynthesis. Growth rates may be restricted by shortages of water or mineral nutrients.

6

a Only a small proportion of the energy in crop plants is transferred to biomass in primary consumers such as cattle. People therefore obtain more energy when they are primary consumers rather than secondary consumers.

b Animals such as cattle and sheep can feed on plants such as grass that humans are unable to use. In marginal lands these may be the only plants that grow. Also, humans use only some parts of crop plants and animals may make efficient use of the rest.

Reducing the greenhouse effect

1 The dark trees absorb radiation, which will slightly increase their temperature. Snow and ice, being white, are highly reflective and absorb much less.

2 In the soil, algae would be broken down by decomposers, releasing the carbon dioxide again. Crop plants would not absorb carbon compounds directly from the soil.

3 54 000 square kilometres. (Rather more than the area of England!)

Nitrogen fixation

1 The enzyme reduces the activation energy of the reaction. Each substrate is attracted to active sites in the enzyme molecules, forming enzyme-substrate complexes. Molecular interactions in the enzyme molecules change their shape and bring the substrates together.

2 By diffusion through the pores in the outer layers of the nodules, from air pockets in the soil.

3 The xylem transports water and mineral ions to the bacteria and nodule tissues. The phloem brings a supply of sugars from the leaves for respiration, and transports the amino acids produced in the nodules to the growing points of the plant.

4 The leghaemoglobin has a dissociation curve similar to haemoglobin. High concentrations of oxygen that diffuse into the nodules combine with the leghaemoglobin. If the concentration falls to a low level, the leghaemoglobin dissociates and releases oxygen.

Chapter 11

1
a 0.0625 m².
b 1.25 m².
c 0.57 %.

2
a 25%.
b Leguminous plants have nitrogen-fixing bacteria in root nodules. These bacteria use gaseous nitrogen to produce organic nitrogen compounds, including amino acids and proteins. When clover plants, or their roots and nodules, die, they are decayed by saprophytic bacteria. Then, nitrifying bacteria make nitrates from the ammonium ions produced. The improved supply of nitrate ions enables the grass to grow more quickly.

3 Oarweed; 0 to 25 cm.
Toothed wrack; 30 cm to 75 cm.
Knotted wrack; 90cm to 150 cm.
Bladder wrack; 75cm to 85 cm.
Spiral wrack; 150cm to 180 cm.
Channelled wrack; 200cm to 245 cm.

4
a 20 x 20 cm.
b Tor grass, Rock rose, Ribwort plantain.
c Some species, such as the daisy, have short stems and spreading leaves. They grow well where the grass is short because they get plenty of light, and their leaves are not easily damaged by trampling. To the side of the path, grasses can grow tall and overshadow them.

5 The pH scale is not linear. The difference between pH 4 and pH 5 is not the same as the difference between pH 5 and pH 6. It is therefore not valid to add pH values together and then divide to find a mean.

6 Hydrogen ions are attracted to the charges on amino acids in a molecule of a protein. They disrupt the tertiary structure of the protein molecules of an enzyme and change the shape of the active site. The enzyme molecules can no longer bind with their substrate and their activity is destroyed. Heavy metal ions are non-competitive inhibitors. They attach to enzyme molecules and alter their shape, thus also affecting the active site.

7
a The temperature rose slowly as the tide receded during the morning, as the covering water became more shallow. Once the pool was exposed the temperature rose rapidly to a maximum level at which it remained until late afternoon. The rapid rise occurred because the air temperature was much higher than the water temperature, and there was only a small volume of water in the pool to heat up. There was then a slow fall until 1900 hours, as the air temperature decreased. When the pool was again flooded by cold sea water, the temperature fell rapidly.
b The oxygen concentration will reduce, as oxygen is less soluble in warm water. It would be harder for animals to obtain enough oxygen for respiration.
c Seaweeds photosynthesise, and therefore produce oxygen. Oxygen concentration would rise during daylight hours. At night, however, there would be a reduction in concentration due to the respiration of the seaweeds.
d When the pool is exposed, water can evaporate and increase the salinity. Heavy rainfall can dilute the sea water in the pool and decrease the salinity. Changes in salt concentration can cause osmotic effects in organisms, with high salt concentrations causing water loss from cells. Low concentrations may cause water to enter cells, and in animals may burst cells.

Application boxes

Can pollution make fish change sex?

1
a Vitellogenin stimulates the development of egg yolks.
b Male fish start to develop eggs in their testes. They also produce some sperm, so are said to have become hermaphrodites.

2 Discussion question, no answer provided.

3
a If male fish become incapable of fertilising the normal eggs produced by female fish, the population will start to decline.

b Steps should perhaps be taken to investigate the major sources of the chemical pollutants responsible so that their rate of discharge into the water supply can be reduced.

Blue butterflies run out of thyme

1
a Fence off an area that is being grazed, so that no rabbits can get in. Make a grid plan in the grazed area and the ungrazed area. Use a table of random numbers to select the positions of a sample of quadrats in each area. Record the species found in each of the quadrats. Repeat at regular intervals.
b Grazing by sheep and rabbits stopped, as a result of changes in farming practice and myxomatosis. Grasses were able to grow taller. They shaded out small plants like wild thyme. The caterpillars had no wild thyme to feed on, so the life cycle of the butterfly was interrupted.

Chapter 12

1 **a**; Population. **b**; Habitat.
c; Ecosystem. **d**; Abiotic factor.
e; Community. **f**; Biotic factor.

2 Predators feed on other animals. Only a small proportion of the energy in the primary consumers is transferred to the predators. The biomass of the primary consumers, and the energy that it contains, must be much greater than that of the predators that it supports.

3 Food in soil is a niche exploited by few animals. The first animals to do so were probably quite small, perhaps able to enter natural tunnels and crevices. In the populations of both ancestors there would be differences between forelegs due to genetic variation. Those animals with forelegs with the largest claws and most powerful muscles would be likely to be most successful in obtaining food and surviving. Natural selection would occur, with the genes for advantageous features being passed on through many generations. Because the environmental conditions in soil would be similar in both Australia and Europe, selection pressures resulted in both types of mole having similar features.

Fig 12.Ans14b

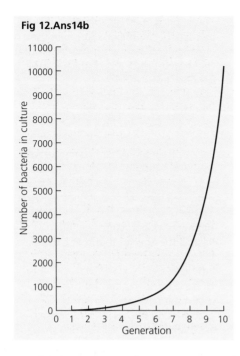

4

a

Generation	Number of bacteria
1	20
2	40
3	80
4	160
5	320
6	640
7	1280
8	2560
9	5120
10	10 240

b See Fig 14.Ans4b.
The graph shows an increasingly steep curve. This pattern of population growth is called exponential.

c The pattern is similar in that there is slow growth at first, followed by a steep increase. The increase is rather irregular, probably because the cells do not all grow and divide at exactly the same rate. The increase in population size levels off after about 15 days.

d Light and mineral ion availability.

5 Possible answers:

a Water availability, temperature.

b Temperature, wind speed, depth of soil.

c Water current, mineral ion availability.

d Lack of stable attachment surface, wave action, salinity.

e Acidity, mineral ion availability, high water content reducing oxygen availability for roots.

6

a The population of this colony would decline, and the colony might well die out, because the total number of rabbits at the end of the season (39) was much smaller than the number at the start (70).

b A rabbit colony can produce a large number of young very quickly and so the population could recover rapidly if the population of predators dropped. If the colony were completely wiped out, the predators would die or move away. Immigration from other colonies could then take place. Also natural selection might occur, whereby the young that are better at avoiding predators would survive, perhaps by being more cautious or having more acute senses. These more successful rabbits could pass on their characteristics to their offspring.

7 The Arctic fox population would follow a similar cycle, increasing in numbers shortly after the lemming population increases and falling sharply after the lemming numbers crash. The total numbers of Arctic foxes would be much lower than those of lemmings.

8 In the grazed field the herbivores prevent the growth of taller herbaceous plants. Once the grazers are removed herbaceous plants with tall stems can grow. By overshadowing they out-compete the smaller plants . Similarly shrubs out-compete the herbaceous plants, and eventually trees replace these by competing more successfully for light and other resources.

Application boxes

Sand dune succession

1 Low water content; high wind speeds; instability of sand; high salt content.

2 For example: The network of underground stems provides anchorage in unstable sand; thick tough outer cuticle protects from wind-blown sand and prevents water loss; hinge cells shrink when dry, causing leaves to roll up; rolled leaves maintain humidity inside cylinder and reduce transpiration from inner surface; hairs restrict air movement and hence loss of water; limited number of stomata tucked away at base of leaf channels, keeping humidity high and reducing diffusion gradient.

3 Mainly by wind-blown seeds. These tend to settle in the sheltered areas on the land side of the ridges. Some grass seeds may be transported by animals or humans.

Chapter 13

1

a Less air means lower oxygen availability around the roots. This reduces the rate of root growth by affecting respiration and also can reduce active uptake of ions. Poor root growth reduces yield by decreasing the amounts of water and ions available for the growth of parts of the crop above ground.

b Bacteria are essential for the cycling of carbon and nitrogen compounds in the soil. Once the populations of these bacteria fall, organic matter is no longer broken down rapidly. When crop material is ploughed into the soil, for example in autumn after harvesting, its constituents are not quickly made available for the growth of the next crop and the mineral ion content of the soil is further depleted.

c Wind can damage mature crops such as cereals by breaking the stems and making harvesting difficult. It has a severe drying effect, and water shortage can restrict growth. It can also cause closure of stomata, which reduces carbon dioxide uptake and thus reduces the rate of photosynthesis. The cooling effect due to increased evaporation can lower the temperature of leaves and hence lower the rate of photosynthesis and other metabolic processes.

2

a Evaporation is reduced close to the hedge. Evaporation reduces because moisture is not dispersed by the wind, so humidity close to the soil increases, thus decreasing the diffusion gradient. Therefore less moisture is lost from the soil. The temperature is increased near the hedge because the cooling effect of evaporation is reduced.

b At about 14 m from the hedge.

c The hedge may shade the crop and reduce photosynthesis. There may also be competition for mineral ions and water from the roots of the hedge.

d The area below the curve for yield showing an increase is greater than the area above the curve showing a decrease.

e The wind may not blow consistently from the same direction.

3

a During spring and summer plants and other producers such as algae grow and use nitrates from their water for protein synthesis, etc.

The nitrate concentration rises again as these organisms decay slowly during the autumn and winter.

The steep rise in ammonium concentration occurs soon after the vegetation dies back in early autumn.

Ammonium ions are the first products of saprophytic breakdown.

The ammonium ions are slowly converted by nitrifying bacteria to nitrates as part of the nitrogen cycle. This process occurs relatively slowly in the lower water temperatures of late autumn and winter.

b It is unlikely that there is serious pollution. The nitrate concentration falls almost to zero during the summer, suggesting that there is not a large excess of organic material reaching the lake. Ammonium ion concentration stays at a fairly low level during spring and summer, again suggesting that there are not large amounts of organic matter being broken down.

4

a To prevent any photosynthesis, which would generate oxygen in the light.

b Reasons include: few bacteria being present when sample taken; poisons in the effluent which kill the bacteria; substrates like cellulose or wood whose breakdown is slow; limited oxygen supply in effluent tested.

5

a Urea.

b Nitrates are vital for protein synthesis, both for structural compounds in cytoplasm and for enzymes. They are also needed for nucleic acid synthesis.

c In phospholipids for plasma membranes, in ATP and in nucleic acids.

6

a They photosynthesise and produce oxygen, thus cancelling out use of

oxygen for respiration.

b The do not contain excess nutrients.

c Some of the algae are toxic.

7

a Producers to primary consumers × 5.75; primary consumers to secondary consumers × 9; secondary consumers to tertiary consumers × 12.75.

b 528 000.

c The predator is much larger so the amount absorbed from each prey will be spread through a larger body mass. Also not all the DDT in the prey will be absorbed into the tissues of the predator.

8

a Animal tissues provide a higher concentration of protein, needed for the growth of the chicks.

b More insects, etc survive and there is more food to feed the young.

c With a lower density of food available the partridges have cover a larger area to find enough food for the chicks. With more energy used in searching for food a higher proportion is likely to die.

d Differences in survival rate and distance moved were both significant, as they were below the 5% level. However the differences in area were not statistically significant as they were between 5 and 10%.

e Retention of hedges and provision of more cover in small areas of woodland, etc. Leaving wide strips next to hedges uncultivated, and avoiding use of pesticides on these strips. Allowing vegetation to grow long to give cover for nest sites.

Application boxes

Sewage effluent

1

a The oxygen concentration decreases in the first 500m because the large population of bacteria uses it for respiration. Below this the oxygen concentration slowly recovers because there are fewer bacteria, oxygen from the air dissolves in the water and the increasing numbers of algae and green plants restore oxygen by photosynthesis.

b The nitrate concentration rises as the nitrogen compounds are decomposed to ammonium ions that are then

converted by nitrifying bacteria to nitrates. Further down river the concentration declines again as they are absorbed by algae and plants, and as a result of dilution.

c The number of bacteria is highest at the point of discharge where the concentration of organic matter is highest. The sewage itself will contain many bacteria and the population will thrive near the outfall. Down river the numbers decline as the amount of organic matter goes down.

d Few algae grow close to the discharge, possibly due to limited light penetration or toxic materials in the sewage. The numbers of algae rise to a peak about 1km from the discharge where the availability of nitrates, and other ions from the sewage, is highest. Numbers decrease beyond this as the supply of nutrients is used up.

2 BOD is a measure of the quantity of oxygen consumed by the bacteria that are breaking down the organic matter in the sewage. This declines as the amounts of sewage and bacteria decline. The actual concentration of oxygen decreases much more rapidly as it is used up by large numbers of bacteria. The demand for oxygen remains high while there is still organic matter, even though there is a limited supply of oxygen.

3 The reduced amount of water in the river and the slower current cause the sewage to become more concentrated near the discharge because their is less dilution effect. There is less oxygen dissolved in warmer water, so the rate of breakdown is lower.

Index

A band 88
abiotic factors 169-70, 174, 179
   measuring 163-4
ABO blood groups 107, 119
absorption spectra 6
acceptor molecules 8, 9, 13
accommodation 71
accuracy, experimental 202
acetylcholine 60, 61, 63, 91
   drugs block 63-4, 65
   parasympathetic nerves secrete 81
acetyl coenzyme A 11, 12, 13, 14
actin filaments 87-9
action potentials 57-9
   across synapses 60-2
in muscle contraction 90, 91
action spectra 6
active transport 39
   in muscle contraction 91
   and resting potential 56
   in selective reabsorption 42
actomyosin bridges see cross bridges
acuity 75-6
adaptation, synapse 60, 62
adaptations 169, 171, 175
   human 127
   on rocky shores 163
   in speciation 132
   and variation 131
   xerophytic 178
   see also dark adaptation
adenosine diphosphate (ADP) 4, 5, 7, 12
adenosine triphosphate see ATP
ADH (anti-diuretic hormone) 44-5, 47
ADP (adenosine diphosphate) 4, 5, 7, 12
adrenal glands 46
adrenaline 31
aerobic bacteria 186
aerobic respiration 3, 11-15
afferent arteriole 40
algae 173, 179
   and organic effluent 185-6, 187
   as phytoplankton 145, 185
algal bloom 185-6
allele frequency 132
alleles 97, 104
   codominant 105, 107
   in crossing over 103
   in dihybrid crosses 110
   dominant 104, 108, 110
   recessive 104-5, 108
   in speciation 131, 132-4
alligators 120-1
all-or-nothing principle 57
alpha cells 20, 21, 22
amino acids 34, 36-7
   in the nitrogen cycle 152-3
ammonification 152-3
ammonium compounds 152-3, 185
amphetamines 64-5
anabolic steroids 37

anaemia, sickle cell 106-7, 127
anaerobic bacteria 186
anaerobic respiration 11
Animalia 137
animals
   alligators 120-1
   breeding of 108, 110-11
   as consumers see consumers
   energy flow in 148
   exoskeletons 94
   farm animals 183, 185, 191-2
   see also birds; fish; insects; mammals
anions 56
   see also chloride ions
ANP (atrial natriuretic peptide) 41
antagonistic effects
   in homeostasis 22
   and muscles 92
   in neurone action 81
   in pupil control 69
antagonistic pairs 22, 92
antibiotics, discovery of 197
antibodies and blood groups 107
anti-diuretic hormone (ADH) 44-5, 47
antigens 107
   HLA types 119, 121
antiseptics, testing 200, 203
ants in butterfly life cycle 165
aquatic ecosystems 142, 146, 147
   marine 145
   pollution 158, 185-8, 192
   ponds 169-71, 173, 174
   wetlands and marshes 191, 194
aqueous humour 68, 69
area graphs 215
arterioles
   in kidneys 40
   in thermoregulation 25, 26, 27
arthropods, exoskeletons 94
artificial selection 130
assays 203
association areas 79-80
associations 204-6, 211
atmosphere 6
   carbon dioxide in 2, 140, 150
      in the carbon cycle 148, 149, 151
   oxygen in 6, 7
ATP (adenosine triphosphate) 3-4
   and muscles 89, 93
   in nitrogen fixation 152
   in photosynthesis 8, 9
   in respiration 11, 12, 13, 14
   in selective reabsorption 42
atrial natriuretic peptide (ANP) 41
atropine 64
Australia, rabbit problems 168, 172
autonomic nervous system 81-4
averages see mean
axes, graph 214
axons 48, 50, 51
   and action potentials 57, 58

myelin sheath 50, 51, 52, 59
   and resting potential 56-7

bacteria 6
   in algal bloom 186
   in decomposition 149
   in the nitrogen cycle 152-4
bacterial lawns 200, 203
barren landscape, succession in 179
basal metabolic rate (BMR) 210
basement membrane 40, 42
beta-blockers 61, 64
beta cells 20, 21, 22
bile 38
bilirubin 38
binomial system 135
bioaccumulation 190
bioassays 203
biochemical oxygen demand (BOD) 187-8
biodegradable pesticides 189-90
biodiversity 130-4
   see also diversity of species
biomass
   and ecosystem productivity 175
   pyramids of 144-5, 190
biotic factors 163, 169-70, 179
bipolar cells 73-4, 75
birds
   finches 126, 133
   population decline 192-3
bivalents 100, 101
bladder 39
bleaching, photosensitive 71, 73
blindness 68
blood
   in haemophilia 114
   in kidney function 38-46
   liver regulates 36
   red cells 38, 106-7
   in thermoregulation 25, 26, 28, 30
   water content 44-5, 47
   white cells 119
blood glucose 18, 19, 20-4
blood groups 107, 119, 121
blood pressure 44-6, 217
blood sugar (glucose) 18, 19, 20-4
blood water potential 36, 44-5
BMR (basal metabolic rate) 210
BOD (biochemical oxygen demand) 187-8
body temperature regulation 18, 25-31
bones, collagen in 92
Bowman's capsules 39, 40
brain 49, 77-80, 82-3
   and blood glucose 20
   hypothalamus see hypothalamus
   neurotransmitters 65
breadth of knowledge for essays 226
breeding animals and plants 108, 110-11
brown fat 29, 31
burning, energy in 11
butterflies 165

244